DISCOVERING MATHEMATICS 1A

Teacher Guide

Authors:

Victor Chow, Jill Borcherds,
Lana Laidler, Ann Lui, Andrea Wickham
UK Consultant: Robert Wilne
Singapore Consultant: Berinderjeet Kaur

OXFORD
UNIVERSITY PRESS

C000062224

Great Clarendon Street, Oxford, OX2 6DP, United Kingdom

Oxford University Press is a department of the University of Oxford. It furthers the University's objective of excellence in research, scholarship, and education by publishing worldwide. Oxford is a registered trade mark of Oxford University Press in the UK and in certain other countries.

British Library Cataloguing in Publication Data
Data available

978-0-19-842186-3

5 7 9 10 8 6

Paper used in the production of this book is a natural, recyclable product made from wood grown in sustainable forests. The manufacturing process conforms to the environmental regulations of the country of origin.

Printed and Bound by CPI Group (UK) Ltd, Croydon, CR0 4YY

Acknowledgements

The authors and publishers would like to thank consultants Berinderjeet Kaur and Robert Wilne who have advised on the content. All of their contributions and advice have been invaluable.

Editorial team: Dom Holdsworth, Julie Thornton, Matteo Orsini-Jones and Sarah Dutton. With thanks also to Katherine Bird and Rosie Day for editorial contributions.

The publishers would like to thank the following for permission to use copyright material:

p6: Oxford University Press; p132: Monkey Business Images/ Shutterstock; p133: Adam Gilchrist/Shutterstock; p133: Aquila/ Shutterstock; p135 (BR): sawaddeebenz/Shutterstock; p135: sawaddeebenz/Shutterstock; p139: mareandmare/Shutterstock; p144 (T): Coprid/Shutterstock; p144 (B): Happy monkey/Shutterstock; p148: akiyoko/Shutterstock; p156 (L): Sakarin Sawasdinaka/ Shutterstock; p156 (R): Apl56/Shutterstock; p156 (R): Adam Gilchrist/ Shutterstock; p168: Francesco83/Shutterstock; p178 (TL): Happy monkey/Shutterstock; p178 (TR): Africa Studio/Shutterstock; p178 (BR): ArchMan/Shutterstock; p178 (BL): Gravicapa/Shutterstock; p183 (T): LanKS/Shutterstock; p183 (B): clearviewstock/Shutterstock; p184 (T): nimon/Shutterstock; p184 (BL): hursina Viktoriia/Shutterstock; p184 (BR): Chursina Viktoriia/Shutterstock; p190: Tom K Photo/ Shutterstock; p197: Yulia Glam/Shutterstock; p203 (TL): Duda Vasilii/ Shutterstock; p203 (BL): xpixel/Shutterstock; p203 (BR): Jim Barber/ Shutterstock; p203 (TR): Duda Vasilii/Shutterstock; p204: ronstik/ Shutterstock; p205 (T): Geolilli/Shutterstock; p205 (B): Terdsak bundi/ Shutterstock; p207 (L): Leftleg/Shutterstock; p207 (R): donatas1205/ Shutterstock; p208 (TR): chutima kuanamon/Shutterstock; p207 (TL): Marco Uliana/Shutterstock; p207 (ML): desertfox99/Shutterstock; p207 (MR): Max Maier/Shutterstock; p207 (BL): musicman/ Shutterstock; p207 (BR): Siberian Photographer/Shutterstock; p212 (TL): Alexey Kljatov/Shutterstock; p212 (TR): Christos Georghiou/ Shutterstock; p213: art designer/Shutterstock; p216 (L): Roman Sotola/Shutterstock; p216 (M): Becky Stares/Shutterstock; p216 (R): notbad/Shutterstock; p217 (TL): Phatthanit/Shutterstock; p217 (TM): LiukasArt/Shutterstock; p217 (TR): Igor Kovalchuk/Shutterstock; p217 (BL): Pro Symbols/Shutterstock; p217 (BM): Standard Studio/ Shutterstock; p217 (BR): Martial Red/Shutterstock; p238: Gts/ Shutterstock; p247 (T): optimarc/Shutterstock; p247 (B): PeterVrabel/ Shutterstock; p254: Pixfiction/Shutterstock; p258: siamionau pavel/Shutterstock; p266: fizkes/Shutterstock; p267 (L): NeMaria/ Shutterstock; p267 (R): cherezoff/Shutterstock; p268 (L): canon_ shooter/Shutterstock; p268 (R): cynoclub/Shutterstock; p269: Vilor/ Shutterstock; p272: David Ross/BritainExpress.com

Artworks: Thomson

Cover: Steve Bloom Images/Alamy Stock Photo

Although we have made every effort to trace and contact all copyright holders before publication this has not been possible in all cases. If notified, the publisher will rectify any errors or omissions at the earliest opportunity.

Links to third party websites are provided by Oxford in good faith and for information only. Oxford disclaims any responsibility for the materials contained in any third party website referenced in this work.

CONTENTS

THE DISCOVERING MATHEMATICS SERIES

Discovering Mathematics provides comprehensive support for **three tiers** – Foundation, Middle and Higher – across **all three year groups** in Key Stage 3. The series is an adaptation of the renowned Singaporean secondary series of the same name. The course has been expanded and revised to cover fully the Key Stage 3 National Curriculum. It has been developed by the original Singaporean author team, in conjunction with a large team of UK and Singaporean reviewers and mastery practitioners.

In Singapore, considerable emphasis is placed on using high-quality resources. All secondary schools adopt a textbook series and over 60% of them have chosen *Discovering Mathematics.* This UK adaptation gives you the full suite of resources, as well as an optional programme of professional development.

Student Resources

Student Books and **Workbooks** are available for all three tiers in Years 7–9.

Discovering Mathematics Kerboodle Books provides online access to all nine Student Books for use in school or at home.

Teacher Resources

Teacher Guides are available to support all nine Student Books. Each one contains a Scheme of Work, Notes on Teaching and Fully-worked Solutions for all questions and activities.

Series Guide for Teachers, available in print and as a digital edition on Kerboodle, provides a clear summary of the core principles behind mastery, and how to implement it successfully in your school using this series.

Professional Development courses offer practical, expert support to teachers at all stages of their career on how to implement the mastery approach and how to use *Discovering Mathematics*. For more information, email discoveringmathematicspd@oup.com

Discovering Mathematics Kerboodle contains all nine digital Student Books and videos for front-of-class use, along with interactive assessment resources for students. Additional resources include the digital edition of the Series Guide for Teachers, fully-worked solutions for the Workbooks and a Graded Question Bank providing additional assessment practice for Year 7 Middle and Higher Tiers (some Level 1 and 2 questions will also be useful for Foundation Tier).

Algebra Discs are a manipulative pack providing support for number and algebra activities using the Concrete-Pictorial-Abstract (CPA) approach. Each Class Set contains 20 Student Sets, totalling 1600 discs. These are used throughout Middle and Higher Tiers, and in Years 8 and 9 in Foundation Tier.

HOW TO USE DISCOVERING MATHEMATICS

Teaching for Mastery in *Discovering Mathematics*

Teaching for mastery in *Discovering Mathematics* is:

- for *all* Key Stage 3 maths students: all stages, all levels of attainment
- for *all* secondary maths teachers: experienced and beginning, STEM graduates and non-STEM graduates.

In this series we use 'mastery' in reference to students' outcomes: the learning they develop that is the consequence of the teaching they receive. Students who show mastery in a particular topic or aspect of mathematics are able to solve problems because they have knowledge **THAT**, **HOW** and **WHY** related to that topic.

They have:

- factual knowledge – knowledge THAT (e.g. that the angles in a triangle add up to 180°)

- procedural fluency – knowledge HOW (e.g. how to work out the angles in an isosceles triangle given one of its angles)
- conceptual understanding – knowledge WHY (e.g. why the sum of the angles in a triangle is 180°)

We have adapted *Discovering Mathematics* for the UK towards our vision of teaching for mastery for all.

Teaching for mastery prioritises depth over breadth: an insistence that a student truly grasps the fundamental concepts and connections within the mathematics before they move on to the next topic. A lesson for mastery may be focused on one idea only, and that one idea is explored in depth: with examples and followed by consolidation.

Problem-solving is seen as the end goal of teaching for mastery: the ultimate test that a student has truly grasped the maths. In this section, we'll show how *Discovering Mathematics* supports the mastery approach.

Lesson Design

When designing a lesson for mastery, decide first what you want students to **think** in the lesson, and then decide what the students will **do**. Both in the Notes on Teaching in this book and in the Student Book, *Discovering Mathematics* encourages this approach. How it does this is described in more detail on the next pages.

1. **Motivating Students' Learning** (see page 3): students are shown upfront how each topic is related to real life, as well as being encouraged to reflect on their prior learning to develop their knowledge further.

2. **Guided Discovery** (see pages 4–5): students learn best when they discover new concepts for themselves, with guidance from you, the teacher. *Discovering Mathematics* is structured to support this journey of discovery. Not every lesson will look the same, but there are certain elements that are carefully included:
   - the **class activities** and **discussions** to sharpen the students' reasoning, and to prompt them to make connections within the current topic and between others

   - the design and sequencing of the **intelligent practice** that students undertake: the questions, tasks and activities that embed and deepen their factual knowledge, procedural fluency and conceptual understanding.

3. **Concrete-Pictorial-Abstract** (see page 6): the series supports the use of concrete and pictorial representations of a new concept, so students can understand it in the abstract.

4. **Mathematical Language** (see page 7): precise language and vocabulary is introduced, used and reinforced, so that students can express themselves clearly and accurately.

5. **Assessment** (see page 8): activities are included to assess students' learning in the current lesson, to inform design of the next lesson and to allow for rapid intervention to prevent gaps 'in the moment'. Support is given so that *all* students make progress and develop secure and connected knowledge of, fluency with and understanding about the mathematics in each lesson.

Scheme of Work – Chapter 8 Measures and Angles:

Scheme of Work defines lessons to teach in each week

Chapter lengths are different; each one determined by the time required to master key mathematical ideas

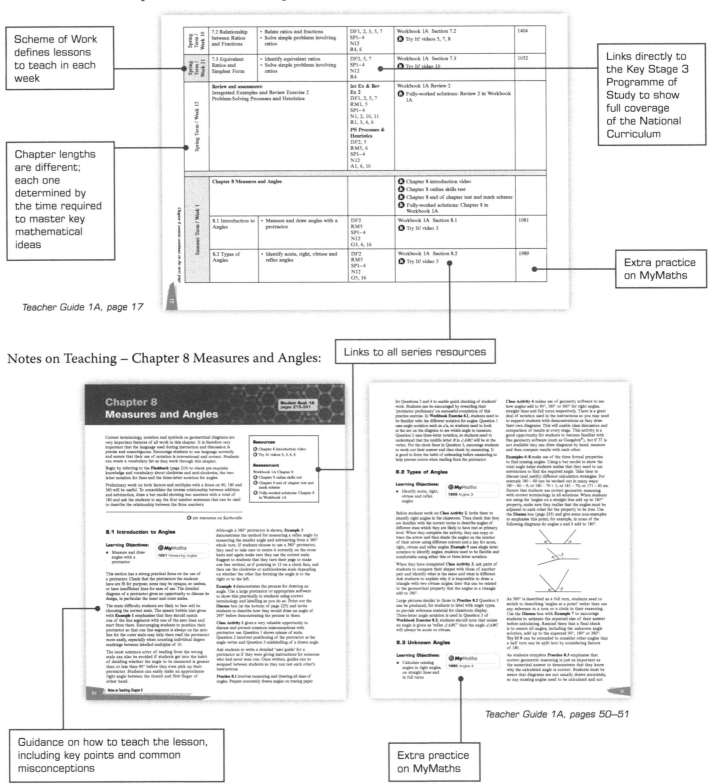

Teacher Guide 1A, page 17

Links directly to the Key Stage 3 Programme of Study to show full coverage of the National Curriculum

Extra practice on MyMaths

Notes on Teaching – Chapter 8 Measures and Angles:

Links to all series resources

Guidance on how to teach the lesson, including key points and common misconceptions

Extra practice on MyMaths

Teacher Guide 1A, pages 50–51

Consolidation is provided throughout the **Student Book** as well as in the **Workbook exercises, Graded Question Bank exercises** (mainly for Middle and Higher Tiers), and the **online assessments on Kerboodle.**

Fully-worked solutions for all exercises, to encourage full understanding, are provided in the Teacher Guide (for the Student Book) and on Kerboodle (for the Workbook and Graded Question Bank).

Motivating Students' Learning

It is vital to show students *why* they learn mathematics, alongside *how*. Although not exclusive to teaching for mastery, this is essential to it.

Every Student Book chapter starts with an example of how the maths can be related to real life. This is supported by a **film on the digital book** on Kerboodle

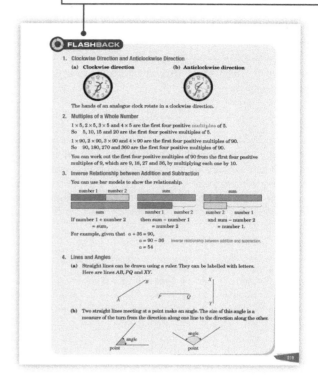

Learning objectives at the beginning of every chapter state what is covered

Student Book 1A, pages 218–219

Flashbacks (and **Recall boxes**, see page 4) are where you can check on your class' prior learning and they are a core feature of *Discovering Mathematics*. For a Foundation set, the transition from Key Stage 2 is a particularly important time. You will find the Flashback at the start of every chapter a valuable way of checking your students' knowledge and identifying any gaps before you move into the main content of the chapter.

At the end of every chapter, **Review** summarises the key learning points that have been covered. This can be used for revision

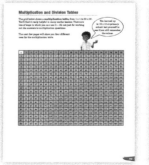

Student Book 1A, page 238

The **Number Hacks** tables at the end of the book support students with basic four-operation arithmetic, so that difficulty with calculation *procedures* doesn't curtail them developing their understanding of mathematical *concepts*. Suggestions to use the tables are given alongside Class Activities, Try It! and Practice questions.

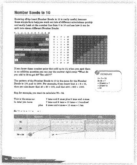

Student Book 1A, pages 358, 359 and 362

Guided Discovery

In Singapore, educators talk about '**Discovery**' rather than '**Mastery**'. The aim is to **guide** students on a journey of **discovery** to uncover mathematical concepts for themselves. When a student grasps a new concept or operation for themselves, they retain it more reliably than when they are fed it.

In *Discovering Mathematics*, Class Activities in the Student Books allow students to work through the problems with the teacher in class and encourage discussion and group learning. The activities should be mostly done through **pair work** and **small group work**, harnessing peer support.

The **Class Activities** are there to prime and motivate students. They encourage students to reason and engage with the underlying mathematics. This is the essence of the mastery approach: helping students to figure out the WHY of a mathematical operation (conceptual understanding) will lead to them having a much surer grasp of the HOW, the procedural fluency. (By contrast, when lessons are designed 'fluency first, reasoning afterwards', many students never reach the reasoning and so never secure their understanding.)

Technology supports some of the learning experiences in the Class Activities. A specific section on IT Exploration in every chapter in the Foundation Tier Workbooks encourages development of IT skills.

In a traditional Mathematics textbook series in the UK, class activities are confined to the Teacher Guides. In *Discovering Mathematics* they are a more central part of the course. They appear throughout the Student Books, to encourage students to engage with their own learning

---

Objective is clearly defined to show students what they are aiming to achieve in the Class Activity

Remark boxes remind students to use the Number Hack tables to help with basic calculations

The reasoning catalysed by the Class Activities prepares students to develop procedural fluency

Student Book 1A, pages 33–34 and 292

Place value counters are used as a concrete resource to develop deep understanding of the four operations in Foundation Tier Year 7. (Note that: Algebra discs are introduced in Year 8 and 9 in Foundation Tier but are used in all three years in Middle and Higher Tiers)

Questioning: students are asked to *think* about and *explain* their reasoning

Discuss boxes encourage paired and group working

In *Discovering Mathematics*, **Examples** with full solutions appear throughout the Student Books. The solutions are always written in full sentences to encourage language development. Additional notes are provided to support understanding and to support the application of the maths in other contexts. The aim is to develop students' confidence and independence.

Examples are always followed by **Try It!** practice questions. They are designed to secure progression in small steps. They allow continuous assessment and rapid intervention.

Fully-worked solutions for all Try It! questions are given in the Teacher Guide. Key Try It! questions also have narrated solution videos on Kerboodle. Both formats show how to present mathematical solutions using precise mathematical language and encourage development of reasoning skills.

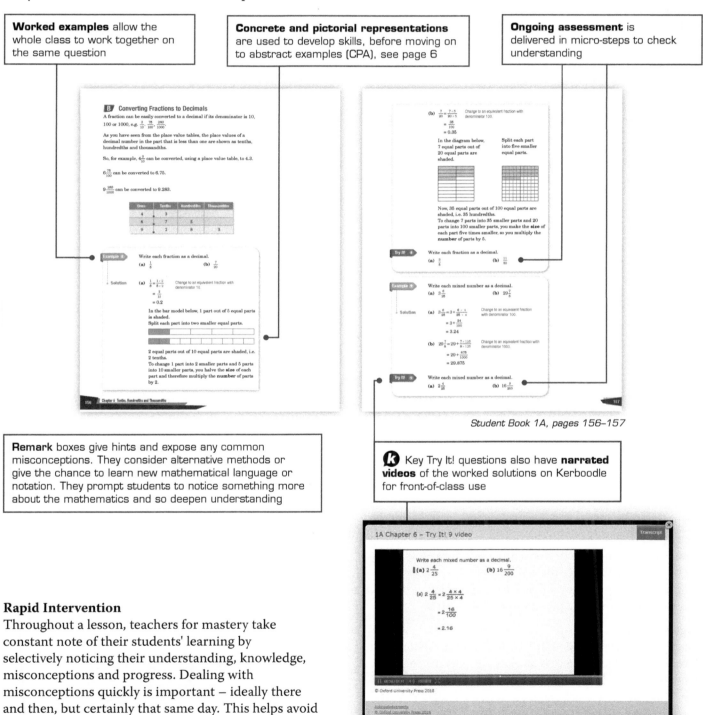

Worked examples allow the whole class to work together on the same question

Concrete and pictorial representations are used to develop skills, before moving on to abstract examples (CPA), see page 6

Ongoing assessment is delivered in micro-steps to check understanding

Student Book 1A, pages 156–157

Remark boxes give hints and expose any common misconceptions. They consider alternative methods or give the chance to learn new mathematical language or notation. They prompt students to notice something more about the mathematics and so deepen understanding

🅚 Key Try It! questions also have **narrated videos** of the worked solutions on Kerboodle for front-of-class use

Rapid Intervention

Throughout a lesson, teachers for mastery take constant note of their students' learning by selectively noticing their understanding, knowledge, misconceptions and progress. Dealing with misconceptions quickly is important – ideally there and then, but certainly that same day. This helps avoid errors becoming embedded.

Concrete-Pictorial-Abstract (CPA) Approach

It matters how students learn. Most students develop secure mathematical knowledge by:

- experiencing **concrete** examples, e.g. imagine going to a shop on Monday and buying two teas and three muffins for £5.10 and on Tuesday buying two teas and one muffin for £2.90
- moving to **pictorial** representations, e.g. using two red bars and three blue bars to represent 510, and two red bars and one blue bar to represent 290
- progressing to **abstract** statements using words, e.g. expressing the information as $2x + 3y = 510$ and $2x + y = 290$.

In *Discovering Mathematic*s, we believe that *all* students should reason with concrete manipulatives and pictorial representations before doing so with abstract words and symbols. These different representations of mathematical concepts are key to developing deep understanding. Just as teaching for mastery is for all students, so are manipulatives and practical resources.

Word of warning: you and your students will need to invest some time in grasping new pictorial and concrete models for representing mathematics. When teaching for mastery, it's important to introduce new models sparingly, and then to use them consistently.

In *Discovering Mathematics 1A*, we focus on bar models and place value counters but we suggest other concrete resources in the Student Book and in the Notes on Teaching in this guide, and algebra discs are used in Foundation Tier in Years 8 and 9.

Bar Models

Bar models are used throughout the series in problem-solving. It's a big leap for students to take a word-based problem and then formulate an abstract mathematical solution. Bar models are a valuable stepping stone to achieving that. You will need to take time with your students: when they first encounter a bar model, it might even take them longer to solve the problem than without a bar model. But with practice, they'll find the bar model becomes a powerful tool, especially for problems requiring multiplicative reasoning.

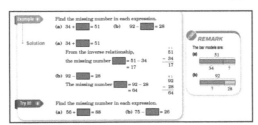

Student Book 1A, page 18

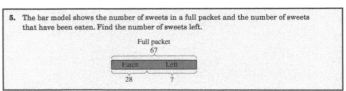

Student Book 1A, page 20

Place Value Counters

Place value counters are presented pictorially in worked examples and class activities in the Student Books. These counters are widely available to purchase. Used together, these concrete and pictorial resources help students to visualise and understand the four basic operations on numbers: addition, subtraction, multiplication and division.

In the example shown here, multiplication is modelled using place value discs. Students can manipulate the physical discs and practice drawing them for calculations, such as 54 x 3. Together these support *all* students to progress to the grid method and then the column method, and to understand *why* the methods are related.

Algebra Discs

Algebra discs are included in Year 8 and 9 Foundation Tier. A class set of algebra discs is available as part of the series. The discs will help guide your students as they explore new concepts, ultimately helping them to master algebra in its abstract form.

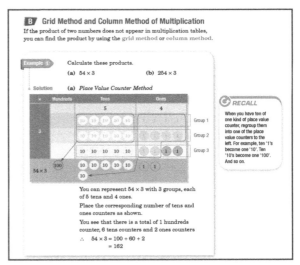

Student Book 1A, page 36

Precise Mathematical Language

Discovering Mathematics places great emphasis on the use of precise mathematical language. Teachers for mastery strive to give all their students the confidence, the vocabulary and the opportunity to explain themselves and justify their mathematical conclusions. This is as relevant in Early Years as it is in Key Stage 3, GCSE and A-level. Maintaining consistent language will support understanding.

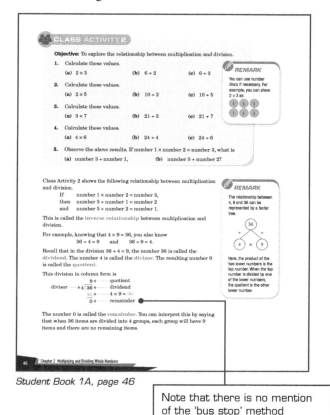

Student Book 1A, page 46

Note that there is no mention of the 'bus stop' method for division – division has no connection with bus stops!

Solutions are given in full sentences in the Student Books, and in the fully-worked solutions in the Teacher Guide and on Kerboodle.

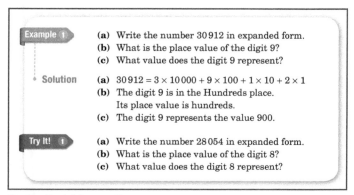

Example 1	(a) Write the number 30 912 in expanded form.
	(b) What is the place value of the digit 9?
	(c) What value does the digit 9 represent?
Solution	(a) $30\,912 = 3 \times 10\,000 + 9 \times 100 + 1 \times 10 + 2 \times 1$
	(b) The digit 9 is in the Hundreds place. Its place value is hundreds.
	(c) The digit 9 represents the value 900.
Try It! 1	(a) Write the number 28 054 in expanded form.
	(b) What is the place value of the digit 8?
	(c) What value does the digit 8 represent?

Student Book 1A, page 6

The use of complete sentences encourages students to think clearly, it helps them to grasp the mathematical language, and it allows you, the teacher, to check they have truly understood a given concept.

Mathematical reasoning is encouraged in the approach to questioning.

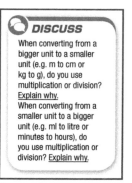

DISCUSS

When converting from a bigger unit to a smaller unit (e.g. m to cm or kg to g), do you use multiplication or division? Explain why.
When converting from a smaller unit to a bigger unit (e.g. ml to litre or minutes to hours), do you use multiplication or division? Explain why.

Student Book 1A, page 166

2. Robert says that 'every angle is either acute, obtuse or reflex'. Do you agree with Robert? Explain your answer.

Student Book 1A, page 230

Questions and discussion points ask students to 'Explain' or to 'Justify'. This is an opportunity for students to engage in reasoning and demonstrate their depth of understanding of a concept. This supports students to develop mastery, shown by their not just knowing how to 'do the math', but also developing an understanding of *why* it works.

Open questions, which have more than one possible answer, are flagged in the series. These questions encourage students to develop depth of understanding and allow them to see that there can be more than one correct answer to a mathematics question.

10. Create more than one algebraic expression in x such that the value of each expression is 7 when $x = 3$.

OPEN QUESTION

Student Book 1A, page 101

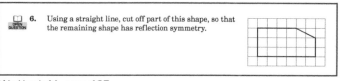

6. Using a straight line, cut off part of this shape, so that the remaining shape has reflection symmetry.

OPEN QUESTION

Workbook 1A, page 137

Try encouraging students to create a mathematics glossary in the back of their exercise books. Give them time to add to it when they meet new mathematics vocabulary.

Assessment

Assessment is at the heart of *Discovering Mathematics*. The teaching for mastery methodology for assessment is, at its core, straightforward:

1 **Formative assessment**: check students' understanding of a topic and identify weak spots.

2 **Gap-filling**: support students with any weak spots.

3 **Summative assessment**: test students' progress towards mastery of the topic.

1 Formative assessment

(a) End-of-chapter section exercises

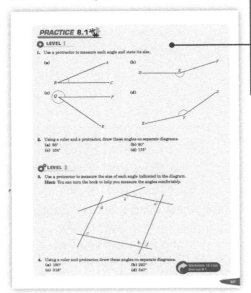

Student Book 1A, page 227

Split into Levels 1 and 2 to allow for differentiation within class:
Level 1 – fluency;
Level 2 – application and word-based problems

The teacher-facing fully-worked solutions in the Teacher Guide have *GCSE grades assigned to each Level

(b) Number Hacks

These tables and the information in them have an implicit assessment function alongside their direct purpose. If your students need to use the Subtraction Within 20 table to complete the tasks and activities in Chapter 1, for example, this suggests that it would be time well spent to revisit and reinforce Number Bonds up to 20.

Number Hacks	358
Addition and Subtraction Within 20	358
Multiplication and Division Tables	359
Number Bonds to 10	362

Student Book 1A, pages 358–63

(c) Online skills test for every chapter **k**

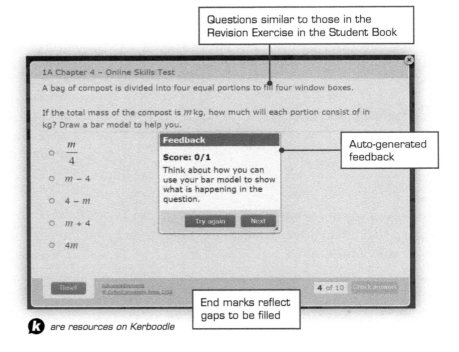

Questions similar to those in the Revision Exercise in the Student Book

Auto-generated feedback

End marks reflect gaps to be filled

k *are resources on Kerboodle*

2 Gap-filling

By gap-filling, we mean helping the student to re-visit and master any weaker areas identified by the formative assessment. The Review sections, Examples and Try It! questions in the Student Books, and the Try It! videos on Kerboodle are all valuable resources for remedial work

It can be very effective to share students' solutions and explanations with their peers – exemplary ones but also those that reveal a misconception, or those that reach a solution in a novel or sub-optimal way.

③ Summative assessment

(a) 'Challenge' activity for every chapter

Intended for all students, the activities provide extra opportunity to deepen understanding and to practise problem-solving methods

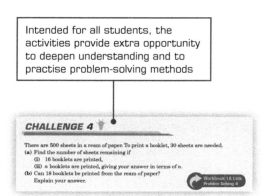

Student Book 1A, page 102

(b) Revision Exercise for every chapter

Covers all content of the chapter

Science and Finance contexts flagged to encourage cross-curricular working

Questions ramp-up in difficulty

Problem-solving questions clearly identified

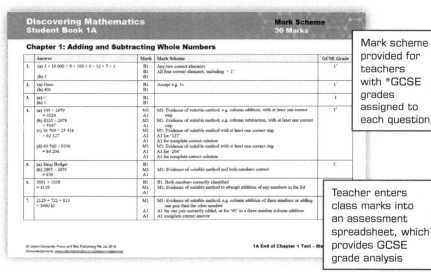

REVISION EXERCISE 4

Where necessary, draw and label bar models to help you represent the relationship between the variables.

1. The capacity of a bowl is 240 ml more than that of a cup. Find the capacity of the bowl when the capacity of the cup is
   (a) 250 ml, (b) 280 ml, (c) x ml.
2. In a basketball match, Sophia's score is nine less than Aria's score. Find Sophia's score if Aria's score is
   (a) 13, (b) 26, (c) a.
3. The monthly salary of a manager is four times the monthly salary of a clerk. Find the monthly salary of the manager if the monthly salary of the clerk is
   (a) £2000, (b) £2350, (c) £y.
4. Sulfur powder is divided equally into five portions for an experiment. Find the mass of each portion if the total mass of the sulfur powder is
   (a) 120 grams, (b) 325 grams, (c) m grams.
5. Find the value of $56 + p$ when
   (a) $p = 12$, (b) $p = 39$.
6. Find the value of $q - 15$ when
   (a) $q = 17$, (b) $q = 24$.
7. Work out the value of $3r$ when
   (a) $r = 7$, (b) $r = 14$.
8. Evaluate the value of $\frac{s}{9}$ when
   (a) $s = 18$, (b) $s = 45$.
9. The temperature of water in a sauce pan is $(13 + 5t)$°C, after being heated on the stove for t minutes.
   (a) Find the temperature when $t = 11$.
   (b) What is the initial temperature of the water?
10. The amount of money left on a travel card after x journeys is £$(73 - 5x)$.
    (a) Find the amount left after 12 journeys.
    (b) Can you use the expression to work out the amount left after 15 journeys? Explain your answer.

Student Book 1A, page 103

The teacher-facing fully-worked solutions in the Teacher Guide have *GCSE grades assigned to each question

(c) Online end-of-chapter printable test 🅚 (with associated spreadsheet for class monitoring)

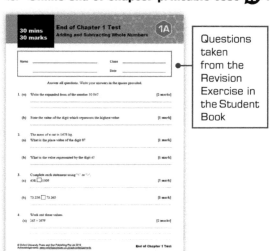

Questions taken from the Revision Exercise in the Student Book

Mark scheme provided for teachers with *GCSE grades assigned to each question

Teacher enters class marks into an assessment spreadsheet, which provides GCSE grade analysis

Supplementary Assessment

Additional assessment opportunities can be found throughout the Foundation Tier resources.

Student Book:
- Integrated Examples and Review Exercises appear after every few chapters
- Problems in Real-world Contexts question the content of the whole book in real-life situations
- The self-assessment booklet on Kerboodle allows students to reflect on their own strengths and weaknesses 🅚

Workbook:
- Each chapter is matched to the corresponding Student Book chapter
- Questions are split into Levels 1 and 2 as in the Student Book
- Problem-Solving and IT Exploration exercises can be found at the end of every chapter
- The self-assessment checklist can be used by students to track confidence levels

Graded Question Bank:
- Questions are split into Levels 1–3
- Each chapter directly corresponds to the Student Book chapter for Middle and Higher Tier but you will find many of the Level 1 and 2 questions useful for Foundation Tier students
- Available in editable format on Kerboodle for teachers to make up their own tests 🅚

*GCSE grades are an assessment of actual grade, not a projection to GCSE result.
Three sub-grades are allocated, e.g. 1⁻, 1, 1⁺, 2⁻, 2, 2⁺ etc.

Metacognition

Throughout *Discovering Mathematics*, students are encouraged to reflect on new concepts they've learnt and to test their own understanding. This self-reflection is a proven way of accelerating learning.

A **Write in Your Journal** feature at the end of every chapter asks students to reflect on concepts covered in the chapter and to practise communicating mathematically. We recommend providing a separate exercise book for your students, which they can use exclusively as their mathematics journal.

Write in Your Journal

Josh wants to buy a box to store his collection of comics. Each comic is 20 cm wide and 25 cm long, and a few mm thick. Draw or describe a box that it would be sensible for Josh to buy. What are the dimensions of the box? Explain why you have chosen these dimensions for the box.

Student Book 1A, page 310

Discuss boxes appear in each chapter. These provide opportunities for students to work in pairs or groups to think and communicate mathematically.

DISCUSS

Can you use curved lines to draw an angle? Discuss your answer with a partner.

DISCUSS

Which method of multiplication do you find easiest to understand and use? Give your reason.

Consider alternative methods

Student Book 1A, pages 221 and 38

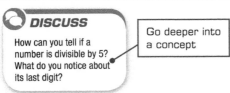

DISCUSS

How can you tell if a number is divisible by 5? What do you notice about its last digit?

Go deeper into a concept

Discuss possible misconceptions

Student Book 1A, page 62

Problem Solving

Skill and confidence at problem-solving is seen as the ultimate goal of teaching for mastery. It equips students to use mathematics in the real world, through their careers and through their lives.

Every exercise in the series includes problem-solving questions, with an emphasis on real-life contexts. They are all clearly identified in the Student Books, Workbooks and Graded Question Bank.

Every chapter in the Workbook has a Problem-solving activity at the end. This is to give students more opportunities to develop their understanding of problem-solving methods.

Every Student Book also has two separate sections dedicated to problem-solving:

1. **Problem-solving Processes and Heuristics** – help students to learn about the steps to take to solve a problem: understand the problem, devise a plan, carry out the plan, and then look back. Examples are given to work through the problem-solving strategies.

2. **Problems in Real-world Contexts** – help students to recognise where mathematics is useful in everyday life, consolidate their learning of problem-solving strategies, and consider what mathematics they have learnt that is relevant to each problem.

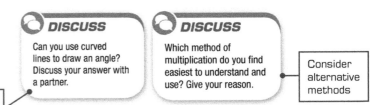

12. Sophia takes $\frac{3}{4}$ of an hour to do an assignment. Donna takes $\frac{3}{5}$ of an hour to do the same task.
    (a) Who is faster? Explain your answer.
    (b) How many minutes does the faster person take?

Student Book 1A, page 144

PROBLEM SOLVING 6

Jenny is trying to find a particular decimal number with three decimal places.

1. The decimal is between $\frac{3}{4}$ and $\frac{17}{20}$.
2. The decimal has the digit 8 in the hundredths place.
3. The thousandths digit is the highest common factor (HCF) of 10 and 14.

Find Jenny's particular decimal number.

Workbook 1A, page 104

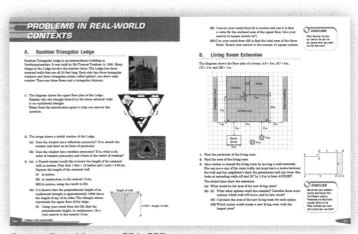

Student Book 1A, pages 354–355

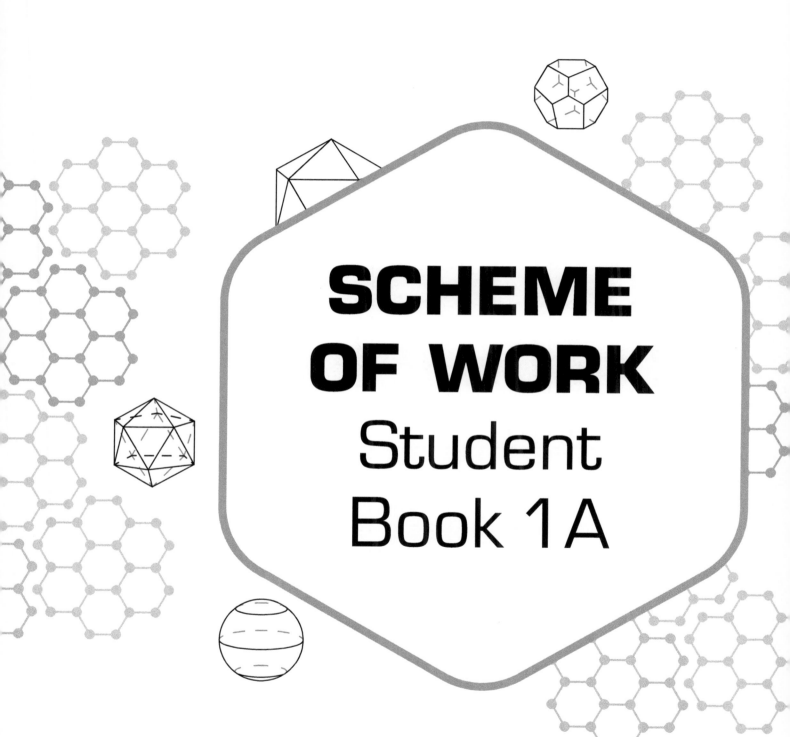

SCHEME OF WORK
Student Book 1A

The *Discovering Mathematics* full series Schemes of Work can be found at www.oxfordsecondary.co.uk/discoveringmathematics

This **Scheme of Work** is for *Discovering Mathematics Student Book 1A*. The detailed Schemes of Work and KS3 POS matching grids for the whole series of *Discovering Mathematics* can be found at www.oxfordsecondary.co.uk/discoveringmathematics

Discovering Mathematics has been adapted from the Singapore series to match fully with the Key Stage 3 Programme of Study (KS3 POS), which is available at www.gov.uk/government/publications/national-curriculum-in-england-mathematics-programmes-of-study

References to the KS3 POS in this Scheme of Work have been abbreviated as follows:
DF – Developing Fluency; **RM** – Reason Mathematically; **SP** – Solve Problems; **N** – Number; **A** – Algebra; **R** – Ratio, Proportion and Rates of Change; **G** – Geometry and Measures; **P** – Probability; **S** – Statistics.

(K) in the Series Resources column shows content available on *Discovering Mathematics Kerboodle* at www.kerboodle.com.

Term / Week	Chapter / Chapter Section	Learning Objectives	KS3 Programme of Study Reference	Series Resources (in addition to Student Book 1A)	MyMaths Codes
	Chapter 1 Adding and Subtracting Whole Numbers			(K) Chapter 1 introduction video (K) Chapter 1 online skills test (K) Chapter 1 end of chapter test and mark scheme (K) Fully-worked solutions: Chapter 1 in Workbook 1A	
Autumn term / Week 1	1.1 Place Values and Order of Numbers	• State the place values of the digits in whole numbers • Order and compare whole numbers	DF1, 2, 5, 7 RM1, 5 SP1–4 N1, 2, 12	Workbook 1A Section 1.1 (K) Try It! video 1	1918
Autumn term / Week 2	1.2 Addition	• Add whole numbers, using different methods • Use addition to solve real life problems	DF2, 5, 7 RM1, 5 SP1–4 N4, 12	Workbook 1A Section 1.2 (K) Try It! video 6	1399
Autumn term / Week 3	1.3 Subtraction	• Subtract whole, numbers, using different methods • Use subtraction to solve real-life problems • Recognise and use the inverse relationship between addition and subtraction	DF2, 5, 7 RM1, 5 SP1–4 N4, 6, 12	Workbook 1A Section 1.3 (K) Try It! videos 7, 9	1903, 1908, 1398, 1400
Autumn term / Week 4	1.4 Efficient Addition and Subtraction by Hand	• Add and subtract whole numbers using mental methods, using different methods	DF2, 5, 7 RM1, 5 SP1–4 N4, 12	Workbook 1A Section 1.4 (K) Try It! video 13	1398, 1342, 1344

Term / Week	Chapter / Chapter Section	Learning Objectives	KS3 Programme of Study Reference	Series Resources (in addition to Student Book 1A)	MyMaths Codes
	Chapter 2 Multiplying and Dividing Whole Numbers			♥ Chapter 2 introduction video ♥ Chapter 2 online skills test ♥ Chapter 2 end of chapter test and mark scheme ♥ Fully-worked solutions: Chapter 2 in Workbook 1A	
Autumn term / Week 5	2.1 Multiplication	• Multiply whole numbers, using different methods and techniques • Use multiplication to solve real-life problems • Calculate square and cube numbers and write these numbers using indices	DF1, 2, 5, 7 RM1, 5 SP1–4 N4, 6, 7, 12, 15	Workbook 1A Section 2.1 🅺 Try It! videos 4, 7	1367, 1024, 1025, 1904, 1911, 1401
Autumn term / Week 6	2.2 Division	• Divide whole numbers, using different methods and techniques • Recognise the inverse relationship between multiplication and division • Use division to solve real life problems	DF2, 5, 7 RM1, 5 SP1–4 N4, 6, 12	Workbook 1A Section 2.2 🅺 Try It! video 12	1905, 1767, 5682
Autumn term / Week 7	2.3 Multiplying and Dividing Efficiently Without a Calculator	• Multiply and divide whole numbers, using different methods and techniques	DF2, 5, 7 RM1, 5 SP1–4 N4, 6, 12	Workbook 1A Section 2.3 🅺 Try It! videos 14, 18	1910
Autumn term / Week 8	2.4 Factors, Multiples and Prime Numbers	• List factors, common factors and find highest common factors • List multiples, common multiples and find lowest common multiples • List primes and prime factors	DF2, 7 RM1, 5 SP1–4 N3, 12	Workbook 1A Section 2.4 🅺 Try It! videos 20, 22, 24	1035, 1032

Term / Week	Chapter / Chapter Section	Learning Objectives	KS3 Programme of Study Reference	Series Resources (in addition to Student Book 1A)	MyMaths Codes
	Chapter 3 Calculation			Chapter 3 introduction video Chapter 3 online skills test Chapter 3 end of chapter test and mark scheme Fully-worked solutions: Chapter 3 in Workbook 1A	
Autumn term / Week 9	3.1 Rounding Numbers	• Round numbers to the nearest 10, 100, 1000 or 10000	DF2, 5, 7 RM1, 5 SP1–4 N2, 12, 13	Workbook 1A Section 3.1 Try It! video 2	1003, 1840
Autumn term / Week 10	3.2 Estimation	• Estimate answers to calculations	DF2, 7 RM1, 5 SP1–4 N12, 13, 14	Workbook 1A Section 3.2 Try It! video 5	1002
	3.3 Order of Operations	• Use the order of operations	DF1, 2, 7 RM1, 5, 6 SP1–4 N4, 5, 7, 12	Workbook 1A Section 3.3 Try It! videos 8, 12, 14	1167
	3.4 Using a Calculator	• Use a calculator	DF2, 7 RM1, 5 SP1–4 N4, 5, 7, 12, 13, 14, 15	Workbook 1A Section 3.4	
Autumn term / Week 11	**Chapter 4 Use of Letters**			Chapter 4 introduction video Chapter 4 online skills test Chapter 4 end of chapter test and mark scheme Fully-worked solutions: Chapter 4 in Workbook 1A	
	4.1 Using Letters to Represent Numbers	• Use letters to represent numbers	DF2, 3, 5, 7 RM1, 3, 5 SP1–4 N12 A1, 3, 6, 10	Workbook 1A Section 4.1 Try It! videos 2, 4	1158

Week	Topic	Learning objectives	Codes	Resources	Page refs
Autumn term / Week 12	4.2 Substitution of Numbers for Letters	• Substitute numbers for letters	DF2, 3, 4, 7 RM1, 3, 5 SP1–4 N12 A1, 2, 3, 6, 10	Workbook 1A Section 4.2 ⏯ Try It! video 6	1187
	Review and assessment: Integrated Examples and Review Exercise 1		DF1, 2, 4, 7 RM1, 3, 5, 6 SP1–4 N1, 2, 3, 4, 5, 6, 7, 12, 13, 14 A1, 2, 6, 10	Workbook 1A Review 1 ⏯ Fully-worked solutions: Review 1 in Workbook 1A	
	Chapter 5 Understanding Fractions			⏯ Chapter 5 introduction video ⏯ Chapter 5 online skills test ⏯ Chapter 5 end of chapter test and mark scheme ⏯ Fully-worked solutions: Chapter 5 in Workbook 1A	
Spring Term / Week 1	5.1 Idea of Fractions	• Understand and use fraction notation	DF1, 2, 5, 7 RM1, 5 SP1–4 N12 R3	Workbook 1A Section 5.1 ⏯ Try It! videos 5, 7	1369, 1220
Spring Term / Week 2	5.2 Improper Fractions and Mixed Numbers	• Convert between improper fractions and mixed numbers	DF1, 2, 5, 7 RM1, 5 SP1–4 N4, 12 R3	Workbook 1A Section 5.2 ⏯ Try It! videos 8, 9, 11	1019
	5.3 Equivalent Fractions	• Identify equivalent fractions	DF1, 2, 5, 7 RM1, 5 SP1–4 N12	Workbook 1A Section 5.3 ⏯ Try It! videos 12, 15	1042
Spring Term / Week 3	5.4 Comparing Fractions	• Compare fractions with the same numerator or denominator	DF1, 2, 5, 7 RM1, 5 SP1–4 N2, 4, 12	Workbook 1A Section 5.4 ⏯ Try It! video 18	1906, 5683
Spring Term / Week 4	5.5 Fractions of Quantities	• Calculate fractions of quantities	DF1, 2, 5, 7 RM1, 5 SP1–4 N11, 12 R3	Workbook 1A Section 5.5 ⏯ Try It! video 20	1402, 1841

Term / Week	Chapter / Chapter Section	Learning Objectives	KS3 Programme of Study Reference	Series Resources (in addition to Student Book 1A)	MyMaths Codes
Spring Term / Week 5	**Chapter 6 Tenths, Hundredths and Thousandths**			Chapter 6 introduction video; Chapter 6 online skills test; Chapter 6 end of chapter test and mark scheme; Fully-worked solutions: Chapter 6 in Workbook 1A	
	6.1 Decimal Place Values	• Identify the tenths, hundredths and thousandths in decimals • Order decimals up to three decimal places	DF2, 5, 7 RM1, 5 SP1–4 N1, 2, 12	Workbook 1A Section 6.1; Try It! video 3	1378, 1076, 1009, 1072
Spring Term / Week 6	6.2 Conversion between Fractions and Decimals	• Convert fractions to decimals • Convert decimals up to three decimal places to fractions	DF2, 5, 7 RM1, 5 SP1–4 N2, 12	Workbook 1A Section 6.2; Try It! videos 7, 9	
Spring Term / Week 7	6.3 Multiplying and Dividing by 10, 100 and 1000	• Multiply and divide by 10, 100 and 1000 • Convert money and measures	DF2, 7 RM1, 5 SP1–4 N4, 6, 12 R1	Workbook 1A Section 6.3; Try It! videos 15, 17	1027, 1013, 1091
Spring Term / Week 7	6.4 Introducing Percentages	• Define percentages • Express percentages • Relate fractions, decimals and percentages	DF2, 5, 7 RM1, 5 SP1–4 N10, 12	Workbook 1A Section 6.4; Try It! videos 19, 20, 22	1029
Spring Term / Week 8	6.5 Percentages of Quantities	• Find percentages of quantities	DF2, 5, 7 RM1, 5 SP1–4 N10, N11, 12	Workbook 1A Section 6.5; Try It! video 25	5688, 1030
Spring Term / Week 9	**Chapter 7 Introduction to Ratio**			Chapter 7 introduction video; Chapter 7 online skills test; Chapter 7 end of chapter test and mark scheme; Fully-worked solutions: Chapter 7 in Workbook 1A	
	7.1 Idea of Ratios	• Write a ratio between two quantities	DF2, 5, 7 SP1–4 N12 R4	Workbook 1A Section 7.1; Try It! video 3	

Spring Term / Week 10	7.2 Relationship between Ratios and Fractions	• Relate ratios and fractions • Solve simple problems involving ratios	DF1, 2, 3, 5, 7 SP1–4 N12 R4, 6	Workbook 1A Section 7.2 k Try It! videos 5, 7, 8	1404
Spring Term / Week 11	7.3 Equivalent Ratios and Simplest Form	• Identify equivalent ratios • Solve simple problems involving ratios	DF2, 5, 7 SP1–4 N12 R4	Workbook 1A Section 7.3 k Try It! video 10	1052
Spring Term / Week 12	**Review and assessment:** Integrated Examples and Review Exercise 2 Problem-Solving Processes and Heuristics		**Int Ex & Rev Ex 2** DF1, 2, 5, 7 RM1, 5 SP1–4 N1, 2, 10, 11 R1, 3, 4, 6 **PS Processes & Heuristics** DF2, 5 RM5, 6 SP1–4 N12 A1, 6, 10	Workbook 1A Review 2 k Fully-worked solutions: Review 2 in Workbook 1A	
Summer Term / Week 1	**Chapter 8 Measures and Angles**			k Chapter 8 introduction video k Chapter 8 online skills test k Chapter 8 end of chapter test and mark scheme k Fully-worked solutions: Chapter 8 in Workbook 1A	
	8.1 Introduction to Angles	• Measure and draw angles with a protractor	DF2 RM5 SP1–4 N12 G3, 6, 16	Workbook 1A Section 8.1 k Try It! video 3	1081
	8.2 Types of Angles	• Identify acute, right, obtuse and reflex angles	DF2 RM5 SP1–4 N12 G5, 16	Workbook 1A Section 8.2 k Try It! video 5	1989

Chapter 8 content continues on the next page

Term / Week	Chapter / Chapter Section	Learning Objectives	KS3 Programme of Study Reference	Series Resources (in addition to Student Book 1A)	MyMaths Codes
Summer Term / Week 2	8.3 Unknown Angles	• Calculate missing angles in right angles, on straight lines and in full turns	DF2 RM5 SP1–4 N12 G5, 10, 16	Workbook 1A Section 8.3 ▶ Try It! videos 6, 8	1990
Summer Term / Week 3	**Chapter 9 Symmetry**			▶ Chapter 9 introduction video ▶ Chapter 9 online skills test ▶ Chapter 9 end of chapter test and mark scheme ▶ Fully-worked solutions: Chapter 9 in Workbook 1A	
	9.1 Reflection Symmetry of Plane Figures	• Identify reflection symmetry and lines of symmetry • Create symmetrical figures and patterns	DF2, 7 RM5 SP1–4 N12 G5	Workbook 1A Section 9.1 ▶ Try It! video 1	1230
Summer Term / Week 4	9.2 Rotation Symmetry of Plane Figures	• Identify rotation symmetry • State the order of rotation symmetry	DF2, 7 RM5 SP1–4 N12 G5	Workbook 1A Section 9.2 ▶ Try It! video 4	1116
	Chapter 10 Perimeter and Area of Rectangles, Squares and Triangles			▶ Chapter 10 introduction video ▶ Chapter 10 online skills test ▶ Chapter 10 end of chapter test and mark scheme ▶ Fully-worked solutions: Chapter 10 in Workbook 1A	
Summer Term / Week 5	10.1 Perimeter of Squares and Rectangles	• Find the perimeter of squares and rectangles	DF2, 7 RM5 SP1–4 N12 G2, 7, 16	Workbook 1A Section 10.1 ▶ Try It! video 1	

Term / Week	Section	Objectives	Codes	Resources	
Summer Term / Week 6	10.2 Area of Squares and Rectangles	• Calculate the area of squares and rectangles	DF2, 7 RM5 SP1–4 N12 G7, 16	Workbook 1A Section 10.2 ▶ Try It! video 5	
Summer Term / Week 7	10.3 Perimeter and Area of Triangles	• Find the perimeter of triangles • Calculate the area of triangles	DF2, 7 RM5 SP1–4 N12 G1, 7, 16	Workbook 1A Section 10.3 ▶ Try It! videos 9, 12	1110
Summer Term / Week 8	**Chapter 11 Volume and Surface Area of Cuboids, including Cubes**			▶ Chapter 11 introduction video ▶ Chapter 11 online skills test ▶ Chapter 11 end of chapter test and mark scheme ▶ Fully-worked solutions: Chapter 11 in Workbook 1A	
	11.1 Nets of Cuboids, including Cubes	• Draw nets of cuboids, including cubes • Sketch cubes and cuboids	DF2, 7 RM5 SP1–4 N12 G15	Workbook 1A Section 11.1	
	11.2 Surface Area of Cuboids, including Cubes	• Calculate the surface area of cuboids, including cubes	DF2, 7 RM5 SP1–4 N12 G15, 16	Workbook 1A Section 11.2 ▶ Try It! video 4	
Summer Term / Week 9	11.3 Volume of Cuboids, including Cubes	• Calculate the volume of cuboids, including cubes	DF2, 7 RM5 SP1–4 N12 G1, 16	Workbook 1A Section 11.3 ▶ Try It! video 9	1137

Term / Week	Chapter / Chapter Section	Learning Objectives	KS3 Programme of Study Reference	Series Resources (in addition to Student Book 1A)	MyMaths Codes
Summer Term / Week 10	**Chapter 12 Collecting, Organising and Displaying Data**			⚡ Chapter 12 introduction video ⚡ Chapter 12 online skills test ⚡ Chapter 12 end of chapter test and mark scheme ⚡ Fully-worked solutions: Chapter 12 in Workbook 1A	
	12.1 Collecting, Classifying and Tabulating Data	• Collect data using different methods • Classify, organise and tabulate data	DF2, 7 SP1–4 N12	Workbook 1A Section 12.1	
Summer Term / Week 11	12.2 Pictograms, Vertical Line Charts and Bar Charts	• Read and interpret pictograms, vertical line charts and bar charts • Represent data in pictograms, vertical line charts and bar charts • Identify the advantages and disadvantages of pictograms, vertical line charts and bar charts	DF2, 7 SP1–4 N12 S1, 2	Workbook 1A Section 12.2 ⚡ Try It! video 4	1205, 1193
	12.3 Grouped Data	• Understand and interpret grouped data • Draw a grouped frequency table • Draw grouped data in a bar chart	DF2, 7 SP1–4 N2, 12 S1, 2	Workbook 1A Section 12.3 ⚡ Try It! video 10	1196
Summer Term / Week 12	**Review and assessment:** Integrated Examples and Review Exercise 3 Problems in Real-World Contexts	**Int Ex & Rev Ex 3** DF2, 7 RM5 SP1–4 N12 G1, 2, 3, 5, 10, 15 S1, 2 **Probs in Real-world Contexts** DF2, 7 RM5, 6 SP1–4 N4, 10, 12, 13 R1, 4, 6 G1, 2, 3, 5, 15	Workbook 1A Review 3 ⚡ Fully-worked solutions: Review 3 in Workbook 1A	

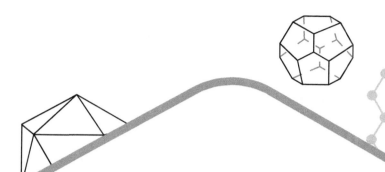

NOTES ON TEACHING
Student
Book 1A

Chapter 1
Adding and Subtracting Whole Numbers

Student Book 1A
pages 3–29

This chapter focusses on the importance of place value whilst looking at the properties of addition and subtraction and the relationships between these operations. The laws covered in this chapter are the foundation for understanding calculations and for later progression into algebra. Students should use place value charts, place value counters and other manipulatives such as base-ten blocks (e.g. Dienes®), in order to feel really confident in their understanding of place value, addition and subtraction. Give students enough time to familiarise themselves with partitioning and regrouping of numbers in order to improve their agility within calculations.

You could start this chapter with Section 1.4 as this section develops students' conceptual understanding of addition and subtraction. All the strategies in Section 1.4 should be shown concretely and pictorially, as students need to see, literally, why the addends can be reordered and why the tens and the ones of the addends can be separated and recombined in 'nicer' ways.

The bar model is introduced in this chapter as a pictorial representation to allow students to visualise what is happening in the calculations. Linking the concrete with the abstract in this way will help consolidate understanding. The bar model will need developing and practising so that it becomes a tool students are familiar with and happy to apply in different situations. It will be revisited on many occasions.

k are resources on Kerboodle

Resources

k Chapter 1 introduction video
k Try It! videos 1, 6, 7, 9, 13
Place value counters

Assessment

Workbook 1A Chapter 1
k Chapter 1 online skills test
k Chapter 1 end of chapter test and mark scheme
k Fully-worked solutions: Chapter 1 in Workbook 1A

1.1 Place Values and Order of Numbers

Learning Objectives:

 **MyMaths**

1918 Greater than and less than

● State the place values of the digits in whole numbers
● Order and compare whole numbers

Students should already be familiar with place value, whole, even and odd numbers and the term 'digit'. (See Part 1 of the **Flashback** on page 4.) It is important to spend time checking students have a secure understanding of place value and that they can read large numbers and understand the use of zero as a place holder. It is also important that students are aware from this early stage that equals means 'the same on both sides' and not just 'the answer is'. The **Recall** box on page 5 emphasises this point.

Students often find it difficult moving from thousands to ten thousands, so additional practice with these numbers is important. Ask students to use place value counters

and a place value table to show different numbers. Include some numbers containing the digit zero and ask students to explain how this is shown in the table. Discuss what would happen if the zero was not written in the number 7308 and how it would change the value represented by the other digits; use the **Discuss** box (page 6) to check understanding. Note that 'ones' and not 'units' is used for the first place value; this helps students understand the value of that column and is now being used widely in primary schools.

Ask students to use place value counters to build a number on the place value grid; start with small numbers and build up to larger numbers. Each time, ask the students to write the number in expanded form. This is a key skill which will help with future work, so make sure all are fluent. Discuss with students the place value of a digit and the value represented by a digit. Make sure these terms are used correctly and confidently before moving onto **Examples 1 and 2**.

Introduce ordering numbers through the use of number lines. Draw a partial number line on the board, for example from 7 to 12, and invite students to give you the next number to the right or to the left. Keep building this way so students can see the number line grow. Draw a new number line and place a number on the line. Give students sticky notes and challenge them to put a number on the line that is bigger than the first, smaller than the first, between two of the numbers etc. Try this with different starting numbers e.g. 15, 200, 375 etc. Another good activity is to draw three or so blank lines of the same length, one above the other, each labelled with a different scale (e.g. 0 to 100, 0 to 200 and 0 to 500), and ask students to mark 50 on each one.

Next indicate two numbers on the number line, ask students which is bigger or which is smaller. Do this a few times and then ask them to write a sentence about the position of a number in relation to another number and whether it is bigger or smaller. At this point introduce the inequality signs < and > and look at some examples. The following diagrams are a visual representation of the signs and can aid understanding. These can also be made using cubes or other objects.

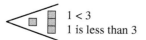 1 < 3
1 is less than 3

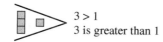 3 > 1
3 is greater than 1

The **Remark** box (page 6) also mentions the signs ≤ and ≥ for completion which you may also want to discuss, though these signs are not used in this chapter. Complete **Class Activity 1**. Questions 1 and 2 should be accessible to all, but some students may find plotting the numbers in Questions 3 and 4 challenging; if this is the case use some more number lines where the numbers are shown on the line before returning to these questions. If students find using the number line difficult then make the numbers with base-ten blocks and see which has more blocks (by value not number). Using the numbers as monetary values may help students to interpret the size of number more easily because this translates the abstract concept of 'number size' into a familiar concrete representation.

Discuss with students how numbers can be compared using place value and which digit(s) need to be considered. Work through **Example 3**; demonstrate the solutions using place value counters so that students can link the concrete to the abstract.

Practice 1.1 gives students the opportunity to consolidate their learning. Questions 3 and 6 will challenge their thinking about place value; ask students why they chose the answer they did and why they rejected the other numbers. Ask students to share their answers to Question 10 and discuss with each other why the different answers are correct. The **Workbook Exercise 1.1** presents a further opportunity for students to engage with this work.

1.2 Addition

Learning Objectives:

- Add whole numbers, using different methods
- Use addition to solve real-life problems

 **1399** Adding together

Students should be familiar with addition using place value counters and the column method when the sum of the digits in each place value does not exceed nine, see Part 2 of the **Flashback** (page 4). If students are not confident then spend some time working with this type of sum using the place value grid and place value counters. When they are confident, introduce the pink regroup section at the bottom of the chart explaining that when the digits in the ones column add to more than nine, ten (or twenty, or thirty etc.) of the ones are regrouped to make one (or two, or three etc.) extra ten(s) in the tens column, and so 1 (or 2, or 3 etc.) is added to the sum of the digits already in the tens column. Ensure students are using the correct language of 'regrouping' and that they don't use the term 'carrying'. Work with these questions for a while and build up to the question demonstrated on page 10. The **Remark** box on page 10 points students towards the addition table in the Number Hacks section of the Student Book, where they can check their calculations. Make sure students understand the regrouping before introducing the column method on page 11. **Class Activity 2** uses place value counters alongside the column method to help students link the concrete to the abstract. Question 3 highlights the similarities between methods and should deepen students' understanding. **Example 4** introduces numbers of different orders of magnitude (e.g. numbers in the thousands); discuss the importance of lining up the digits using place values. Show this calculation with base-ten blocks or place value counters.

Examples 5 and 6 use the bar model to show how to form a sum from information given in a question. Take time to explain the pictures if students are not familiar with the bar model. Again use place value counters alongside the column method to reinforce the regrouping. The **Discuss** box (page 13) asks a very important question. When students are convinced the answers are the same, discuss which method they feel is more efficient. Students should complete **Practice 1.2**. Make place value counters available so students can choose to use them if required. You may also want to encourage students to draw them in some questions so they have a pictorial as well as concrete experience. It is important to check early that students are positioning their numbers correctly in Questions 2 and 3 using place value. Challenge students further with Question 8 to see if they can answer the questions with no regrouping, with regrouping once, twice etc. then discuss their answers. Question 10 will be challenging for the students; it is a good idea to work on mini-whiteboards to encourage trial and improvement, and it may work best as a paired activity. Encourage the use of bar models for worded questions in **Workbook Exercise 1.2**.

1.3 Subtraction

Learning Objectives:

- Subtract whole numbers, using different methods
- Use subtraction to solve real-life problems
- Recognise and use the inverse relationship between addition and subtraction

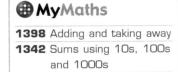

⊕ **My**Maths

1903 Introducing column subtraction

1908 More written methods

1398 Adding and taking away

1400 Comparing: finding the difference

Students should be familiar with subtracting numbers using place value counters and the column method where regrouping is not required, see Part 3 of the **Flashback** (page 5). Use some of these questions to make sure students have a good understanding then look at the question on page 15. Ask the students what is different about this question and why it may be more difficult to answer. Ensure students understand that when setting out a subtraction in column form, the number being subtracted is written at the bottom and that when carrying out the calculation the bottom number is always subtracted from the top. Explain why this time the red regroup space is placed at the top of the calculation. Work through the question using the place value counters, discussing the regrouping that is taking place and why it needs to happen. Again, take care with the language used throughout and remind students of the subtraction table mentioned in the **Remark** on page 15. Spend time practising questions with the place value grids and counters until students are confident with regrouping in this way.

Class Activity 3 uses the column method alongside the visual method so that students can make the link between the concrete and the abstract. Allow them to practise questions when one column is regrouped into the next column. Only when they are happy should you discuss **Example 7**. Give students time to practise the written method (after first evaluating using place value counters) using Questions 1 and 2 from **Practice 1.3** and Questions 1 and 2 in **Workbook Exercise 1.3**.

Class Activity 4 explores the inverse relationship between addition and subtraction. Ask students to draw bar models to show what is happening in each question and to help them see the link between the calculations. Continue to use bar models when discussing **Examples 8–10**. Students find this a difficult concept so spend time with different numbers until they are confident. Some students may find using plain counters with small number examples an easier starting point than the bar model; others will find using base-ten blocks, place value counters or number lines more accessible. If this is the case then build up to using bar models, as these pictures will be more useful as they move forward. Use both a concrete and pictorial representation for the examples to support understanding.

Complete the remaining questions from **Practice 1.3** and **Workbook Exercise 1.3**. Question 10 in the student book and Question 12 in the Workbook can be extended by asking students for answers where regrouping is and isn't required. Discuss these answers in pairs or as a class.

1.4 Efficient Addition and Subtraction by Hand

Learning Objectives:

- Add and subtract whole numbers, using different methods by hand

⊕ **My**Maths

1398 Adding and taking away

1342 Sums using 10s, 100s and 1000s

1344 Mixed sums over 100

Class Activity 5 explores the properties of addition. The questions help students notice what is happening in the sums and how the addition sums can be manipulated. Reveal that these are the commutative and associative laws of addition, and use bar models and place value counters to represent these laws pictorially. Ask the students to use the names of these laws each time they discuss a manipulation in a question in order to embed the understanding. Work through **Example 11** showing how these laws can make a calculation easier to solve. Discuss with students how they know whether a pair of numbers will give a multiple of 10 using the **Remark** on page 22 and look at the Number Hacks section to see number bonds to 10 (as mentioned in the final **Remark** box on page 22). Work through **Example 12** and then discuss the statements on page 23. Ask students to give numerical examples for each of these statements to consolidate understanding.

Work through **Example 13** looking at partitioning the second number. Again, place value counters may help here. Pay attention to the signs when completing the subtraction calculations. Discuss with students when a number is close to a multiple of 10 or 100 and how the use of near numbers can help to calculate an expression.

Money contexts can help students become confident with using near numbers; if you have 23p and you want 49p more I can give you 50p and then you give me back 1p, hence 23 + 49 = 23 + 50 − 1 = 73 − 1 = 72. Practising re-writing numbers using near numbers will give students confidence before looking at calculations. Work through **Examples 14 and 15**. Discuss if there is an alternative way to answer **Example 15** that may be easier (possibly −20 + 3) so students appreciate that there may be different methods.

Complete **Practice 1.4**. Encourage students to discuss a number of Level 1 questions with a partner explaining which method they used and why. Consolidate further using **Workbook Exercise 1.4**.

Ask students to complete **Challenge 1** (page 28) and make up some problems of their own for their classmates to solve.

Revision Exercise 1 allows students to review the learning in this chapter. Ask them to draw bar models for Questions 6–9 to practise this skill. Question 10 is best tackled using whiteboards or pieces of paper for each number so that they can manipulate the positions easily.

When completing **Write in Your Journal**, ask students to draw a bar model to show the problem and then to answer the questions in full sentences. Ask a few students to read these out to the class as this encourages thoughtful reasoning and strong explanations.

Use **Problem Solving 1** in the Workbook to assess whether students can apply the inverse relationship between addition and subtraction. This can be extended by asking students to design their own picture; encourage them to think about the minimum number of values they need to give to make solving it possible.

Use **IT Exploration 1** to generate numbers to work with. Students can then compare with the shortest two motorways in the UK or with motorways in other countries.

Chapter 2
Multiplying and Dividing Whole Numbers

Student Book 1A
pages 30–68

The **Flashback** (page 31) reminds students of the link between addition and subtraction, which can be modelled using a bar model. Ask students to write down the four relationships that can be seen for the bar model that corresponds with the generalised wording in Part 3.

Throughout this chapter consider the patterns within multiplication that enable students to link related multiplication calculations and consider the relationship between multiplication and division. Use counters to produce arrays for simple multiplication and division, as shown in Part 4 of the **Flashback**, to help students understand how to find answers before moving to the abstract methods. Continue to use bar models to bridge the thinking between worded questions and answers.

k are resources on Kerboodle

Resources

k Chapter 2 introduction video

k Try It! videos 4, 7, 12, 14, 18, 20, 22, 24

Place value counters

Assessment

Workbook 1A Chapter 2

k Chapter 2 online skills test

k Chapter 2 end of chapter test and mark scheme

k Fully-worked solutions: Chapter 2 in Workbook 1A

2.1 Multiplication

Learning Objectives:

- Multiply numbers, using different methods and techniques
- Use multiplication to solve real-life problems
- Calculate square and cube numbers and write these numbers using indices

⊕ MyMaths

1367	Mixed tables 2 to 12
1024	Multiply single digit
1025	Multiply double digits
1904	Short multiplication
1911	More short multiplication
1401	Comparing: how many times more?

Using counters, make some arrays and show explicitly the link between repeated addition and multiplication in a similar way to the chairs example on page 32. Using counters, discuss how 4 rows of 5 chairs is the same total as 5 rows of 4 chairs. Introduce the terms 'times' and 'product' and use these throughout the chapter. Look at the multiplication grid and ask students to explain how they use can use it to find products. Complete **Class Activity 1** (page 33) and discuss the properties of multiplication that are highlighted making sure students are aware of the commutative law of multiplication. Give pairs of students a copy of a square multiplication table and ask them to put a pair of different coloured counters on the products for each pair of calculations throughout Questions 1 and 2 of the activity. You can extend from Question 2 by asking students what's the same and

what's different about a set of related products such as 6×5, 6×10, 12×5 and 12×10. Manipulation of an array of counters or number rods (such as Cuisenaire®) may be helpful here. It is vital that students are fluent with the multiplication tables; help them to learn them by playing games involving multiplication, for example Fizz Buzz, or by using a pack of cards and, in pairs, turn two over and multiply the numbers together. Make sure that multiplying by zero is covered frequently as this can often be a stumbling block for some students. Give students sets of cards which include two arrays, two multiplication calculations and a product for them to match up as equivalent. The **Remark** on page 33 directs students to the multiplication table in the Number Hacks section.

Questions 3, 4 and 5 of **Class Activity 1** enable students to use place value counters to consolidate their understanding of multiplication by multiples of 10 and 100, which is essential for understanding multiplication of numbers beyond 12×12. Ask students to explain how the digits move when a number is multiplied by 10, 100 and so on; avoid descriptions of zeros being added as these may lead to misconceptions when decimal numbers are involved. Check student understanding by asking them to match the equal products in the **Discuss** box on page 40.

In Section B, both the grid method and column method are shown for multiplication, so that students can compare the efficiency of the methods as they work through the examples; use the **Discuss** box (page 38). Compare what is happening in both methods so that students understand they are equivalent. Point out that the products 12, 150 and 600 which appear in the grid method are written in the column method working from right to left, with one digit carried to the next column where necessary. The use of place value counters is illustrated; laminated blank grids to write and arrange counters on may be helpful for students who need additional support. Consolidate multiplying by a single digit number in **Examples 1 and 2** (notice the **Recall** box on page 36) before moving onto multiplying by the double digit numbers in **Examples 3 and 4**; students will often need much support to make this transition. The **Remark** box alongside Example 3 considers the use of place value counters to find 30×80. Alternatively, a pictorial approach using graph paper may be used: 3 big squares by 8 big squares makes 24 big squares each of which contains $10 \times 10 = 100$ small squares, hence 2400 small squares.

Example 3 shows two parts of the calculation separately as 36×2 and 36×80 before the combined column method for 36×82 is given. Some students may find it helpful to practise with the calculations shown separately before they are confident with the combined formal method. The **Remark** box for **Example 4** supports students by providing details of the interim steps.

A useful way to promote understanding is to consider the area of rectangles. When using the written method it is useful to write the calculation on each answer line until the students understand the place value of the second line.

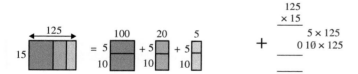

The application examples in Section C allow students to see these multiplications in context. Again, the use of the bar models can aid students' understanding. **Example 5** involves scaling and so an alternative approach would be to use a double number line labelled 1, 2, 3, 4, 5 along the top scale with 124, 248, 372, 496, 620 matching up on the scale directly underneath.

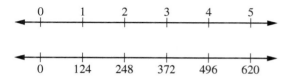

For **Example 6** point out the **Discuss** box and ask students to identify how they know that multiplication is required as they read through the problem. Discuss how the two multiplications can be calculated in any order – particularly as students may be able to find 16×4 mentally by equating it with $2 \times 8 \times 4$ or 8×8.

When working through Section D on square and cube numbers, use a practical approach with square tiles and cubes to deepen student understanding. To begin

with, give students 12 or 18 tiles and ask them to make different rectangles and thus identify factor pairs with a product 12 or 18. Expect a one tile wide rectangle to be included. Students can then try 10 tiles followed by 11 and 9. The fact that 11 can only be arranged as a one tile wide rectangle can be linked to the fact it has only two factors and thus is prime. Arranging 9 tiles as a 3×3 square offers a concrete representation of a square number. Using 16 tiles shows that whilst 16 is a square number, as tiles can be arranged 4×4, there are other rectangles that can be made. Ask students to make a variety of squares with square tiles; identify the corresponding multiplications and square numbers and then write using index notation. Carry out a similar process making large cubes from smaller interlocking cubes such as Multilink®. Work through **Example 7** then use the **Discuss** (page 43); students may support their reasoning with tiles or cubes.

At the start of **Practice 2.1,** when students complete a blank multiplication grid, make sure that they use suitable reasoning if they do not know all answers from recall. They should make good use of symmetry, completing rows and columns in matching pairs. Once the multiples of 2 and 3 are completed, students can double to find multiples of 4 and 6 respectively. Discuss any other patterns students spot that help them complete the grid. For further practice, students can complete multiplication squares which do not have the numbers 1 to 12 shown consecutively.

Blank grids and counters may be helpful for Question 2 and comparing the number of counters used for parts (i) and (ii) will help students explain how 53×2 and 4×53 are related. Students may struggle writing down their explanations for the reasoning parts of the Level 1 questions, so ask students to discuss their answers, first with a partner and then as a whole class. Ask students to make up their own word problems that require the same calculation as in Question 10. Students may wish to draw double number lines for some Level 2 questions; discuss the practical limitations of this and point out that whilst a diagram may be feasible in Questions 7 and 8 of **Workbook Exercise 2.1**, it would be very unwieldy for scaling for 38 desks in Question 9.

2.2 Division

- Divide whole numbers, using different methods and techniques
- Recognise the inverse relationship between multiplication and division
- Use division to solve real-life problems

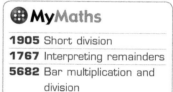

MyMaths

1905 Short division
1767 Interpreting remainders
5682 Bar multiplication and division

Start by using counters to divide numbers which give whole number solutions. Division can be thought of in two ways: 12 divided by 3 can be thought of as 'share 12 into 3 equal groups' or 'find how many 3s fit into 12'. Discuss these two methods so that all students understand both. When 12 is shared into 3 groups, each of the 12 coins is shared one by one into 3 groups – just as a set of 12 playing cards could be dealt between 3 people. To find how many groups of 3 fit into 12, purses are filled up one by one with 3 coins in each – just as 3 cards at a time are taken from the set of 12 until all 12 have been used up. The answer, 4, has a different meaning in the two models. When sharing 12 coins between 3 groups, the answer (the quotient) means that each group has 4 *coins*. When making groups of 3 *coins*, the quotient means that 4 *groups* can be filled.

Show the division using the division sign and as a fraction and explain that they mean the same thing. Use the **Discuss** on page 45 and share ideas as a class.

Complete **Class Activity 2** in order to explore the relationship between multiplication and division. Discuss the inverse relationship. Give students some products and ask them to write what else they know, e.g. if $5 \times 7 = 35$ what else can you tell me? The second **Remark** box on page 46 shows a factor tree representation of division; ask students to use a similar diagram to show how the factor pair 5 and 7 relate to 35, together with the two associated division calculations.

Introduce division in column form and explain the terms 'dividend', 'divisor', 'quotient' and 'remainder' (see page 46); use these terms frequently so students become familiar with them and are able to use them correctly. Work slowly through both parts of **Example 8**; using place value counters here is a good visual representation for students to follow and helps them understand why they are doing each step. Crucially, in part (b), they need to understand the process of regrouping the 2 remaining tens counters (after the 6 tens counters are divided by 4) to form 20 ones counters to add to the 7 ones counters. Showing what the result means using the pictorial representation in this example helps students to understand what they have found out. The **Remark** box on page 48 reminds students that they can use the Number Hack tables to check their calculations. Discuss that if a remainder is zero then the dividend is divisible by the divisor. Part (a) of **Example 9** involves regrouping but has no final remainder; for part (b) the use of counters is somewhat unwieldy with 60 tens.

Students may have looked at short division rather than long division at primary level so take time to work through this method. Concentrate first on dividing a double digit number by a single digit number so students become familiar with how to write the method. This type of calculation should be practised both without and with remainders before moving onto three digit dividends etc.

The **Remark** box next to **Example 10** shows a factor tree to relate the two division calculations and one multiplication calculation in the 'missing number' problem. This structure will help students use known multiplication facts to perform related division calculations; encourage them to represent the problems in **Try It! 10** using a factor tree.

When the students are confident with long division, show them how this can be done using short division; make a direct comparison between the two methods by solving the same question simultaneously, explaining the reasoning at each step. Work through **Examples 11 and 12** to put the division into a contextual situation. In **Example 12**, the context matches the concept of division as grouping or filling up; in this case, trays of 24 are being filled up until all 367 bottles are used. Notice the **Discuss** box on page 54. The remainder 7 is a partly filled tray. In this particular context this final tray is needed, so the final answer to the problem will not involve 7 bottles as a remainder but will round up to include the extra tray. Remind students that division can be written as a fraction so the final 7 remainder can be represented by the fraction $\frac{7}{24}$ and, as part trays are not realistic, this fraction is rounded up to a whole tray.

Make sure that students are clear about their reasoning for Question 1 in **Practice 2.2** and that they appreciate that if the same dividend is divided by a smaller divisor, the quotient will be greater. Explain that if the size of the groups is smaller, a greater number of groups can be filled and vice versa. Tackling the real world Questions 5, 7, 8 and 9 will help them to understand how division can be used to solve problems. Highlight the situations where the context clearly suggests that groups are being filled: egg boxes in Question 8 and buses in Question 9.

For Question 9 of **Workbook Exercise 2.2** students must appreciate that they are working backwards and will need to multiply to solve the problem; when they make up their own question for Question 10, they may choose to make up a similar problem or use a sharing or grouping situation instead.

2.3 Multiplying and Dividing Efficiently Without a Calculator

- Multiply and divide whole numbers, using different methods and techniques

You could begin this section by giving students a partially completed multiplication grid with the factors in the 1st row and some of the products filled in, but with the factors in the 1st column hidden behind an ink blot. Challenge students to work out the products in some highlighted squares. Students should reason about the relationships between the columns, for example that the products in the 4-column must all be twice the corresponding products in the 2-column, and half those in the 8-column.

×	2	4	8	3	6	9	10	100
	18							
		52						
			144					
							300	
								4500
				144				

Remind students about the commutative law and introduce the associative law of multiplication. Use the **Discuss** box (page 56) to think about how to use these rules with division; make sure students are aware when they can and cannot use them. These laws will mean students can reorder numbers to make mental calculations easier. Work through **Examples 13–15** to look at different strategies for calculations. Discuss the benefits of doubling and halving using the **Remarks** on pages 56 and 57. Number rods can be used to show how doubling and then doubling again is equivalent to multiplying by four; double again to show multiplication of the original rod by eight. Use an array of counters to show that multiplication of a single row by ten and then dividing the rows into two groups and discarding one group is the equivalent of multiplying by five.

Introduce the distributive laws of multiplication and division over addition and subtraction using red and green counters to represent the apples in the example given on page 57. Students can lay the counters into rectangular arrays of 4 × 3 and 4 × 5 and compare with the single array of 4 × 8. In **Example 16**, point out that sometimes the first factor is partitioned and sometimes the second; students need to become familiar with strategies for making multiplication easier, to help them decide which way to partition. Ask them to suggest calculations that they will try to incorporate, such as multiplication by 10 and multiples of 10. The **Discuss** box next to part (a) of **Example 17** offers two possible partitions for division, both of which involve multiples of the divisor 6 but Boris's method making use of a complement to 100. In part (b) of **Example 17**, highlight the explanation that ÷ 15 is the same as ÷ 3 ÷ 5; point out that the order could be switched to ÷ 5 ÷ 3 and ask students to draw similar diagrams to represent division by 12 as ÷ 3 ÷ 4 or ÷ 2 ÷ 6. Point out that the ÷

2 ÷ 3 method could be used for part (a) and see which students prefer.

Encourage students to think of the easiest way to tackle the questions in **Practice 2.3** so that they are applying all the methods discussed. Point out the variety of command words used: calculate, evaluate and compute as well as work out. Students can work in pairs and compare their 'thinking stages' when answering the calculations. For the Level 2 questions, which are set in various contexts, students need to initially decide the calculation required and then apply an appropriate strategy.

2.4 Factors, Multiples and Prime Numbers

- List factors, common factors and find highest common factors
- List multiples, common multiples and find lowest common multiples
- List primes and prime factors

MyMaths

1032 Factors and primes
1035 Multiples

This section develops work previously done with tiles but with the expectation of systematic working. Once more, give students 12 square tiles and ask them to make as many different rectangles as possible, recording the dimensions as they build them. Discuss that the product of the dimensions each time gives the total number of squares and therefore each of the numbers fit exactly into 12. These can then be named as factors. Discuss how this activity could be done systematically as the starting number of squares increases. How do they know when they have found all the factors? The fraction wall shown in the first **Remark** box on page 61) illustrates all the factors of 12; this could be reproduced using number rods to help demonstrate that all factor pairs have been identified. The second **Remark** box on page 61 shows another way of thinking about factors using square tiles.

Work through **Example 19**, labouring the need to be systematic in finding factors. Use **Example 20** to look at common factors and highest common factors (HCF). Investigate when numbers are divisible by 2, 3, 5, 6, 9 and 10 and decide on some rules; this will help students when they are finding factors.

Introduce the definition of a multiple and work through **Example 21**; ensure students are aware that there are an infinite number of multiples of any number.

When looking at common multiples, discuss ways of making the solution more efficient. For example, in **Example 22** students can write down the multiples of both numbers at the same time or they can write down the first few multiples of the larger number first and then write multiples of the smaller number to 'catch up' and find a common multiple. Notice the **Remark** box (page 62) which suggests how the multiplication table in the Number Hacks section can be used to find common multiples. This example can also be arranged using number rods, shown as a bar model or as an equivalent double number line.

Ask students to write down the factors of each of the numbers from 1 to 30. Students could do this using a factor table, with the numbers 1 to 30 across the bottom and factors 1 to 30 up the side, by shading the cells to indicate the factors for each number.

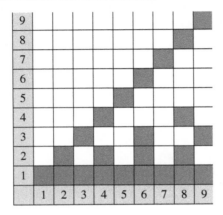

Students should consider which numbers have an odd number of factors. Ask what can be said about the numbers that have exactly two factors and introduce these as prime numbers. Make sure students can explain why 1 is not a prime number. Prove by counterexample that 15 is not a prime number.

For **Example 24**, expressing a number as the product of prime factors, point out how division can be used systematically, gradually working up the prime numbers using 2 then 3 then 5 as a divisor. The factor tree approach is also shown; demonstrate that whatever factor pair is chosen at the start, the same prime factors

will always be found eventually. When students factorise larger numbers, encourage them to use any factor pairs they can see, even if neither factor is prime. For example, they can factorise 600 first as 6×100, then as $6 \times 10 \times 10$, and then as $2 \times 3 \times 2 \times 5 \times 2 \times 5$.

In **Practice 2.4**, there are several justifiable responses to Question 4 so make sure that students explain their reasoning really carefully. Students may find a bar model or double number line very helpful to support their reasoning for Question 8.

In **Workbook Exercise 2.4**, Question 7(b) develops reasoning about divisibility for 25; discuss student approaches to this with the whole class, considering patterns in the list of multiples of 25. Question 8(a) demonstrates the fact that the square of a prime number has exactly three factors; develop this by asking students to find the number of factors for the square of other numbers and then present reasoning about why all square numbers have an odd number of factors.

IT Exploration 2 in the Workbook asks students to research the Sieve of Eratosthenes method to determine all the prime numbers from 1 to 100. Give students a 1 to 100 grid to help them do this.

Challenge 2 (page 67) will really make students think, as well as practise their multiplication skills with reference to place value to maximise the product. When students complete later questions in **Revision Exercise 2** they will first have to decide whether the context requires multiplication or division and then interpret their answer, including any remainder, correctly.

When completing the **Write in Your Journal** activity encourage students to write an example for each method they have covered. They should annotate their examples, to indicate their reasons for choosing that method and also to highlight any likely possible mistakes, before sharing as a class discussion.

The rounding and estimation skills developed in this chapter will be used throughout students' mathematical journeys, so it is important to develop a strong understanding of these concepts. Take time to look at how to label number line segments when rounding to different degrees of accuracy; for instance, when rounding to the nearest 10 then the scale should go up in 10s, similarly when rounding to the nearest 100 the scale should go up in 100s. Students can then plot their number and decide whether to round up or down. It is also important to consider the numbers that will round to give a particular number. For example, ask students to give you a number which rounds to 300 when rounded to the nearest 100. How does this differ if the number rounds to 300 when rounded to the nearest 10?

k are resources on Kerboodle

Resources

k Chapter 3 introduction video
k Try It! videos 2, 5, 8, 12, 14

Assessment

Workbook 1A Chapter 3
k Chapter 3 online skills test
k Chapter 3 end of chapter test and mark scheme
k Fully-worked solutions: Chapter 3 in Workbook 1A

3.1 Rounding Numbers

Learning Objectives:

● Round numbers to the nearest 10, 100, 1000 or 10 000

MyMaths

1003 Rounding to 10, 100
1840 Rounding and accuracy

Students should already be familiar with place value from Chapter 1, but recap if necessary by checking the **Flashback** (page 70). Look at some real-life examples of numbers on the Internet or in newspaper or magazine articles, where the numbers have most likely been rounded; for example, attendance at a concert or football game, profits of a large company etc. Ask students why they think these numbers have been used. Check they understand that these numbers have been rounded and so are approximations of the original number.

Class Activity 1 allows students to consider the reasons why a number is rounded up or down. Discuss Question 3 with the students and agree how to round a number that is exactly half way. Drawing number line extracts is a concrete way to help students when rounding; use the **Discuss** box (page 73) to check students understand how to best label these.

Students need to appreciate that different labels will be used on the number line depending on what 87 452 is being rounded to. For example, to round to the nearest 10, draw a line showing 87 450 and 87 460 and split it into 10 equal lengths, each representing 1, Hence an arrow marking 87 452 shows that it is less than the midpoint at 87 455. Then, rounding to 100, draw a line from 87 400 to 87 500 marked off in tens to show that 87 452 is greater than the midpoint 87 450. Discuss with

students how when rounding to the nearest 100 we look at the tens digit. Continue this demonstration and discussion for rounding to 1000 and 10 000.

Ask students to write down the steps to be considered when rounding and then check these against the steps on page 73. It is vital that students write the degree of accuracy with their answer. Work through **Examples 1 and 2** then practise the skills in **Practice 3.1**. Remind students to keep using number lines. The Level 2 questions give a variety of contexts to show the usefulness of rounding. Students will find that Question 6(b) increases the number of digits when they round to the nearest 1000. Discuss with students when rounding to a given degree can affect more than just the digit in the place value of rounding; for example, round 97 to the nearest 10, or 1965 to the nearest 100.

The initial Activity in **Workbook Exercise 3.1** involves matching pairs of cards showing exact numbers and numbers rounded to certain degrees of accuracy. Point out to students that the card showing, for example, the rounded number 400 needs to state the degree of rounding; we cannot assume that 400 is a number rounded to the nearest 100 just because the tens digit is zero.

3.2 Estimation

Learning Objectives:

● Estimate answers to calculations

MyMaths

1002 Estimating introduction

This section begins with **Class Activity 2** using estimation in a real-life situation. Once students have worked out the estimates that both Leanne and William would reach, discuss why in this context William is correct to round *up* rather than to the nearest £10. Discuss what could happen in a similar situation if the prices would normally have been rounded down.

Work through **Examples 3 and 4** highlighting the use of the symbol for 'approximately equal to'. Again, remind students to use number lines and to always state the degree of accuracy. Consider the actual answer and compare it to the estimated answer to check it is a good estimate. **Examples 5 and 6** consider whether an estimate is an under-estimate or over-estimate in a purchasing situation. Discuss the real-life repercussions of this in the given situations: buying too little or too much. For the paint example, point out that the required quantities for each room are already estimates and in reality these values would be added and then the total rounded with reference to the number of litres in the cans of paint being purchased. Complete **Practice 3.2** where Questions 7–10 give contextual problems to solve, allowing students to see the usefulness of approximating calculations. Discuss with students that approximations are also useful for checking answers to actual calculations.

3.3 Order of Operations

Learning Objectives:

- Use the order of operations

1167 Order of operations

Write the calculation $3 + 4 \times 5$ on the board and invite students to give you answers. The students' responses will reveal two possible solutions, 23 and 35, which can often result in a good debate. Ask students to come up with a story for each of the answers. For example: if you have 4 bags of 5 green apples and 3 more red apples then you have a total of 23 apples; but if there are 3 green and 4 red apples in a bag and you have 5 bags then the total number of apples is 35.

Explain that we should only have one possible story for any expression and that we need some rules so everyone is thinking of the same story and gets the same answer. Introduce the convention that multiplication and division are calculated before addition and subtraction and show why this means that $3 + 4 \times 5$ is interpreted as 23 (the first story) and not 35 (the second story). Perform the calculation on a scientific calculator to show that it has been programmed with these rules so it also gives the agreed answer. Work through **Example 7** showing all the steps of working.

Continue by introducing indices and then brackets, working through **Examples 8–10**. You may wish to replace some numbers in the examples with smaller numbers so that the order of operation is not clouded by difficult numerical calculations. Students may well have previously

come across the mnemonic 'BIDMAS' to remember the correct order of operations. It is essential they appreciate that division does not have priority over multiplication and that addition and subtraction are usually carried out from left to right. The correct priority is given as:

- brackets
- indices
- multiplication and division, usually from left to right
- addition and subtraction, usually from left to right
so either BIDMAS or BIMDAS are mnemonics to be used with great care, if at all.

Working through multiplication and division or addition and subtraction from right to left is *usually* the best approach, but you should use the **Discuss** box on page 79 to explain that sometimes this is not sensible. For example $123 + 50 - 49$ is easier if we calculate the subtraction first to give $123 + 1$. Similarly $30 \times 6 \div 2 = 30 \times 3$ is easier than $180 \div 2$. However, this requires care since $123 - 50 - 49 \neq 123 - 1$ and $30 \div 6 \div 2 \neq 30 \div 3$. Students should not get into trouble if they stick to working from left to right, but do not insist that this is the only approach since this will cause confusion later: when simplifying algebraic expressions by collecting like terms we do not work rigidly from left to right.

Class Activity 3 gives students an opportunity to practise calculations using the correct order of operations with relatively small numbers, given that the digits 1, 2, 3 and 4 are used. Students need to appreciate the requirement to keep the digits running consecutively in a row whether or not they are combined to form another integer (such as 12). You can also introduce students to the 'Four Fours' activity where students aim to write an expression for every number from 0 to some maximum using exactly four integers and any of the operation signs $(+, -, \times, \div)$.

Examples 11 and 12 are more complicated with expressions involving four or more numbers, so may be considered after students have completed the Questions 1–8 in **Practice 3.3**. When answering Question 8, help students to look carefully at the four pairs of expressions. You want them to recognise that sometimes inserting brackets makes a difference to the answer to a calculation and sometimes it doesn't.

Examples 13 and 14 give situations where a subtraction or addition takes place before multiplication. In both cases, students should use brackets on their calculator or find the answer to the addition or subtraction before multiplying. When they calculate a mean, encourage students to consider if their answer is within the set of values and so reasonable. This will help them avoid making a common error of forgetting to find the total before dividing.

Look at the worded Questions 9 and 10 and discuss how to write an expression; ask students to write the full expression before calculating as some may answer in several stages. **Workbook Exercise 3.3** gives further practice at both numerical and worded questions. Encourage students to show clear line by line working in their answers.

3.4 Using a Calculator

Learning Objectives:

● Use a calculator

It is important that students become familiar with their own calculators as some will work differently to others. Ask students to check that their own calculator uses the correct order of operations using a previous question. For this section students need to be able to enter indices and brackets and convert fractional answers to decimals. Instil in students that it is good practice to estimate the answer so they are confident their calculator answer is correct.

Example 15 covers use of a calculator for calculations including indices; students should check carefully which keys to use on their own calculator. **Example 16** shows how to find the remainder for a division calculation when their calculator shows the quotient as a recurring decimal; many students may find this challenging. Show them that if $356 \div 11 = 32.363636...$ then $356 = 11 \times 32 + 11 \times 0.3636363636...$ which can be written $356 = 352 + 4$ to show the remainder 4 clearly. An alternative approach is to calculate $32 \times 11 = 352$ and then $356 - 352 = 4$, so the remainder is 4.

Example 17 gives a real-life context where the answer to a division calculation needs rounding to an integer – in this case up to a whole number of coaches so no-one is left behind. For the Try It! context, students will need to round down as they need to find the number of full servings and disregard the part serving left over.

Example 18 uses bar models to help visualise the problem of finding a missing data value given the mean. The equal length bars demonstrate that the total can be

made up of four equal mean values or the four actual data values.

When students complete **Practice 3.4** make sure that they write down the full calculation before typing it into the calculator for Questions 5–9. Refer back to **Example 18** to support students with Questions 7 and 9 which involve calculating means. A bar model may be helpful especially for Question 9 where students first need to find the total number of minutes for all four students by multiplying the mean 43 by 4. **Workbook Exercise 3.4** offers further practice on the range of questions that students can answer using a calculator.

Challenge 3 (page 89) offers another chance for students to practise using the correct order of operations with a restricted number of digits.

The final five questions of **Revision Exercise 3** are set in real-life contexts. In Question 7, ask students to repeat their area calculation for part (a), rounding each of the three part-areas to the nearest 10 first, before carrying out any calculations; they can then compare this answer with the final answer obtained by rounding at the end. Here the answer will be the same, but further work adjusting the values used could lead to a useful discussion about premature rounding of interim answers during multi-stage calculations. Compare, for example, the effect of rounding to the nearest 10 before and after calculating $74 + 88$, $76 + 88$ and 74×88 to demonstrate that sometimes intermediate rounding does affect the answer and sometimes it doesn't.

Workbook Problem Solving 3 asks students to put brackets into expressions to ensure the calculated answer given is correct. Give students sets of cards with numbers, operations and brackets for them to rearrange to find the correct position for brackets. These may also prove useful for the **Write in Your Journal Activity**.

Before students calculate the mean area for England, Wales, Northern Ireland and Scotland for **IT Exploration 3**, ask them to predict which of the countries will have an area above the mean and which will be below.

Chapter 4
Use of Letters

It is important to make a smooth transition from arithmetic expressions to algebraic expressions as this can often be a stumbling block for students. Constant comparison with numerical examples will build confidence and understanding. The use of bar models will help students to visualise problems and develop their understanding of the abstract algebra because 'x' represents an unknown exactly as a bar does.

Students will generalise simple daily-life scenarios to understand the importance and value of using variables.

k are resources on Kerboodle

Resources

k Chapter 4 introduction video

k Try It! videos 2, 4, 6

Assessment

Workbook 1A Chapter 4

k Chapter 4 online skills test

k Chapter 4 end of chapter test and mark scheme

k Fully-worked solutions: Chapter 4 in Workbook 1A

4.1 Using Letters to Represent Numbers

● Use letters to represent numbers

MyMaths

1158 Rules and formulae

By exploring some daily-life scenarios, as in **Class Activity 1**, students should find that the use of letters is an easy and efficient way to express a relationship between two or more quantities. Use the numerical situation to understand the calculations taking place in order to then generate the algebraic expression. Notice the **Discuss** box on page 93. Situations involving age, mass, height and money are all very accessible and relevant to students.

Students need to understand that a variable can represent any number and is used to represent an unknown quantity. It is important not to confuse students by assigning a letter to an object. For example 3 apples is not $3a$, but rather a stands for the amount of something. So if a represents the number of apples in a bag, then $3a$ represents the total number of apples in three bags; but if a represents the mass of an apple, then $3a$ represents the mass of 3 apples. Ask students if it matters which letter they use for the unknown, e.g. does it matter if they choose to represent the mass of a baby as b kg, m kg or x kg?

Class Activity 2 lists various statements which students must match to the appropriate expression. Ask students to discuss the pairings and explain why more than one statement links to one expression. Use **Example 1** to discuss further what the simple expressions mean and look at a variety of statements that can be made. Bar models, as used in **Examples 2–4** are a pictorial way of

helping students to represent relationships and form expressions, and will help to embed understanding before moving to the abstract. If students are confident drawing bar models you may wish to show them a double number line as an alternative, to show the price of watches and pens in **Example 3**.

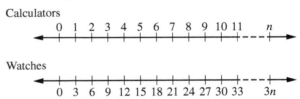

When solving problems it is important students understand that a variable does not have a unit, only the whole expression does, and therefore brackets should be used (see **Remark** on page 95).

It is important in **Example 3** to discuss that $3 \times n$ and $n \times 3$ are both written as $3n$ and that the convention is that when we want to multiply a variable by a number, or a variable by a variable, we write them next to each other without the × sign: '$4b$' not '$4 \times b$', and 'jk' not '$j \times k$'. Similarly, we can write a division of a variable by a number or a variable, or the division of a number by a variable as a fraction. Use the **Discuss** box on page 96 to make sure students understand the different notation.

Complete **Practice 4.1**. In Questions 6–9 remind students to write down the numerical calculations, and not just the answers, so they can see the patterns which will then help them to form the algebraic expressions. The final questions 10 and 11 of **Workbook Exercise 4.1** show expressions for volume and price with units included. Students need to appreciate that these letters and symbols are not variables and are not themselves part of the algebra.

Ask students to discuss in pairs or small groups the rules for writing expressions. As a class, create a poster of the rules for the classroom wall. (For example, write division as $\frac{x}{y}$ as well as $x \div y$, variables do not have units, do not write multiplication signs when writing the products of numbers and variables, etc.)

4.2 Substitution of Numbers for Letters

● Substitute numbers for letters

1187 Substitution 1

Ensure students understand the meaning of the word substitution. Relate it to a sporting substitution to embed the idea of a variable being exchanged for a number. Students need to understand that different values of a variable can be substituted into the same expression and this may give different answers. Recap again what $3x$ means, reminding them to refer to the poster they made in Section 4.1. Ask students to explain why, when $x = 5$, $3x = 15$ and not 35.

Work through **Examples 5–7**. Pay attention to the **Discuss** box beside **Example 7**, to make sure that students relate their answer to the problem. When students complete Question 1 of **Class Activity 3**, checking answers against the numbers in the circle will give them confidence in their own work. For Question 3, the hint indicates that the expression will include both multiplication and addition; students could draw a two-step function machine and think about a multiplication to use for one step and an addition to use for the other that will give the required outputs for the y inputs given.

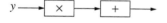

Complete **Practice 4.2**. It is worth discussing and making sure everyone understands Question 9b as this use of the word 'initial' to mean time is zero will appear in many future problems. Question 10 could be completed on the board with students adding their expressions to a cloud burst diagram. Challenge students to produce expressions containing one of the four operations and then increasingly more complicated expressions. By working as a class it will help those less sure to gain confidence. Extend this thinking with Questions 11 and 12 from **Workbook Exercise 4.2**.

Ask students to complete **Challenge 4** (page 102); discuss their answers to (a)(ii) and check that everyone has the correct expression. Discuss any misconceptions then ask them to complete **Problem Solving 4** from the Workbook.

Consolidate skills by completing **Revision Exercise 4**. Question 9 again requires students to understand the use of 'initial' to mean that time is equal to zero. Question 10(b) makes students think about the validity of an expression and relate it to the context of the problem.

In **IT Exploration 4** students are expected to be able to use formulae in a spreadsheet to generate numbers and then look at the patterns created. This could be extended by considering different expressions such as $3n - 2$, $3n + 2$, ... to see if students can make any generalisations.

The **Write in Your Journal** addresses the most common misconception in substitution. Ask students to read out their explanations so that precise language can be modelled.

Integrated Examples and Review Exercise 1

The purpose of this section is to consolidate the learning from the previous four chapters by combining the topics into integrated questions. Before working through the solutions, discuss with students which knowledge will be useful in helping them solve the problems. When reading through the examples, ask students to explain the meaning of the mathematical words to refresh their understanding and usage of them, in particular the words 'estimate' and 'evaluate'. Encourage students to show all their working, looking back at previous work to consider the most efficient methods.

Example 1 involves long multiplication and division, and the inverse relationship between addition and subtraction. Students also need to understand the definition of a prime number and factor. **Try It! 1** mirrors the question to allow students to practise this type of problem solving, however, discuss part (c) as a class. As the missing number is odd, it is more challenging to identify whether or not it is prime and students will need support with the reasoning required to decide which numbers they need to divide by to check for factors other than 1 and itself.

In part (a) of **Example 2**, remind students to show the values on a number line to reinforce how values are rounded. The example involves rounding, estimating, efficient calculation, order of operations and divisibility. Discuss with students what other efficient calculation methods they could use for part (a)(ii). Ask students to compare their answers to (a)(i) and (a)(ii) and consider whether part (i) produced an over- or under-estimate and why. Use parts (b) and (c) of this example to ask students to explain the order of operations and the definition of a multiple. Emphasise the importance of setting out working clearly, as shown in the example. Again **Try it! 2** mirrors the example so that students can follow through and link the learning together.

Example 3 involves place value, rounding, writing an expression and substitution into an expression. Students should use a place value table and number line to explain parts (a) and (b).

Review Exercise 1 provides practice questions for students to become fluent with the skills they have developed over the previous four chapters. Encourage students to look back at their work if they are finding questions challenging. Remind them of the manipulatives and pictures, such as place value counters and bar models, which will help them to explain their reasoning.

You may need to remind students of the definition of common factors and multiples for Question 7 (and Questions 8 and 9 in **Workbook Review 1**). When working through the calculations in Questions 8 and 9, students should write down intermediate answers. Students need to be confident using inequality signs for Question 11 and are likely to need a reminder about the mean for Question 14.

Question 13 requires students to decide which mathematical operations to carry out. Encourage students to draw a diagram or bar model to represent the situation; they should always be prepared to explain their methods when questioned. Question 16 (and Workbook Questions 15 and 16) require students to interpret their answers within the context of the question. Students will need support with the written explanations; it is helpful to discuss these questions as a class with the aim of producing a well-worded explanation that all students can understand. It is important that *all* students know and can use correct mathematical vocabulary.

Continue to consolidate learning by using **Workbook Review 1**, which is substantial and contains questions to review all aspects of the first four chapters.

Chapter 5
Understanding Fractions

The idea that a fraction represents part of a whole is reinforced throughout this chapter. It is important that the whole is defined; sometimes the whole is a single object, sometimes the whole is a group of objects. Make the connection between a fraction and the division it represents to deepen understanding.

k are resources on Kerboodle

Resources

k Chapter 5 introduction video

k Try It! videos 5, 7, 8, 9, 11, 12, 15, 18, 20

Assessment

Workbook 1A Chapter 5

k Chapter 5 online skills test

k Chapter 5 end of chapter test and mark scheme

k Fully-worked solutions: Chapter 5 in Workbook 1A

5.1 Idea of Fractions

Learning Objectives:

● Understand and use fraction notation

⊕ MyMaths

1369 Introducing fractions
1220 Simple fractions

Make sure that students understand that the whole can be a single object such as a pizza, as on page 113, or a group of objects, as in **Class Activity 1**. The key concept is that the *denominator* of the fraction represents the total number of equal parts the whole is divided into, or the total number of parts that make up the whole group, and the *numerator* represents the specific number of these parts that we want to choose, or identify as important. Emphasise that the parts must be equal using the second **Remark** on page 113. In **Class Activity 1**, the students need to make a tessellation of the identical shapes and draw around the outline of the whole that is formed. Discussion about whether their whole is made of an odd or even number of shapes will inform whether half the outline can be filled. The second part of the activity, where students challenge each other to decide what fraction of the outline is filled, is an opportunity for them to practise estimation and spatial awareness.

Discuss student explanations to Questions 3 and 4 in **Class Activity 2** to emphasise that the parts of the whole must be equal with regards to the property of the whole or group being considered. (In Question 2 the six children wearing jeans are 'equal parts' if we are considering 'jeans-wearing', but they are not 'equal parts' if we consider 'height' or 'age'.) This concept of a whole being dividing into equal parts leads to the important connection between fractions and division. The process of marking a fraction on a number line in **Example 1** consolidates this by requiring a line segment from 0 to 1 to be physically divided into four equal parts before $\frac{3}{4}$ can be marked.

Class Activity 3 and **Examples 2 and 3** emphasise thinking of a fraction as representing

 $\dfrac{\text{number of specified parts}}{\text{total number of equal parts}}$ using a variety of contexts from

daily life. Encourage students to suggest their own examples and distinguish between those where the whole is a single object and those where the whole is a group of objects. The connection with division when sharing equally or 'fairly' in daily life should be highlighted in these examples.

Relate the bar models in **Examples 4–6** to those used to represent division previously. They show the whole bar as the dividend (i.e. the dividend is always the whole 1). The sharing model of division is represented: the denominator is the divisor and is the number of equal sections that the bar is divided into. Later in Section 5.5, the whole will be greater than 1 when a bar model is used to find fractions of a quantity. Draw the bar model and ask students to describe it in a number sentence with words and then fractions. Highlight the **Remark** (page 117), stating that $\frac{7}{7}$ is one whole, to make it clear to students that whenever the numerator and denominator are equal, and neither equals 0, the fraction is equal to 1. Ask students to give statements in words, 'seven sevenths make a whole 1', 'eight eighths make a whole 1' and so on. Develop a stem sentence with the students for part (b) of **Example 4**; for example, 'three sevenths plus four sevenths equal seven sevenths which makes a whole'. Ask students to read out the sentences in their answers to encourage clear explanations. This will not only embed the pairs of fractions adding to 1, but also prepare students for conversion between mixed numbers and improper fractions. The use of a bar model will help address and prevent the misconception that $\frac{3}{7} + \frac{4}{7} = \frac{7}{14}$ by showing that the whole bar has only 7 parts, and not 14, when the two fractions are added.

Example 7 highlights the importance of using the same units for measurements in the numerator and denominator of a fraction. It provides an opportunity to practise working with units of time. Use the **Discuss** box while working through this example.

Students may find it helpful to draw bar models when tackling the Level 2 questions in **Practice 5.1**. When they complete Question 10, make sure that they choose a shape for the whole that can be divided into 16 equal parts easily by successive division by two; discourage the use of a circle and recommend a rectangle, or strip, that enables comparison with other fractions easily, in preparation for future work on equivalent fractions. Extend this by drawing 'fraction of a group' representations, not always with 16 (or whatever the denominator is) parts. For the similar Question 10 in **Workbook Exercise 5.1**, a grid is given for the students to use; challenge them to draw several diagrams that show equivalent fractions.

5.2 Improper Fractions and Mixed Numbers

Learning Objectives:

- Convert between improper fractions and mixed numbers

1019 Improper and mixed fractions

The generalisation that $\frac{n}{n} = 1$ for any non-zero n should be linked to the statements such as, 'seven sevenths make a whole 1' made previously. Pizza examples show clearly how converting improper fractions to mixed numbers relates directly to division. Give students concrete models of fractional parts of a whole, to model their own further examples of combining parts to form wholes and parts, and writing statements such as '7 thirds make 2 wholes and 1 third'.

For **Class Activity 4**, point out to students that the diagrams show several fully-shaded shapes, each labelled as a whole and, in Question 2, a partly-shaded shape which is a fraction of a whole. Demonstrate to students how to build up wholes and write the remainder as the fractional part. In the case of **Example 11** this is done in a practical daily-life context. In **Example 9** mixed numbers are converted to improper fractions in two

ways; in both methods the first step is to convert the whole number part to the correct number of wholes written as a fraction, e.g. $\frac{7}{7}$; this is then added to the fractional part. Use the blue text in **Examples 8–10** to encourage students to think about the denominator as the 'unit' and the numerator as the 'quantity'. In the same way that 3 cm + 3 cm = 6 cm, so 3 thirds + 3 thirds = 6 thirds. This will help students avoid the mistake that $\frac{3}{3} + \frac{3}{3} = \frac{6}{6}$.

Example 10 shows a number line being used to represent fractions; point out the importance of dividing the appropriate number line segment between two integers into the correct number of equal lengths according to the denominator of the fractional part being represented.

For **Practice 5.2**, encourage students to draw their own diagrams to help. Question 8 has a practical context and students need to interpret this to work out that the answer needs to be rounded up to the next integer so everyone can have a slice of cake. When students have completed Question 9, ask them to compare their answers with a partner; student choices for this question may reveal their confidence and preference for fraction diagrams or number lines. In **Workbook Exercise 5.2**, Question 10 has a context which gives a practical meaning to the parts of a mixed number in terms of the number of full racks and the fraction of the final partly-filled rack. Question 11 requires a time interval in hours and minutes to be written as a mixed number and as an improper fraction; emphasise to students that they should use 60 as the denominator to try to avoid the misconception that there are 100 minutes in an hour when writing times in decimal form.

5.3 Equivalent Fractions

Learning Objectives:

- Identify equivalent fractions

1042 Equivalent fractions

The paper folding activity in **Class Activity 5** introduces equivalent fractions by starting with $\frac{1}{2}$ (a fraction in its simplest form) and doubling successively to find other equivalent fractions. This may be an unfamiliar approach to students who may have previously dealt with equivalent fractions only in the process of simplification. The folding in half is equivalent to doubling the numerator and denominator. Ask students to consider what happens if the paper is folded into three equal parts each time. Three more diagrams representing $\frac{1}{2}$ are shown after the class activity; ask students to identify what is the same and what is different compared to the diagrams generated by the paper folding activity.

Examples 12 and 13 consolidate the concept that equivalent fractions can be found by multiplying the numerator and denominator by the same non-zero integer; encourage students to draw labelled arrows in their own work, as seen in the **Remarks** (page 130). Parts (c) and (d) of **Example 13** require division and so naturally lead to work on simplification of fractions to their lowest terms.

Students need to be confident with finding common factors for the work on reducing fractions to simplest form, so discuss a strategy for doing so systematically. Demonstrate that there may be several ways to simplify a fraction; some students may find it easier to use several steps if they are less secure with recognising multiples of larger numbers. Refer to the **Discuss** on page 132 and point out that in the solution to part (b) of **Example 15** both the numerator and denominator are divided by six but that this could have been replaced by the two-step process of dividing by two and then three. Students can show arrows between pairs of numerators and pairs of denominators labelled with the division. The **Remark** box (page 132) beside **Example 16** shows a pictorial representation of equivalent fractions and the **Discuss** box on page 133 shows different ways of simplifying fractions.

When completing the Level 2 questions in **Practice 5.3**, students may find it helpful to draw arrows to show the factor being used. Point out that the direction of the arrow and whether it is labelled with multiplication or division will depend on the position of the missing number.

Workbook Exercise 5.3 begins with **Activity 2** where students investigate pictorial representations of equivalent fractions by shading. For Question 6, where students are asked to find the fraction which is *not* equivalent to $\frac{2}{10}$, discuss possible strategies and whether they would first look for fractions which *are* equivalent. Students can make up their own version of this question by writing five fractions on pieces of paper and then asking a partner to explain which might be the odd one out. Question 8, comparing fractions of £1, is a good link to the convention of writing money as a decimal which always show hundredths of £1 because £1 = 100 pence.

5.4 Comparing Fractions

Learning Objectives:

- Compare fractions with the same numerator or denominator

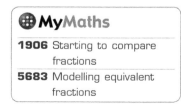

1906 Starting to compare fractions

5683 Modelling equivalent fractions

A fraction wall is used as a key pictorial representation to embed the relative sizes of unit fractions in **Class**

Activity 6. This introduction enables students to compare fractions with a common numerator as well as comparing fractions with a common denominator. Guide the discussion to elicit the reasoning and conclusions given on page 135. Throughout their work on comparing fractions, discuss with students which of the methods is better for each case they meet. Discuss when it is more efficient to compare fractions using a common numerator rather than defaulting to the common denominator method. As well as comparing 'fractions of one' diagrams, as in a fraction wall, show students 'fractions of a group' images as well.

Use bar models in **Examples 17 and 18** to consolidate the pictorial representation shown in the fraction wall. **Example 19** uses a number line to show the relative positions of the two fractions as mixed numbers. Encourage the students to see how these two fractions can be compared without complete conversion of $\frac{23}{4}$ into a mixed number. For example, by establishing that there are more than 3 wholes in $\frac{23}{4}$, students can deduce it is the larger fraction.

Make sure that students are confident with the use of < and > symbols for **Practice 5.4**. Answers to Questions 1 and 2 can be read aloud to ensure correct language for this notation is understood.

Discuss with the students that although Question 7 has three fractions, it is not necessary to convert all three to a common numerator or common denominator. Comparison of the two pairs $\frac{5}{7}, \frac{5}{8}$ and $\frac{5}{7}, \frac{13}{7}$ is sufficient to rank all three. Discuss why the relative sizes of the fractions make this possible and contrast this situation with what would be the case if the fractions were, for example $\frac{5}{7}, \frac{5}{4}$ and $\frac{13}{7}$.

In **Workbook Exercise 5.4**, Question 8 asks for a fraction between $\frac{5}{8}$ and $\frac{5}{10}$; discuss students' reasoning for their answers to this and compare it with the reasoning for the situation in Student Book Question 9, where the pair of fractions $\frac{3}{4}$ and $\frac{13}{4}$ have the same denominator rather than numerator.

5.5 Fractions of Quantities

Learning Objectives:

- Calculate fractions of quantities

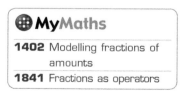

1402 Modelling fractions of amounts

1841 Fractions as operators

The pictorial representations showing six slices for six lots of $\frac{1}{3}$ and a bar model for $\frac{1}{3}$ of six consolidate the key concept that the two expressions are equivalent and have the same value. The bar model showing the whole six divided into three equal parts demonstrates once more the link between fractions and division, showing clearly that $\frac{1}{3}$ of 6 is the same as $6 \div 3$.

Finding a fraction of a quantity by building up from a unit fraction of the quantity is shown in Method 1 of **Examples 20 and 21**. Method 2 then shows how to use multiplication of the quantity by the fraction. Highlight that in all of **Examples 20–22**, cancellation before multiplication is an efficient strategy to avoid large numbers.

The Level 1 questions in **Practice 5.5** give further practice at finding fractions of a quantity. Students should make sure that they include the correct units in their answers for Question 3 onwards.

When students complete the table finding the same fractions of different quantities in Question 1 of **Workbook Exercise 5.5**, encourage them to spot the relationship between answers as they work across the table.

Challenge 5 (page 143) gives an opportunity for students to see a variety of methods to solve a problem. Some may identify themselves that $\frac{3}{24}$ can immediately be simplified to $\frac{1}{8}$. Discuss with students the fact that both

quantities are of the original £3600 so the two fractions could be added to find the $\frac{3}{8}$ spent or the $\frac{5}{8}$ remaining rather than first calculating the individual amounts spent.

Revision Exercise 5 gives further practice in all the processes covered in this chapter. For Question 12, discuss how the fractions themselves can be compared for part (a) and, once the faster person is established, a calculation of time taken is only needed for them in part (b).

IT Exploration 5 in the Workbook involves expressing the relationship between miles and kilometres as a fraction; ask students to do the same for other pairs of units and make sure that they are confident which numbers should be the numerator and denominator.

For the **Write in Your Journal** activity, students will need to find equivalent fractions with either a common numerator or a common denominator. Encourage students to show both methods and make sure that, in each case, they can make the correct decision as to which fraction is greater.

Chapter 6
Tenths, Hundredths and Thousandths

Student Book 1A
pages 145–179

Throughout the chapter, place value tables and number lines provide visual models for decimals. These help students gain a better understanding of the relative sizes of decimal numbers. Care needs to be taken with language; make sure that students really appreciate the difference between whole number and decimal place values, for example hundreds and hundred*ths*. When you are reading decimal numbers, for example 3.18, you should emphasise the correct language and read this as 'three and one tenth and eight hundredths' or 'three and eighteen hundredths'. Your students will be used to 'three point one eight', which is a reading that verifies fluency but not understanding. Whenever practical, ask your students to say a decimal number in more than one way to make sure they understand exactly what the decimal represents. Bead strings of 100 beads alternating colours in groups of 10 are a useful concrete representation, and laminated empty place value charts, blank hundred squares and blank number lines may also be useful resources for students to write on during some of the class activities.

Resources

k Chapter 6 introduction video

k Try It! videos 3, 7, 9, 15, 17, 19, 20, 22, 25

Assessment

Workbook 1A Chapter 6

k Chapter 6 online skills test

k Chapter 6 end of chapter test and mark scheme

k Fully-worked solutions: Chapter 6 in Workbook 1A

k are resources on Kerboodle

6.1 Decimal Place Values

Learning Objectives:

- Identify the tenths, hundredths and thousandths in decimals
- Order decimals up to three decimal places

⊕ MyMaths

1378 Introducing decimals
1076 Decimal place value
1009 Decimal number lines
1072 Ordering decimals

Column headings given as fractions for decimal place values builds on work covered in the previous fractions chapter. Writing decimals in expanded form, and using correct language when saying decimals, helps students see the relative size of the digits in a number. Use the **Remark** box (page 148) to emphasise correct language and the **Discuss** box to ensure that students appreciate the value of zeros as place holders within a decimal and the redundancy of trailing zeros.

In **Example 2**, highlight that when writing down the value represented by a digit, students should do so in words or with a fraction rather than a decimal e.g. 7 hundredths or $\frac{7}{100}$ rather than 0.07.

When considering how to order decimals in section B, discuss how to represent 7.93 using a hundred square. Ask the students how to represent seven using hundred squares, and then how to represent the 0.93. What number will they represent if they shaded in one more square on the 0.93 hundred square? Discuss why it is not very easy to represent three decimal places using a hundred square. A similar approach can be used with bead strings to identify 0.93 and 0.94.

Before considering the use of number lines to compare decimals, give the students a number line with only two numbers labelled and ask them to label values marked at equal intervals between them. This will consolidate understanding of number lines and give students confidence to use them for non-integer values. **Examples 3 and 4** extend this work, magnifying a number line further to position decimals with two and then three decimal digits. Students have to answer questions involving familiar units with two decimal places for pounds and three decimal places for kilograms; the contexts here may aid student understanding. Use the **Discuss** box on page 152 to prevent the misconception that you consider the last digit when ordering decimals.

Using a place value table encourages students to line up digits and decimal points when comparing decimals. Having mastered this, students may just write the decimal numbers in columns rather than a table. **Example 5** compares decimals with different numbers of decimal places. Refer to the **Remark** (page 153) to discuss how trailing zeros can be helpful when comparing decimals. This may help students compare numbers such as 0.587 and 0.59; although only the 5 tenths and 8 or 9 hundredths need to be compared, seeing the extra 0 thousandths in 0.590 may help some students match up the crucial tenths and hundredths columns more easily. If the number of decimal places are the same, students are effectively comparing 587 thousandths and 590 thousandths, which they may feel more secure doing.

When students write decimal numbers in expanded form for Question 1 in **Practice 6.1**, ask them to read their answers aloud. Articulating the place value of each digit will help students to improve their conceptual understanding as well as procedural fluency. Encourage students to understand that while they can read 9.34 as 'nine point three four', the number actually represents the value 'nine and three tenths and four hundredths'. Using a place value table and trailing zeros may be helpful in Questions 4 and 5. In Question 9, point out that once they have established that the missing digit cannot be 6, only the hundredths column of the two numbers need to be considered.

Workbook Exercise 6.1 Question 8 emphasises that trailing zeros do not change the size of a number; we often use them when writing money, for example £3.80 not £3.8. For Question 9 part (a), the division of the line into five spaces between 2.4 and 2.5 rather than ten may prove tricky, especially as both points to plot are between marks; suggest to students that they add extra marks to show tenths along the number line. In Question 12, students may need a reminder that 0 is even.

6.2 Conversion between Fractions and Decimals

Learning Objectives:

- Convert fractions to decimals
- Convert decimals up to three decimal places to fractions

Previous work on equivalent fractions will help students convert the expanded form of a decimal number to a mixed number by expressing all digits after the decimal point as fractions with the same denominator – corresponding to the place value of the final digit. Once the fraction over 10, 100 or 1000 has been found, students can use their knowledge of simplifying fractions. The pictorial representation in the note for **Example 6** shows how when the 75 squares on a 100 square grid are arranged in a particular way, it is clear that they are equivalent to $\frac{3}{4}$. Students may find it helpful to have blank 10 × 10 laminated grids to shade in different ways. Notice the **Remark** boxes while working through this example.

Before students convert fractions to decimals, it may be helpful to ask them to find all the factors of 10, 100 and 1000. These values are the scale factors likely to be needed to find an equivalent fraction, so by familiarising themselves with these, students will find it easier to decide whether the decimal will need one, two or three decimal places. Diagrams accompanying **Example 8** show how fractions can be converted to decimals by dividing the sections of a fraction diagram by this scale factor. It is then straightforward to find the equivalent decimal from the diagram with 10 or 100 parts. Encourage students who can recall the decimal equivalents of unit fractions to use this knowledge to convert other

fractions. For example if they know that $\frac{1}{5} = 0.2$, then they can find $\frac{3}{5}$ from 3×0.2.

For Questions 6 and 7 in **Practice 6.2**, students need to take care with the zeros appearing in the tenths and hundredths columns. In Question 5 of **Workbook Exercise 6.2**, students may find it helpful to label fractions as well as decimals along the number line; they need to note that there are five lengths marked between 0 and 0.1 so each will be 0.02 giving marks at $\frac{2}{100}, \frac{4}{100}, \frac{6}{100}$ and so on. Discuss where $\frac{5}{100}$ will be in relation to 0 and 0.1 so that students understand they can mark it directly at the midpoint without having to count along from 0 in intervals of 0.01.

6.3 Multiplying and Dividing by 10, 100 and 1000

Learning Objectives:

- Multiply and divide by 10, 100 and 1000
- Convert money and measures

⊕ MyMaths

1027 Multiplying by 10 and 100

1013 Multiply decimals by 10 and 100

1091 Converting measures

Use **Class Activities 1 and 2** to show students clearly how the digits move in the place value table when a number is multiplied or divided by a power of 10. It is important students appreciate that the digits are moving left or right to new place value positions. Insist on this rather than the idea of the decimal point moving. Show counters or sticky notes actually moving on a place value table to embed this idea. To do these activities successfully, students need to understand that 70 tenths = 7, 700 tenths = 70 and so on. Use base-ten blocks (or pictorial representations of them) to show students this and use them when discussing Questions 4 and 5 of **Class Activity 1**. A place holder is required in Question 4 which students may need to be reminded about; contrast the redundancy of a trailing zero with the importance of a place holder zero. **Examples 12 and 14** address misconceptions involving placeholders; invite students to explain which answer they think is correct and why. Discussing their answers should help avoid misconceptions.

Make sure that students are familiar with the common metric units used in this section. Units of time can be particularly problematic, so emphasise these conversions to make sure that students avoid the common mistake of using 100 minutes for 1 hour in their calculations. Discuss with students whether 1 minute and 30 seconds is 1.30 minutes. Encourage students to think about 30 seconds as a fraction in relation to 1 minute so that they can convert 1 minute 30 seconds to 1.5 minutes. Use a clock face to show that 30 seconds is equal to half of one minute. Discuss with students the idea of using a place value table where the usual column headings are replaced with units. Choose different units as 'one', and then fill in the rest. For example: if a metre is 'one', then a cm is a 'hundredth' and a kilometre is a 'thousand'; but if a km is 'one', then a metre is 'thousandth'; if £1 is 'one' then 10p is a 'tenth' and 1p is a 'hundredth', etc.

The first **Discuss** box on page 166, which matches conversion from a bigger unit to a smaller unit with division and smaller unit to bigger unit with multiplication, encourages students to use a common sense approach to check answers. Use the second **Discuss** box to remind students that there are 60 minutes in an hour, not 100.

Writing a number on a laminated place value table and then writing again to show the new position of the digits after multiplication or division will help students to complete Questions 1 and 2 in **Practice 6.3**. In Question 5 make sure that students write their answers using correct money notation using an extra trailing zero where necessary. For example, in part (a) they should give £49.50 rather than £49.5. Explaining the choice of the odd one out in Question 6 will address understanding of place holders and Question 7 deals with the common misconception that in every case, to multiply by 10, a zero needs to be added.

In Question 9 of **Workbook Exercise 6.3** students must think about inverse operations to complete missing values. They may find it useful to write both numbers in a place value table and consider the operation needed to move the digits the required number of places.

6.4 Introducing Percentages

Learning Objectives:

- Define percentages
- Express percentages
- Relate fractions, decimals and percentages

⊕ **My**Maths

1029 Frac dec perc 1

This section follows on naturally from previous work on fractions and decimals. A percentage is defined as a fraction with 100 as the denominator, so 100% represents the whole. Students need to understand that both the fraction and the percentage are describing a proportion of the *same* quantity (or the same whole).

Use a hundred square to help students visualise the percentages shaded and not shaded as complementary fractions out of 100, as shown in the **Remark** box by **Example 18**. Encourage students to be flexible when converting fractions to percentages by discussing the two methods given in **Example 19**. If students choose Method 2, multiplying the fraction by 100, make sure they realise that cancelling first may give easier arithmetic. The final **Remark** box on page 169 reminds students that multiplying by 100% is the same

as multiplying by 1; the value doesn't change, but the answer will then be a percentage.

One hundred square diagrams are shown in the **Remark** with **Example 20** to show the fractions equivalent to 40% with denominators 100, 10 and 5.

When considering **Example 21**, use the **Discuss** box to talk about the decimals 0.02 and 0.2, and their equivalent fractions and percentages; this is important as students will often muddle such pairs. Use a hundred square so students can really see how 2% and 20% differ; including a trailing zero to give two decimal places for both decimals 0.20 and 0.02 may help. Consolidate this understanding by asking students to complete **Try It! 21** which involves 0.4 and 0.04 and **Try It! 22** with 60% and 6%. Ask them to work in pairs and explain to each other how 40% and 4% or 6% and 60% differ.

Practice 6.4 gives a variety of questions converting between fractions, decimals and percentages. Ask students to reflect on the methods they are using and compare with each other. Draw a diagram with the three words 'fraction', 'decimal' and 'percentage' at the vertices of an equilateral triangle and then invite students to draw arrows showing links and the methods that they have learnt for conversion.

You can give the Activity at the start of **Workbook Exercise 6.4** as a card sort and encourage students to make their own sets of matching cards so they become familiar with common equivalent fractions, decimals and percentages. Question 10, about £1 and £2 coins, shows how a percentage giving relative proportions using the *number* of coins will be different from the relative proportions involving the *value* of the coins.

6.5 Percentages of Quantities

Learning Objectives:

- Find percentages of quantities

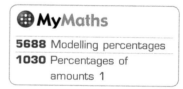

⊕ **My**Maths

5688 Modelling percentages
1030 Percentages of amounts 1

This section builds directly on earlier work on finding fractions of a quantity, since a percentage is a special fraction out of 100. In Example 24, to find 20% of 300 cm, a building-up process from 10% is offered, then a method that first uses the multiplier $\frac{10}{100}$ to find 10% before doubling, and finally a direct method using the multiplier $\frac{20}{100}$.

Make sure students understand that 10% is special and is equivalent to $\frac{1}{10}$ from simplifying $\frac{10}{100}$. A common misconception is to deduce that 20% is $\frac{1}{20}$ and 5% is $\frac{1}{5}$. A fraction wall or bar model can demonstrate how this is not the case.

Using bar models in **Examples 24 and 25** emphasises that the complete bar of 100% represents a whole. Point out to students the alternative methods and remind them that redoing a problem using a different method is an effective way to check their final answer. The **Discuss** box beside **Example 24** shows two build-up methods; ask students if they can think of others. If they are secure with 20% being equivalent to $\frac{1}{5}$ they could immediately find 20% by dividing by five. Previously, division by ten and then multiplication by two was presented as a useful method to divide by five, so a connection to this previous work would be worthwhile. Similarly, many students will know that 75% is the same as $\frac{3}{4}$, so will be able to find 75% of £240 in **Example 25** by dividing by four (to effectively find 25%) and then multiplying by three.

When they are finding the percentage of a quantity, remind students that in this, and similar, contexts the word 'of' means multiply. In the context of percentages, a common mistake is to read the word 'of' as 'off' and deduct the amount calculated from the original quantity as if calculating a decrease. When answering questions in context such as **Example 25**, remind students to take note of whether the reduction or sale price is required. Using a bar model to represent the situation may help prevent confusion.

For the Level 1 questions in **Practice 6.5**, remind students to give correct units to accompany their numerical answers. For the Level 2 questions, in various contexts, encourage students to use bar models to help see the complements of 100% they are dealing with.

For Question 8, a bar model will help students to see the various methods that can be used. It should also encourage an efficient solution to part (b), i.e. finding 55% of 360 directly, by recognising that the percentage of cars that are neither white nor grey can be found from $100\% - 15\% - 30\%$.

Encourage students to consider the various methods possible for **Challenge 6** (page 178) and decide which they prefer. They may use consistent fractions, decimals or percentages.

Questions 2, 3 and 4 of **Review Exercise 6** cover conversions between fractions, decimals and percentages. Ask students to extend the table for Question 4 to include the most commonly used percentages where it is helpful to learn the equivalent fractions and decimals.

Problem Solving 6 in the Workbook helps students think about relative place value and comparison between two numbers. Encourage them to make up similar questions, ensuring each has one unique solution.

Sports results for athletics can provide a rich source of examples for the use of decimal numbers in real life for **IT Exploration 6**; students can identify when the larger number identifies the winner e.g. a long jump length and when a lower number is better e.g. a track event time.

For the **Write in Your Journal** activity, students could refer back to the equilateral triangle diagram showing all conversions between fractions, decimals and percentages that they prepared while working on Section 6.4.

Chapter 7
Introduction to Ratio

Pictorial representations using bar models are very powerful for helping students make the crucial connection between using ratio and fractions to represent information about quantities. They can help ensure that students are clear that the total of the parts of the ratio will represent the whole, as does the denominator of the fractions showing the proportions of each quantity being compared in the ratio.

k are resources on Kerboodle

Resources

k Chapter 7 introduction video
k Try It! videos 3, 5, 7, 8, 10

Assessment

Workbook 1A Chapter 7
k Chapter 7 online skills test
k Chapter 7 end of chapter test and mark scheme
k Fully-worked solutions: Chapter 7 in Workbook 1A

7.1 Idea of Ratios

Learning Objectives:

- Write a ratio between two quantities

Class Activity 1 demonstrates clearly that the order of comparison, and so the order of the numbers written, in ratio notation is crucial. Consolidate this further by discussing how scores in a football match always show the home team first and so writing the numbers the other way around makes a big difference. In the same way, $5:2$ is a different ratio to $2:5$. **Examples 1–4** introduce bar model representations of a ratio; sometimes the ratio is written in the same order as the bar parts, sometimes not. For **Example 1**, read the sentence describing the ratio 'the number of flasks to the number of beakers' out loud so students appreciate that the first quantity is written first and the ratio symbol effectively replaces the word 'to'. This is shown in the diagrams in the solutions to parts (b) and (c). In part (d) of **Example 2**, students write the ratio of a part to the whole; the bar model can be used to show this, with the total for all three bars used for the second part of the ratio. Use the two **Discuss** boxes on page 184 when working through these Examples and Try Its.

Example 3 requires students to give reasons when explaining the mistake regarding order in (b) and confusion between parts and the whole in (c). **Example 4** demonstrates that units are not included when writing in ratio notation; however, students need to be aware that they must be consistent for correct proportions of quantities to be shown.

Encourage students to draw bar models throughout **Practice 7.1**. Invite students to also consider the ratio of blue to white squares for Question 6 and then look carefully at their bar model to begin to develop the concept of equivalent ratios. Care is needed in Question 7(c) where one part of the ratio represents the whole. In this case, the quantities of each ratio on the bar model will effectively overlap. In Question 8 part (a), students must notice that units have been retained in the ratio which should be written without £ signs; for part (b), ask students to suggest how Dani may have obtained her incorrect value 13 for the total. Students need to think carefully about the order of the two quantities when they are writing sentences for the meaning of ratios in Question 9. For Question 10, students could write a question with a set of multiple-choice answers addressing some of the misconceptions dealt with in Examples 1–4 and Question 8.

For the open Question 10 in **Workbook Exercise 7.1**, ask students to show their example in a diagram and write two sentences relating the two quantities.

7.2 Relationship between Ratios and Fractions

Learning Objectives:

- Relate ratios and fractions
- Solve simple problems involving ratio

⊕ MyMaths

1404 Modelling ratio

The introduction to this section shows four ratios that can be written to show how proportional relationships can be described using both fractions and ratios for the five pieces of fruit shown. During discussion use interlocking cubes in two colours to represent the fruit, joining them together to make a bar model. The number of each fruit is first given as a ratio to the total number of fruit giving the ratios $2:5$ and $3:5$; these are matched to the fractions $\frac{2}{5}$ and $\frac{3}{5}$ respectively. The ratio of apples to oranges, $3:2$, is then given and matched to the fraction $\frac{3}{2}$ to represent that the number of apples is $\frac{3}{2}$ of, or $1\frac{1}{2}$ times, the number of oranges. Similarly, the ratio of oranges to apples, $2:3$, is matched to the fraction $\frac{2}{3}$ to represent that the number of oranges is $\frac{2}{3}$ of, or times, the number of apples. The **Remark** box (page 189) makes a crucial note about the number of apples being $\frac{3}{2}$ of the number of oranges not $\frac{3}{2}$ of the total number of fruits. Students must take care to recognise that a fraction represents a proportion of a whole and so they must be very clear as to what quantity that whole is. This whole will be represented by the denominator in the fraction and may be a part or the total of a ratio.

Class Activity 2 considers the relationship between the number of boys and the number of girls in Year 7 to consolidate these concepts. The fraction of boys in Year 7 is given at the beginning of the activity as $\frac{5}{11}$; discuss with students the fact that, unless there really were only a total of 11 students in Year 7, the fraction using the actual numbers has been simplified to give this equivalent fraction. Again, as for the fruit example, use interlocking cubes or number rods to form a bar model and consider the various proportional relationships. Use the **Remark** to emphasise the fact that a ratio describes proportions and not actual amounts. The final Question 5 relates the work to the actual number of students in Year 7. Here, students can note that the total 99 is the denominator in the fraction $\frac{\text{number of boys}}{\text{total number of students}}$ which was simplified to give the equivalent fraction $\frac{5}{11}$; as the denominator of the fraction $\frac{5}{11}$ is $99 \div 9$, the actual number of boys must be $5 \times 9 = 45$. This can be represented pictorially by labelling each of the 11 blocks of a bar model with the number 9 (as $99 \div 11 = 9$) and then deducing that as there are 5 blocks of 9 representing boys, there are $5 \times 9 = 45$ boys. The comment below the Class Activity once more emphasises that the numbers in a ratio of quantities are not necessarily the actual amounts of each quantity.

Work through **Examples 5–8** along with the **Try Its!** to consolidate these concepts before students tackle **Practice 7.2**. In Question 3, in order to give the required ratios, students need to observe that the number of blocks in each part of the bar model is labelled with a letter. The Level 2 questions from Question 5 onwards involve finding the scale factor from a part of the given ratio to the corresponding value that the part represents (e.g. from 2 to 108 in Question 5, and from 7 to 350 in Question 6). This can be shown by labelling each block of a bar model with the actual number of items it represents.

For Question 9 where the ratio of the number of notes and the ratio of the value of those notes is considered, students may find using cards labelled with the values £10 and £50 helpful. These cards can be formed into a bar model of $4 + 9 = 13$. Students can then find the equivalent ratio $8:18$ to find the total value from $8 \times £10 + 18 \times £50$.

The questions in **Workbook Exercise 7.2** give further practice at changing between fraction and ratio representations and at finding equivalent ratios to calculate actual amounts.

7.3 Equivalent Ratios and Simplest Form

Learning Objectives:

- Identify equivalent ratios
- Solve simple problems involving ratio

1052 Ratio introduction

A practical approach can be used in **Class Activity 3** at the start of this section. Give students six squares of brown and eight squares of white paper to put into pairs to make 'sandwiches' to see the ratio $6:8$ appear as $3:4$. Each 'sandwich' is then cut into two giving $6:8$ once more, then cut again to give the ratio $12:16$. Discuss how each of these ratios is equivalent, because the total amount of bread isn't changing, and discuss the scale factor, used to write equivalent ratios, in the context of the sandwich making and cutting that took place.

This concrete activity leads onto the bicycle wheels example shown in the table that follows the activity. The ratios used can be represented with symbols representing bicycles and wheels, for example for $1:2$ show ⮾:◉◉ and for $2:4$ show ⮾ ⮾:◉◉◉◉ Point out to students that for every bike there are two wheels; draw arrows with scale factors to show how each ratio is related to the other equivalent ratios.

The bar models in **Examples 9 to 11** clearly demonstrate the process of simplifying ratios by relating to the equivalent process of simplifying fractions; make sure that students are confident at drawing and using a bar model appropriately for **Example 10**. **Example 11** demonstrates that simplification may take place in stages; show students that division by 6 and then 2 could have been calculated in a single step dividing by 12.

Draw the bar model for **Example 11** and label the individual boxes as £4 to demonstrate the unitary method being used. Students can then do the same for **Try It! 11** and the Level 2 Questions 7 and 8 in **Practice 7.3**. Ask students to discuss their answers to Question 9 in pairs and then explain to the whole class. Make sure that they appreciate that since Beth's height is part of both ratios, Zac and Asha's heights can be compared.

The Activity in **Workbook Exercise 7.3**, which involves matching up two sets of equivalent ratios, can be done as a card-matching activity. You can introduce a single 'odd one out' ratio and you can also ask students to make up sets of their own for a partner to try to match up.

Question 1 about the ratio of different shaped biscuits can be extended to consider related fractions. As the total number of biscuits is 25, which is scaled easily to 100, you could also link this to previous work on percentages.

To solve **Challenge 7** (page 201), students will need to rewrite the ratio $2:3$ as an equivalent ratio with 18 boys. To do so, they will need to find the scale factor from 3 to 18, and then apply this to 2. This can be represented using a bar model. Once they have found the new ratio, ask students to simplify it and consider how they could compare it with the original ratio to deduce that extra boys have been added.

In Question 4 of **Revision Exercise 7**, make sure students appreciate that whilst it is important that the units given for the pairs of quantities are consistent, they should not be included in the ratios they write. The individual parts of Question 10 break the problem down into steps that students could complete and then at the end write a three part-ratio of the areas living room : bedroom : kitchen as $30:10:8$, which can then be simplified to $15:5:4$. A challenging extension to this problem is to offer a similar question and ask for the three-part ratio without giving an actual area as was done with the $10\,m^2$ for the bedroom here.

Work for **Write in Your Journal** once again highlights that the ratio does not generally give actual values and that in this case it is impossible to know the actual number of boys and girls in each club.

In Workbook **Problem Solving 7** students need to consider the ratio of the $1200\,g$ quantity of chicken in the recipe to the $1500\,g$ of chicken that Rose has; the equivalent ratio for potatoes then needs to be found. Students can then try to apply the same method to find the amount of cauliflower and curry paste required; a discussion can be had as to how this scaling would be applied in real life, particularly for the bunch of coriander.

These integrated examples combine work on fractions, decimals, percentages and ratio.

Example 1 begins by asking students to express one quantity (red balls or non-red balls) as a fraction or percentage of the whole number of balls. The bar model is useful to visualise the two parts of the whole. Identifying the whole on the bar model as 100% will help students to find the percentage of non-red balls having worked out the percentage of red balls. Part (d) then goes on to consider the relationship between red and non-red balls as a ratio. In **Try It! 1**, as the total number of chocolate bars is ten, students may be able to recall that $\frac{1}{10} = 10\%$ and so write down 40% directly.

In **Example 2**, students need to take care with the units for juice and water and make sure that they are consistent in order to write a correct ratio. Part (c), converting the juice capacity from litres to millilitres, should prompt them to do this.

Example 3 demonstrates converting a fraction to a decimal in part (a) and then converting both a fraction and a decimal to a percentage for the method used in part (b). Encourage students to consider other possible methods to compare lengths A and B, such as writing both as fractions or percentages. Discuss how the method shown here may be considered the most efficient strategy. For Part (c), once the ratio is simplified to $16:15$, draw a bar model to help students visualise how each of the 15 parts represents 3, from $45 \div 15$.

In Question 1 of **Review Exercise 2**, encourage students to simplify their fraction answer in part (a), but also encourage them to look ahead to see that writing $\frac{8}{20}$

as $\frac{4}{10}$ will help with the conversion to a decimal and percentage. For Questions 3 to 8 make sure that students give appropriate units in their answers. Encourage a variety of methods in Question 4 to compare $1\frac{4}{5}$ and $1\frac{2}{7}$, and ask students to explain their reasoning to each other. Some strategies may not involve directly comparing the two values; for example, a reasonable alternative method would be to compare both quantities with $1\frac{1}{2}$.

Students need to take care to show 1.3 and $2\frac{1}{4}$ correctly on the number line in Question 11 as they fall between the marks shown at 0.2 intervals along the line. Bar models are useful for Question 12 onwards; for Question 15, students must spot that they are given a numerical value for part of the whole, not the total.

The shapes shown shaded in Question 1 of **Workbook Review 2** serve as a reminder that a fraction is a number of *equal* parts of a whole; for figures II and IV, the shapes have not been split into equal parts. When students calculate the discounted price for the lamp in Question 11, they must use the different values for the original whole price at the two different shops. For Question 12, students could write down the ratio of the number of male staff to the number of female staff along with the actual numbers at each stage of the question. In Question 14, the crucial piece of information that there are 72 red counters is only given at the end of the question. Ask students if they can work out the single ratio to compare proportions of all three colours of counter in the form red : yellow : blue.

Problem-solving Processes and Heuristics

This section explains how a four-step problem-solving process can be used to help students become good problem solvers. There are a variety of ways students can tackle problems and the examples here look at how to use different strategies in different situations. For each problem, you should first allow students to tackle the question on their own or with a partner. This will give them time to think about strategies and experience 'productive struggle' before considering and working through the solution given in the Student Book. Don't jump in and offer help too quickly; getting stuck, and getting unstuck on their own, is a very important experience for students.

Give students **Example 1** to tackle on their own or in pairs initially. You could introduce this by asking a student to pick out two of three different coloured items from a bag as a demonstration to ensure that all students understand the problem. Compare the students' methods to the 'Make a Table' strategy in the example, discussing the advantages of this strategy. Ensure that students understand what we mean by working systematically; the **Discuss** boxes encourage this way of thinking. Discuss the four-step strategy with students so they understand what each step involves.

Example 2 uses the 'Draw a Diagram' strategy. Pose this problem to the students; prompt them to try to represent the problem by drawing a diagram without any further guidance before introducing the bar model. Discuss what other diagrams they have used and their advantages and disadvantages. Students may draw a comparative bar model rather than a part–whole diagram; discuss which makes it easier to find the price of two drinks. Some students may prefer to use different length number rods, or cubes of two different colours, to represent the prices of pizzas and drinks before drawing the bar model. Work through the steps using the bar model diagrams and then ask students to comment on how using the diagram has changed the perceived complexity of the problem.

Example 3 uses the 'Guess and Check' and 'Use a Variable' strategies. Guess and check is a really useful method that students often do not like to use as they do not always see it as a 'proper' method. Creating the table as a class, with students suggesting the guesses, gives an opportunity to discuss how to choose values in a sensible way so as to narrow down the range of values you need to look at. This can be a long process so discuss the use of spreadsheets to solve this type of problem. Some students will find the 'Use a Variable' strategy more challenging, so showing how to represent the problem using a bar model (number rods or cubes could be used again) can provide support.

Example 4 uses the 'Work Backwards' and 'Use a Diagram' strategies. There is a lot of information in this example; you will need to read through each sentence in Step 1 carefully so that students can make sense of the question. Allow students to make suggestions for a suitable diagram (some may suggest a clock rather than a bar model or number line – discuss the advantages and disadvantages of this). Work through the steps using the bar model; you can use cubes to build a concrete model of the timeline. Ask students to think about why it is sensible to split the bar model into five-minute sections. Work through the Looking Back section in the opposite direction as a check. You can also use the bar model to ask students other questions, such as 'what time would she finish lunch if she wanted to do 35 minutes of piano practice?'

There are many problems and puzzles you can use to develop further students' understanding and application of these principles. There are a number of good, free websites with questions and challenges that can also be successfully tackled through the Pólya approach.

Student Book 1A
pages 218–241

Correct terminology, notation and symbols on geometrical diagrams are very important features of all work in this chapter. It is therefore very important that the language used during instruction and discussion is precise and unambiguous. Encourage students to use language correctly and ensure that their use of notation is conventional and correct. Students can create a vocabulary list as they work through this chapter.

Begin by referring to the **Flashback** (page 219) to check pre-requisite knowledge and vocabulary about clockwise and anti-clockwise, the two-letter notation for lines and the three-letter notation for angles.

Preliminary work on both factors and multiples with a focus on 90, 180 and 360 will be useful. To consolidate the inverse relationship between addition and subtraction, draw a bar model showing two numbers with a total of 180 and ask the students to say the four number sentences that can be used to describe the relationship between the three numbers.

Resources

k Chapter 8 introduction video

k Try It! videos 3, 5, 6, 8

Assessment

Workbook 1A Chapter 8

k Chapter 8 online skills test

k Chapter 8 end of chapter test and mark scheme

k Fully-worked solutions: Chapter 8 in Workbook 1A

k are resources on Kerboodle

8.1 Introduction to Angles

Learning Objectives:

● Measure and draw angles with a protractor

⊕ MyMaths

1081 Measuring angles

This section has a strong practical focus on the use of a protractor. Check that the protractors the students have are fit for purpose; some may be opaque, so useless, or have insufficient lines for ease of use. The detailed diagram of a protractor gives an opportunity to discuss its design, in particular the inner and outer scales.

The main difficulty students are likely to face will be choosing the correct scale. The speech bubble hint given with **Example 1** emphasises that they should match one of the line segments with one of the zero lines and start from there. Encouraging students to position their protractor so that one line segment is always on the zero line for the outer scale may help them read the protractor more easily, especially when counting individual degree markings between labelled multiples of 10.

The most common error of reading from the wrong scale can also be avoided if students get into the habit of deciding whether the angle to be measured is greater than or less than 90° before they even pick up their protractor. Students can easily make an approximate right angle between the thumb and first finger of either hand.

Although a 360° protractor is shown, **Example 3** demonstrates the method for measuring a reflex angle by measuring the smaller angle and subtracting from a 360° whole turn. If students choose to use a 360° protractor, they need to take care to centre it correctly on the cross hairs and again make sure they use the correct scale. Suggest to students that they turn their page to make one line vertical, as if pointing to 12 on a clock face, and then use the clockwise or anticlockwise scale depending on whether the other line forming the angle is to the right or to the left.

Example 4 demonstrates the process for drawing an angle. Use a large protractor or appropriate software to show this practically to students using correct terminology and labelling as you do so. Point out the **Discuss** box (at the bottom of page 225) and invite students to describe how they would draw an angle of 295° before demonstrating the process to them.

Class Activity 1 gives a very valuable opportunity to discuss and prevent common misconceptions with protractor use. Question 1 shows misuse of scale, Question 2 incorrect positioning of the protractor at the angle vertex and Question 3 mislabelling of a drawn angle.

Ask students to write a detailed 'user guide' for a protractor as if they were giving instructions for someone who had never seen one. Once written, guides can be swapped between students so they can test each other's instructions.

Practice 8.1 involves measuring and drawing all sizes of angles. Prepare accurately drawn angles on tracing paper for Questions 2 and 4 to enable quick checking of students' work. Students can be encouraged by rewarding their 'protractor proficiency' on successful completion of this practice exercise. In **Workbook Exercise 8.1**, students need to be familiar with the different notation for angles. Question 1 uses angle notation such as $\angle a$, so students need to look at the arc on the diagram to see which angle to measure; Question 2 uses three-letter notation, so students need to understand that the middle letter B in $\angle ABC$ will be at the vertex. For the clock faces in Question 3, encourage students to work out their answer and then check by measuring. It is good to form the habit of estimating before measuring to help prevent errors when reading from the protractor.

8.2 Types of Angles

Learning Objectives:

- Identify acute, right, obtuse and reflex angles

1989 Angles 3

Before students work on **Class Activity 2**, invite them to identify right angles in the classroom. Then check that they are familiar with the correct terms to describe angles of different sizes which they are likely to have met at primary level. When they complete the activity, they can copy or trace the arrow and then shade the angles on the interior of their arrow using different colours and a key for acute, right, obtuse and reflex angles. **Example 5** uses single letter notation to identify angles; students need to be flexible and comfortable using either this or three-letter notation.

When they have completed **Class Activity 3**, ask pairs of students to compare their shapes with those of another pair and identify what is the same and what is different. Ask students to explain why it is impossible to draw a triangle with two obtuse angles; later this can be related to the geometrical property that the angles in a triangle add to 180°.

Large pictures similar to those in **Practice 8.2** Question 3 can be produced, for students to label with angle types, to provide reference material for classroom display. Three-letter angle notation is used in Question 3 of **Workbook Exercise 8.2**; students should note that unless an angle is given as 'reflex $\angle ABC$' then the angle $\angle ABC$ will always be acute or obtuse.

8.3 Unknown Angles

Learning Objectives:

- Calculate missing angles in right angles, on straight lines and in full turns

1990 Angles 4

Class Activity 4 makes use of geometry software to see how angles add to 90°, 180° or 360° for right angles, straight lines and full turns respectively. There is a great deal of notation used in the instructions so you may need to support students with demonstrations as they draw their own diagrams. This will enable class discussion and comparison of results at every stage. This activity is a good opportunity for students to become familiar with free geometry software (such as Geogebra®), but if IT is not available they can draw diagrams by hand, measure and then compare results with each other.

Examples 6–8 make use of the three formal properties to find missing angles. Using a bar model to show the total angle helps students realise that they need to use subtraction to find the required angle. Take time to discuss (and justify) different calculation strategies. For example 180 − 69 can be worked out in many ways: 180 − 60 − 9; or 180 − 70 + 1; or 181 − 70; or 171 − 60 etc. Ensure that students use correct geometric reasoning with correct terminology in all solutions. When students are using the 'angles on a straight line add up to 180°' property, make sure they realise that the angles must be adjacent to each other for the property to be true. Use the **Discuss** box (page 233) and give some non-examples to emphasise this point; for example, in none of the following diagrams do angles a and b add to 180°.

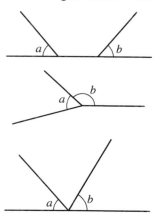

As 360° is described as a full turn, students need to switch to describing 'angles at a point' rather than use any reference to a turn or a circle in their reasoning. Use the **Discuss** box with **Example 7** to encourage students to estimate the expected size of their answer before calculating. Remind them that a final check is to ensure all angles, including the unknown angle solution, add up to the expected 90°, 180° or 360°. **Try It! 9** can be extended to consider other angles that a half turn can be split into by considering factors of 180.

As students complete **Practice 8.3** emphasise that correct geometric reasoning is just as important as the numerical answer to demonstrate that they know why the calculated angle is correct. Students must be aware that diagrams are not usually drawn accurately, so any missing angles need to be calculated and not measured. Students can make up their own puzzles like the problem-solving Question 8 and give to each other to solve.

Extend **Workbook Exercise 8.3** Question 4 by asking what other angles divide exactly into 360°; this work on factors of 360 will be helpful later for work on regular polygons. As students complete the problem-solving questions, ask them to state the geometric property used at each step of their working.

The clock face in **Challenge 8** (page 239) requires students to apply proportion and there is plenty of scope for rich extension work considering the angles between the hands at other times. Questions 1–4 of **Revision Exercise 8** give further practice measuring, drawing and calculating angles. Ensure that students' answers to Questions 5 and 6 are rigorous and use correct vocabulary. Students may find it useful to draw their own sketches of the constituent parts of the diagram for Question 8 where they need to consider the straight line at *B* and the right angle at *C* separately.

To support work on **Problem Solving 8** in the Workbook, students may wish to use a bar model showing three equal parts of a whole. When students complete **IT Exploration 8** they should identify where they find each type of angle on their flags. Challenge them to find a single flag which has several types of angle.

The **Write in Your Journal** activity gives an opportunity for students to attempt some simple proofs. For Bella's statement about two acute angles making an obtuse angle, students can offer a counterexample. Some numerical reasoning relating obtuse angles to right angles should be included in students' responses for Alfie's statement about two obtuse angles always making a reflex angle.

A practical approach using tracing paper to trace diagrams then fold or rotate will be helpful for all work on reflection and rotation symmetry. Some students may also find using a mirror useful.

_k_ are resources on Kerboodle

Resources

_k_ Chapter 9 introduction video
_k_ Try It! videos 1, 4

Assessment

Workbook 1A Chapter 9
_k_ Chapter 9 online skills test
_k_ Chapter 9 end of chapter test and mark scheme
_k_ Fully-worked solutions: Chapter 9 in Workbook 1A

9.1 Reflection Symmetry of Plane Figures

Learning Objectives:

⊕ **MyMaths**

1230 Symmetry

- Identify reflection symmetry and lines of symmetry
- Create symmetrical figures and patterns

When students complete Question 1 of **Class Activity 1**, there may be some discussion as to whether the shape or patterns on each diagram affect the symmetry of the object. For Question 2, encourage students to find one object with one line of symmetry and another object with more than one line. When they have drawn their diagrams, offer a mirror for students to check the accuracy of their freehand drawing. **Class Activity 2** then gives two more accurate methods for producing symmetrical designs using geometry software and tracing paper.

Make sure that students are familiar with the terms 'polygon' and 'regular' used in **Example 1**. Asking students to draw some polygons that are not regular will help remind them that the number of sides only defines the general polygon, although it is the regular version that is often most familiar. Notice the **Discuss** box on page 246

Making their own paper parallelogram, as suggested in the **Discuss** box beside **Example 2**, is a worthwhile activity to avoid the common misconception that a parallelogram has two lines of symmetry. Invite students

to predict whether a parallelogram has any reflection symmetry before they complete the activity. Students can then think about the special properties of a rhombus before repeating the process. In both **Examples 1 and 2** it may be beneficial to ask students to trace the shapes, cut them out and then fold them to show how to find the lines of symmetry. If students are having difficulty with part (b) of **Try It! 3** point out the **Remark** box which suggests they turn their page; making the line of symmetry vertical or horizontal may help them complete the shape.

Work in **Practice 9.1** considering the reflection symmetry properties of letters and road signs can be extended to include more examples and later returned to when rotation symmetry is covered. There may well be some discussion about the number of letters in the alphabet which have reflection symmetry given that various fonts have different shaped letters. Encourage this discussion to get students thinking carefully about how aspects of a shape will affect symmetry properties. For the Level 2 Question 9, ask students to work in pairs and try to convince their partner whether or not there is only one possible square to shade to meet the required condition.

In Question 4 of **Workbook Exercise 9.1**, challenge students to find as many four letter words as possible which end with the letters OOK and have reflection symmetry. Similarly, ask students to compare their answers to Question 6 where there are several different ways to cut part of the shape off so that the remaining shape has reflection symmetry. Ask students to identify how it is possible to make a single cut to obtain a shape with two lines of symmetry (a rectangle) and one with four lines of symmetry (a square).

9.2 Rotation Symmetry of Plane Figures

Learning Objectives:

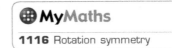

1116 Rotation symmetry

- Identify rotation symmetry
- State the order of rotation symmetry

Ask students to carry out the process of determining the order of rotation symmetry of a rectangle by tracing, as described in this section. It is essential that they realise the importance of labelling the vertices of the rectangle so that they can discern the orientation at every stage. Check that students are familiar with the concept of mapping (the shape 'perfectly covering', or 'matching up' with, itself) when discussing how to decide the order of rotation symmetry for a shape. Make sure they are aware that the letters used for labelling are just that; they are there to help, but it is the perimeter and not the letters that must match up as the shape rotates. You should also discuss that a shape only has a centre of rotation if it has rotational symmetry and that it is meaningless to talk about the centre of rotation for other shapes.

Class Activity 3 enables students to decide the order of rotational symmetry of a figure using geometry software. Point out that once an angle of rotation that maps a shape onto itself is found, the same rotation with an identical mapping can be repeated until 360°, a full turn, is reached. This means that if 360° is divided by the angle of rotation which maps the shape onto itself the quotient is the order of rotational symmetry.

In **Example 4** an alternative method of labelling individual vertices with numbers is used to keep track of rotations. Students may decide to use this method, to simply label one vertex or to put a T at the top of their original tracing. As the first three shapes in **Example 4** are regular polygons, the number of lines of symmetry do match the order of rotational symmetry. However, it is very important that students do not conclude that this is always the case for any shape. The figure used in **Class Activity 3** demonstrates that a shape may have rotational symmetry but no reflection symmetry. Similarly, the keyhole shape in part (d) of **Example 4** shows that a shape can have line symmetry without rotational symmetry.

When discussing order of rotation symmetry, make sure students understand that if a shape has to rotate the full 360° until it maps onto itself again (e.g. a

scalene triangle), then for consistency we can say that it has rotation symmetry order 1; but it is more natural to say that it has no rotation symmetry. To deepen understanding, ask students: What is the order of rotation symmetry of a regular polygon with n sides? What shape(s) other than a regular polygon with n sides will have rotation symmetry of order n? What is the order of rotation symmetry of a circle? Does any shape have rotation symmetry of order 0?

Example 5 involves identifying both reflection and rotation symmetry properties for a variety of shapes and designs. Extending this work by using other letters and playing cards in addition to those seen in **Try It! 5** will help students appreciate that symmetry properties are a very common feature in graphic design work throughout the ages.

Students consider symmetries for more shapes throughout **Practice 9.2**. Question 6 consolidates the fact that a shape may have just one of rotation symmetry or reflection symmetry. The Activity at the start of **Workbook Exercise 9.2** encourages students to look around them and find real-life objects with rotational symmetry. Ask them to distinguish between objects for which the rotational symmetry is essential for their function such as a propeller and those for which it is a more aesthetic design feature such as a logo.

For **Challenge 9** (page 257), consider producing sets of four hexagons in advance for students to shade with the required properties. For some extension work, if students make their own hexaflexagons, they can shade each of the three surfaces then flex to investigate the effect that manipulating the hexaflexagon has on the symmetry properties of their original shading.

When completing Question 8 in **Revision Exercise 8**, you can advise students to turn their paper so the mirror line runs vertically in front of them to complete the shape. Ask students to complete **Problem Solving 9** in the Workbook with a partner and discuss whether there is a unique solution to part (a). This question can be extended into a rich activity by giving students a 6 by 6 grid and asking them to produce designs with specific symmetry properties. For **IT Exploration 9**, students can consider why flags may be designed with symmetry properties and how this affects how they can be flown.

For the **Write in Your Journal** activity tell students that any diagram they draw that proves a statement wrong is called a counterexample.

It is assumed that students will know the terms perimeter and area from previous work at primary level. Here we extend the concept to find formulae for the perimeter and area of squares and rectangles through practical measurement and drawing diagrams. By making connections between the area of a rectangle and a triangle, students will derive the formula for the area of a triangle.

k are resources on Kerboodle

Resources

k Chapter 10 introduction video

k Try It! videos 1, 5, 9, 12

Assessment

Workbook 1A Chapter 10

k Chapter 10 online skills test

k Chapter 10 end of chapter test and mark scheme

k Fully-worked solutions: Chapter 10 in Workbook 1A

10.1 Perimeter of Squares and Rectangles

● Find the perimeter of squares and rectangles

The **Flashback** (page 261) will help students to recall the definitions of perimeter and area. It is useful to highlight 'rim' in pe*rim*eter to help students remember the definition. **Class Activity 1** looks at the connection between the length and width of a rectangle and its perimeter. Use this to determine the formulae for the perimeter of a rectangle and square. Recall the distributive law if students are having difficulty moving from $2 \times$ length $+ 2 \times$ width to $2 \times$ (length $+$ width). This can be demonstrated concretely by making the perimeter with bars or rods and rearranging. Using the string to create other shapes with the same perimeter will help to reinforce the definition of perimeter as the outline of a shape. The method of using the inverse process to answer Questions 2(b) and (c) is formalised when working on **Example and Try it! 2**.

Use **Example 1** to show how to record the substitution into the formulae. Students may need more practice at this before moving onto **Example 2** which looks at finding a missing length. Use the bar model to explain the method and to help develop understanding. The real-world **Example 3** shows why a perimeter may need to be calculated.

Complete **Practice 10.1**; encourage students to draw sketches labelled with the dimensions for Questions 3–5 so they can see what they are trying to find. Encourage students to draw bar models throughout this exercise.

Have students share and explain their methods for answering Question 6; prompt them to explain why they cannot simply halve the perimeter and work with one square. Allow students time to think about Question 7 and then ask them to vote for the correct answer. Asking students to explain how they think each person came up with their answer should encourage a discussion enabling you to reinforce the definition of perimeter as the outline of the shape.

10.2 Area of Squares and Rectangles

● Calculate the area of squares and rectangles

Ask students to create a rectangle with 21 squares which they can rearrange into 3 rows of 7 and 7 columns of 3. Sticky notes, square pattern blocks, square algebra tiles or paper cut outs could be used for this. Students can look at different sized rectangles and spot efficient ways to find the area. Develop the formula for the area of a rectangle (recall how arrays are used for multiplication). Consider how this changes when you have a square and find the formula for a square. Discuss the unit of measurement for area.

Work in pairs on **Class Activity 2**. Draw the plan on squared paper and cut out rectangles for the stalls where 1 m is represented by 1 cm. When a pair think they have a solution they can draw it on their diagram and work out the total profit.

Students need to decide which formula to use in **Example 4** and then use area in context in **Example 5**. Recall the inverse relationship between multiplication and division and use this to find a missing length or width given an area in **Example 6**. Highlight the factor tree representation used in the **Recall** box (page 271).

Practice 10.2 challenges students to use their knowledge to help solve problems. The two financial questions, 7 and 8, will enable students to see some real-world applications of area.

In **Workbook Exercise 10.2**, Question 3 is a multi-step problem where students may need support. Encourage them to use the space to draw a diagram and discuss what else they can find out about the square from the information given in the question. Question 5(b) is a good opportunity for students to explain their mathematical thinking. Encourage students to refer to their definition of perimeter to help them explain the answer.

Students could complete a mini-project working out how much it would cost to paint and carpet the classroom given the costs of materials. This can be extended to adding skirting boards, working out how much smaller the painted wall area will be because of windows etc.

10.3 Perimeter and Area of Triangles

- Find the perimeter of triangles
- Calculate the area of triangles

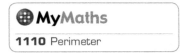

MyMaths

1110 Perimeter

Discuss with students what is meant by the word perpendicular see **Flashback** (page 261). Ask them to sort some examples of pairs of lines into perpendicular and non-perpendicular, explaining their reasoning. Include line segments that would be perpendicular if they were long enough to intersect and those that are not vertical/horizontal.

The perimeter of a triangle is consistent with the work they have done on squares and rectangles, so is just extending their thinking. Try giving the students a range of triangles to measure, including isosceles and equilateral, in order to find the perimeter. Ask them if they need to measure all the sides on each triangle in order to find the perimeter. This can be referred to when looking at **Example 8**. Students may need support to draw the bar model to solve **Try it! 8**.

Class Activity 3 considers the relationship between the area of a triangle and a rectangle. Make sure students draw different types of triangles including right-angled triangles. Make clear to students that the dotted line is the perpendicular height and always talk about perpendicular height. For the obtuse-angled triangle

in Question 4, you may need to support students with finding the area by subtracting a smaller right-angled triangle from a larger one. Discuss the fact that the perpendicular height can be a side of the triangle (in the special case of a right-angled triangle), or it can be inside or outside the triangle.

Students must be able to identify the base and perpendicular height of different triangles. **Class Activity 4** focusses on this. Students may find it helpful to work with paper cut-outs of triangles which they can rotate to make different sides horizontal. Ask students to explain their answers using letter notation to describe sides, for example 'the base is AB', to make it clear that the perpendicular height comes from the third vertex. Ask students which side would not be used as a base and why.

Use **Example 9** and **Try It! 9** to discuss whether it matters which side is the base and which is the perpendicular height, and to discuss when it is best to multiply by the half (see the second **Remark** box on page 278). Ask students to come up with different methods to answer the questions. **Example 10** provides a good opportunity for students to explain which answer is correct and why, using the language of perpendicular height and base. Use **Example 11** to ensure that students can find the area of an obtuse-angled triangle.

Complete Questions 1–5 of **Practice 10.3** to consolidate the use of the formula. Question 6 requires an explanation; encourage students to draw the diagram to help them explain the answer. Consider how to find a missing side given the area by working through **Example 12**. Students can then attempt Questions 7 and 8.

In **Workbook Exercise 10.3**, Question 6 is a multi-step problem. As a starting point, ask students to think about what else they can find out about the rectangle from the information given in the question.

Challenge 10 (page 285) in the Student Book and **Problem Solving 10** in the Workbook both consider composite shapes. This is extending students' thinking, so they may be good activities to work on in pairs. The **IT Exploration** can be a practical project for students to do at home.

Complete **Revision Exercise 10** to consolidate the work of this chapter. Question 9 asks students to find the area of a shape by subtracting an internal section. Students can cut out a diagram of the path on squared paper to see that they need to find two areas and subtract.

The **Write in Your Journal** task will encourage students to think about why the perimeter changes as the shapes are placed in different arrangements, they can then try to use this knowledge with a different amount of squares to find the largest and smallest perimeters.

Ensure students have access to a number of real-world solid objects. Give students opportunities to build cuboids and cubes from their nets to provide a better understanding of the idea of surface area. Similarly, use interlocking cubes to build cuboids and cubes when considering the volume of these 3D solids.

Some students find it difficult to visualise a 3D solid from a 2D net, so will benefit from practical work with manipulatives. Others may struggle to interpret 2D representations of 3D solids on a page. Give these students lots of opportunities to examine 2D representations, ideally not only in the student book but from other sources too.

k are resources on Kerboodle

Resources

k Chapter 11 introduction video
k Try It! videos 4, 9

Assessment

Workbook 1A Chapter 11
k Chapter 11 online skills test
k Chapter 11 end of chapter test and mark scheme
k Fully-worked solutions: Chapter 11 in Workbook 1A

11.1 Nets of Cuboids, including Cubes

Learning Objectives:

- Draw nets of cuboids, including cubes
- Sketch cubes and cuboids

Pose the question 'Is a square a rectangle?' When students can explain their reasoning, extend their thinking to decide if a cube is a cuboid.

Ask students to group a collection of real-world 3D objects into cuboids and non-cuboids, explaining their reasoning as they do so. This is a good opportunity to assess prior knowledge and vocabulary. Discuss which faces of a cuboid are the same and which are different. How does this change if the cuboid has a square face? What about a cube?

Class activity 1 introduces nets of cubes and looks at whether a net will make a cube. Challenge students to see how many different nets they can draw. Ask students how many squares are needed and what rules they need to follow in order to draw a potential net. Challenge them to see how many they can find. Clickable shapes (such as Polydron®) are very useful here for students to test their designs. A useful activity for pairs involves one student drawing a possible net and the other explaining if they think it will make a cube and then testing it out. Students then swap roles. This will then help them to explain their answers in **Example and Try It! 1**.

Students often find drawing 3D objects difficult; **Class Activity 2** shows a good way of drawing cubes and cuboids. They can practise by drawing a variety of sizes. Notice the **Discuss** box on page 292.

Before looking at **Example 2**, give students various cuboid packages they can cut open to reveal the net. Refer back to the discussion on faces and see if they can label the faces that match and work out where these are on a net. Discuss with students which faces on the cuboid have the same area, how they can describe the position of these faces and how this may help when drawing a net.

Complete **Practice 11.1** (and **Workbook Exercise 11.1**) for students to further engage with drawing nets and 3D objects. Students can cut out their nets in Question 6 to check that they create the correct cuboid. Compare students' answers to Question 7 and find all possible correct answers as a class. Ask students how they identified which size rectangle to draw and where it can and cannot be positioned. Use Questions 7 and 8 to reinforce the importance of being able to identify pairs of matching faces in nets of cuboids.

In the Workbook, Question 2 of **Activity 2** contains a further challenge: labelling the vertices on the net. Allow students to use a net which they can label and make into a cuboid to support this activity.

11.2 Surface Area of Cuboids, including Cubes

Learning Objectives:

- Calculate the surface area of cuboids, including cubes

Use the **Flashback** (page 289) to confirm understanding of the area of a square and rectangle, revisiting the formulae used. **Class Activity 3** introduces other solids and considers what their nets will look like. Ask students to bring in different shaped boxes which can be cut up. For Question 3, students will need to have the same box as their neighbour; a supply of the same sized cereal boxes will be ideal for this activity. Discuss with students why different nets of the same cuboid have the same area. Have 3D solids available for students to handle to help them visualise the net. Discuss with them that the surface area will be the same as the area of the net. Question 8 asks students to think about the surface area of a cylinder; discuss with students what the top and bottom faces will look like.

Class Activity 4 then looks at a systematic way of finding the surface area of a square and cuboid by considering equal faces. Discuss with students why the rectangles *A* and *C*, *B* and *D*, and *E* and *F* have equal areas. **Example 4** highlights two methods to calculate the surface area and it is useful to discuss the merits of each. **Example 5** looks at finding the area of one face of a cube given the total surface area; use a factor tree representation to recall the inverse relationship between multiplication and division. Discuss with students the difference between an open and a closed box and ensure they are clear that the surface area of an open box does not include the inside surfaces of the box.

Complete **Practice 11.2**. Encourage the more confident students to complete Questions 1 and 2 without drawing a net. For Question 5, students who need support could draw a net of the tray. As a further challenge, ask students to work out how much paint is needed to cover the inside and the outside of the tray.

Question 4 in **Workbook Exercise 11.2** will be a challenge for students as they try to find a missing length given the surface area of a cuboid; discuss how to use the net in part (a) to solve this problem. Students may also need guidance on how to set out their solution. Discuss with students the most useful way to draw the net for part (b).

11.3 Volume of Cuboids, including Cubes

Learning Objectives:

● Calculate the volume of cuboids, including cubes

1137 Volume of cuboids

It is important for students to understand that the volume of a solid is measured in cubic units. Building a variety of 3D solids from interlocking cubes (or other practical apparatus) and working out their volumes is an important starting point. Also discuss that the volume of an object is always the same; the volume of a liquid inside an object such as a bottle or pot may change, but the total volume of the object won't. It is important that students realise that a hollow box occupies the same volume as a solid object with the same dimensions.

When considering the cuboid (page 302) build it with coloured layers to aid the students' understanding. Build three versions of the cuboid in different ways $(5 \times 2) \times 3$, $(5 \times 3) \times 2$, $(2 \times 3) \times 5$ using (3, then 2 and then 5) coloured layers. Discuss with students the different arrangements and recall that multiplication is associative and commutative. Use **Example 6** to discuss with students other ways that a $6 \times 3 \times 2$ cuboid can be 'sliced'. Use interlocking cubes to do this example and **Try it! 6**. Discuss how this gives the formula for volume of a cuboid and then talk about how this changes for a cube. Use the second **Discuss** box on page 304 to highlight once more the commutative property of multiplication.

Class Activity 5 is a real-world example involving both surface area and volume; this can be extended by considering different shaped cuboids that produce the same volume, and students could then compare the cost for producing each. **Example 9** involves finding a missing dimension given the volume; again refer to the inverse relationship of multiplication and division. Note that **Example 9** and **Try It! 9** are structured slightly differently; in **Example 9** two dimensions are combined in the base area, but in **Try It! 9** the three dimensions are kept separate. You should draw students' attention to the fact that the units are consistent. Make sure they are aware that if the units are different they cannot simply calculate length × width × height, but must first convert the units.

Question 6 in **Practice 11.3** is challenging and will need discussion before students solve this problem; likewise Question 5 of **Workbook Exercise 11.3** will benefit from discussion. **Challenge 11** is very accessible for all students, using interlocking cubes when needed; however, **Problem Solving 11** will provide real challenge.

Completing **Revision Exercise 11** will review the chapter. Ask students to share their answers to Question 6 and challenge them to find as many cuboids as possible; this should generate a good discussion, giving students the opportunity to explain their thinking. This question also links to work on factors. Challenge students by asking how to make a cube with the same volume. Question 9 is a challenge, so you may need to support students to identify the steps needed to solve the problem.

IT Exploration 11 allows students to be creative and embed their understanding of nets. By completing the **Write in Your Journal** activity, students will consider practical reasons for using cuboids.

Chapter 12
Collecting, Organising and Displaying Data

Student Book 1A
pages 311–344

This chapter covers methods for collecting, organising and displaying data, and simple interpretation of pictorial and graphical representations of data, but stops short of the process of interpreting and comparing statistics, which is covered in Year 9. Use the **Discuss** boxes throughout this chapter to remind students to look at what the data tells us and the information they can find out; emphasise the point that we collect and represent data for a purpose.

There is scope for students to carry out their own surveys and to use real statistical data. Real examples of pictograms, line charts and graphs found in the media can be used to generate discussion. Many links can be made to students' work in other subjects, particularly science and geography.

Previous work on fractions and percentages, such as expressing one quantity as fraction of another or a part as a percentage of a whole, is revisited throughout this chapter when interpreting data in frequency tables and charts. As a hook to begin, introduce the **Challenge 12** from the end of the chapter (page 342) and set completing this as an aim.

Resources

𝑘 Chapter 12 introduction video
𝑘 Try It! videos 4, 10

Assessment

Workbook 1A Chapter 12
𝑘 Chapter 12 online skills test
𝑘 Chapter 12 end of chapter test and mark scheme
𝑘 Fully-worked solutions: Chapter 12 in Workbook 1A

𝑘 are resources on Kerboodle

12.1 Collecting, Classifying and Tabulating Data

- Collect data using different methods
- Classify, organise and tabulate data

Discuss with students examples of the different methods of data collection. As well as using the examples in the Student Book, ask students for examples of their own from studies in other subjects such as science, geography and PE. Discuss what makes a good or bad survey question, e.g. 'what's your favourite food?' vs. 'rank these foods from most to least favourite', 'how old are you?' vs. 'which of these age groups are you in?' Ask students to suggest why this information may be collected; for example, why would a marketing department want to know students' favourite foods? Discuss with students that companies other than food producers would be interested in this information to help them reach their target market (e.g. by advertising their product on food packaging).

Students work in pairs to devise a questionnaire of their own in **Class Activity 1**; once designed, they can exchange questionnaires with another pair of students and offer constructive criticism of each other's work. While checking that the questionnaire is straightforward to answer, students should make sure that response boxes are exhaustive and do not overlap. Encourage students to include collection of both quantitative, or numerical, data and qualitative, or categorical, data in their questionnaires.

Students are likely to be familiar with making tally charts of data from primary school but they must also be clear about how to set up the three columns of a frequency table. Completing **Class Activity 2** gives students the opportunity to practise the entire process for discrete data. Point out that the word 'frequency' should always be the title of the final column rather than 'total' or 'number'. Throughout the chapter, keep making the distinction between the data (what has been measured or recorded) and the frequency (the number of times each value has been measured or recorded).

The **Remark** boxes next to **Example 1** highlight the correct interpretation of the expressions 'fewer than' and 'more than' when dealing with discrete data. The **Discuss** box enables students to think about choosing efficient methods; remind them that an alternative method can be used as an effective checking strategy.

When students tally the data given in Questions 1 and 2 of **Practice 12.1**, remind them that a useful check is to make sure that their total frequency equals the number of items of data. Make sure they appreciate that the purpose of a frequency table is to allow a tally mark to be added for each data value in turn. Rather than doing this, some students may be tempted to count the number of each type of data value and then enter the tally and frequency in the table. Discuss with students how accurate this is, especially when dealing with a lot of data values, and how keeping a tally can avoid errors.

Question 4 in **Workbook Exercise 12.1** uses percentages rather than fractions to describe a proportion of the total. Point out to students that, as the total is 50, it is relatively straightforward to find an equivalent fraction with denominator 100 to give the percentage.

12.2 Pictograms, Vertical Line Charts and Bar Charts

- Read and interpret pictograms, vertical line charts and bar charts
- Represent data in pictograms, vertical line charts and bar charts
- Identify the advantages and disadvantages of pictograms, vertical line charts and bar charts

⊕ MyMaths

1205 Pictograms and bar charts

1193 Frequency tables and bar charts

Throughout this work, differences and similarities between the three types of chart should be considered and discussed with students. Talk with them about the advantages and disadvantages of using each of pictograms, vertical line charts and bar charts.

Emphasise the importance of having a key for a pictogram by discussing how the values represented by a pictogram would change with a different key. When students complete **Class Activity 3**, they should consider carefully how many cakes each symbol on their pictogram should represent. For this example, each frequency is a multiple of three; talk to students about whether they would generally use a picture to represent three. When working through the pictogram **Example 3 and Try It! 3** make sure that students understand that the cake diagram used in the Try It! can be easily divided into quarters to represent a single cake whereas it would be difficult to use the symbol in the Example to represent more than two cars. This issue of accuracy is raised in the **Discuss** box next to the initial example, on page 319, where one symbol represents 200 apples. Students need to consider whether the half symbol represents exactly 100 or perhaps 90 or 110 or somewhere in between. The difficulty reading and interpreting data values when part symbols are shown is highlighted as a disadvantage of pictograms.

The **Discuss** boxes next to the first vertical line chart (page 322) and first bar chart (page 326) both invite students to write down facts that they know about the data from reading the graph. Encourage students to identify which aspects of the graph, such as titles or labels, they are using in each case. When considering vertical line charts and bar charts, encourage correct labelling by highlighting how the axis titles match the headings of the 'data' and 'frequency' columns of a corresponding frequency table. The values in the first column then become the line or bar labels. When working through **Examples 4–6**, discuss with students the scale used in each case for the frequency axis. In all cases it must be linear and a scale chosen to make it easy to plot accurately.

Use the **Discuss** boxes next to the horizontal bar chart (page 326) to get students to compare and contrast this chart with the previous vertical bar chart showing the same data. Then talk about what information it is possible to work out even if the frequency axis is not labelled.

Students may be familiar with drawing bar charts using a spreadsheet program as done in **Class Activity 4**. Demonstrate the process and discuss whether it is easier to see the relative proportions of the data in the bar chart or the original table.

For **Class Activity 5**, students have to present real-life data in a pictogram, a vertical line chart and a bar chart. They should consider how simple it is to produce each diagram, how accurately it can display the data and whether data can be interpreted easily from it.

Example and Try It! 7 both give a poorly drawn bar chart for students to criticise. Ask students to look for examples of similar poor diagrams online or in a magazine or newspaper. Extend with a discussion about when a chart may be drawn in a particular way to be misleading and reasons why a person or organisation might want to do this.

Section D introduces compound bar charts. Draw attention to the **Remark** box (page 331) emphasising that a key to indicate which of the two categories a particular bar represents is essential.

Practice 12.2 gives students practice at constructing and interpreting all the types of chart covered. Make sure that students read values from vertical scales accurately; horizontal lines are given in Question 2, but suggest to students that they could use a ruler to read across or add lines themselves if a chart is not presented on a grid. Students are asked to consider proportions of data throughout this exercise. Point out that such statements are often used when the results of surveys are reported in the media and invite students to make up some headline-style statements which include the expressions 'more than' and 'less than'.

In Question 3 of **Workbook Exercise 12.2** students need to plot values carefully using the scale where two small squares represent one cubic metre. Point out that it is easier to read the data directly from the table rather than the graph in order to do the calculations required for parts (b) and (c).

12.3 Grouped Data

- Understand and interpret grouped data
- Draw a grouped frequency table
- Draw grouped data in a bar chart

1196 Grouping data

Students will construct a variety of frequency tables for grouped discrete and continuous (counted and measured) data in this section. When going through **Examples 9 and 10**, discuss the class intervals that have been chosen. Students should note that they are uniform and the number of classes is manageable. The **Flashback** (page 312) gives a reminder of the inequality notation needed for grouped frequency tables. Showing a class interval on a number line may help students understand which values can and cannot be included in it.

Questions 3 and 4 in **Practice 12.3** give students the class intervals to use, but using some real-life data collected by the students will give them the chance to make decisions about classes themselves. Remind students that they need to leave a gap between bars when they complete a bar chart for the grouped data in Question 1 of **Workbook Exercise 12.3** though take care not to encourage the misconception that there should *always* be gaps (for example, this would not be the case if they were to plot a graph for the data Example 10). In Question 5(c), students need to work out equal class intervals for the

data before tallying it; remind them to note the width of two for the class interval given and replicate it for the remaining four classes.

For **Challenge 12** (page 342), encourage students to read the sentences one at a time and construct a bar model diagram with a separate bar showing the information for each sentence. This model will effectively form a draft diagram showing relative proportions that can then be used to work out the actual numbers for each category in order to draw a bar chart.

For **Revision Exercise 12**, students need to complete missing information in frequency tables. These include grouped frequency tables where students will need to work out the size of the class interval being used in order to complete the table. In Question 5, point out that an easy way to do this is to look at the sequence of numbers running downwards on both the left and the right of the inequality symbols. Here they are clearly multiples of five and these can be continued to produce the missing class intervals.

To complete **Problem Solving 12** in the Workbook, students must not miss the initial sentence stating that there are 100 students. When students set up an online poll for **IT Exploration 12**, the data may be collated into a spreadsheet for them automatically. Discuss the advantages and disadvantages of using online polls.

For the **Write in Your Journal** activity, students could produce a checklist to use whenever they carry out surveys and statistical work in any subject.

The Examples and Try Its in this section are designed to consolidate the learning from Chapters 8 to 12 including work on angles, symmetry, perimeter and area of triangles, and data handling.

Example 1 requires students to consider angles, area and symmetry properties for right-angled triangles. Students may need to trace and extend lines for measuring the angle *ACB*. Tracing paper will also be helpful to establish rotation symmetry. The **Try It! 1** triangle is not right-angled and as the vertex *C* is not above the line *AB*, you may need to remind students that the usual formula for area applies and the height *NC*, shown dashed on the diagram, will need to be used. Observing that triangle *BCN* is an isosceles right-angled triangle may lead students to deduce that both angles *CBN* and *BCN* will be 45°. This will provide an alternative strategy for the solution to part (c)(i).

In **Example 2**, encourage students to think strategically when finding pairs of angles that total 360°. Discuss which pairings from acute + acute, acute + obtuse, acute + reflex, etc. can possibly equal exactly 360°. This preliminary work will reduce the number of trials. A similar strategy can be used when finding pairs to total 180° in **Try It! 2**, where the reflex angles can be ignored.

For **Example 3**, it is important to state that the solution given as a net for the cuboid in part (b) is just one possible net. Discuss with students the number of possible nets for this cuboid. Encourage them to use their net diagram when calculating the total surface area to help ensure that they include all six faces. When interpreting the pictogram for part (e) of **Try It! 3** students should note that the key differs from the pictogram in the previous example. Discuss with students why each key may have been chosen for the set of data each pictogram represents.

The first four questions of **Review Exercise 3** allow students to separately practise the skills involved in measuring angles, using angle properties and symmetry. Provide students with tracing paper for the symmetry work and suggest that sketch diagrams may be helpful throughout the exercise. For example, sketches annotated with side lengths will be useful in both parts of Question 5.

On the diagram in part (b) of Question 6 there is a redundant length of 25 cm, which may be used as the height of the triangle in error. This is an opportunity to consolidate the fact that the *perpendicular* height must be used for the area calculation. The triangles in Question 11 gives further practice at identifying the

correct values to use. Students could identify some likely misconceptions themselves and generate some incorrect answers that could be used as distractors for a multiple choice version of this question. In each case they can write a statement that could be given as a hint to someone who chose a particular incorrect answer.

When students have designed their own aquarium tank cuboids for Question 8 ask them to work out the surface area of the five rectangular faces and compare their surface area with a partner. Help the students to notice that a cuboid whose side lengths are most alike will have the lowest surface area and hence a cube will have the least possible surface area for a given volume.

For question 10, direct students to look at the pictogram key first, then discuss how the picture is being used to represent different numbers of daffodils. Ensure students are clear that each petal is representing one daffodil by asking extra questions about the pictogram if necessary.

Question 13 can be extended to consider how this particular net would need to be labelled in order to produce a cube with numbers for a dice in correct positions. This can then be repeated for other cube nets.

In part (a) of Question 14, students are asked to state what the 10–14 range in the table means; this can lead to a discussion of the discrete nature of this data – the number of push-ups will always be a whole number.

Before students complete Question 11 in **Workbook Review 3**, ask them to state, with reasoning, the fraction of the rectangle that is shaded. They may choose to draw additional lines to divide the rectangle into halves or quarters to support their explanation.

Question 12, which involves shading a 25 square grid, can be related to more familiar work with a 100 square grid to help students see that as four 25 square grids make a 100 square, the number of shaded squares × 4 gives the percentage shaded.

Question 13 can be used for further work considering volume and surface area together. Give students 24 interlocking cubes and ask them to make all the possible cuboids and find the associated surface areas using the square face of one cube as a unit. They will deduce that the long 1 × 1 × 24 cuboid has the largest surface area whereas the cuboid with most equal side lengths has the least surface area. The question can then be posed: if a carrot and an apple have the same volume, which has the greatest surface area? Careful peeling of an actual carrot and an apple can offer a powerful demonstration of the correct answer.

Problems in Real-world Contexts

Throughout these problems, there are opportunities to extend the work and incorporate students' own experiences by making links to other curriculum areas such as design and technology, geography and history.

A Rushton Triangular Lodge

A great deal of written material is presented in this question. Use this as an opportunity to discuss relevant and redundant information. Where students are considering the symmetry properties of the window, they should look at the carved trefoil border rather than the square slab. When students make conversions or calculate area and then round their answers, ask them to investigate how the final answers are affected if they round values before using them in their calculations.

B Living Room Extension

The diagram given for the possible extension will help students interpret the letter notation for the shapes and walls given in the question text. Discuss why this notation is used and encourage them to use it in their descriptions of other possible extensions. Students need to interpret the limitations for the outer walls and may find it helpful to trace the diagram and annotate the loci of possible positions for the extension sections when working on the final part of this question. The **Discuss** box (page 355) asks students to think about the Pólya problem-solving process and how it applies to this problem; refer back to the four-step problem-solving process (page 210) and work through this with students, referring to this question and indeed others throughout the chapter.

C Extendable Table

Students may be unfamiliar with this type of table so sketch diagrams will be invaluable. A practical approach adding a third table between a pair of classroom tables could be used to demonstrate the problem to students. For the particularly challenging Question 3, students will first need to work out the area of the extended top and thus find the volume given the thickness of 4 cm. They will need to use the hint or alternatively you can provide a value for the density of pine.

D Carat Gold

As indicated in the **Remark** box, (page 356), bar models showing the proportions of gold and other metal in each type of gold will help students visualise the problem. There is a great deal of information given in Question 3, so students should take care to read the sentences one at a time and write down the key facts. It is essential that students appreciate that it is the mass of gold and other metals that defines the carat. Given the total mass of 48 g for each bracelet, students should be able to scale up from the total 24 for each ratio and identify that a 22 carat bracelet uses 44 g of gold whereas a 9 carat one uses 18 g. Multiples of 44 and 18 then need to be combined to get as close to 200 g as possible; students may well use a trial and error strategy for this stage.

E Height of a Tree

As long as it's a sunny day, taking students outside to use this method to find heights of objects around the school grounds would be a valuable practical activity.

Number Hacks: Reference Sheets

Lower prior attaining students often have difficulty recalling key arithmetical facts, such as times tables, or they rely on inefficient methods with a high cognitive load, for example, reciting the whole times table to reach a particular multiple, or counting on or back in ones when adding and subtracting within 20. This impacts adversely on both their progress and their confidence: they think they 'can't do maths' because they don't remember that $7 \times 8 = 56$ or $9 + 6 = 15$. It is likely that you will be encouraging students to improve their knowledge and retrieval of the sorts of numerical facts and relationships that higher attaining students have 'at their fingertips', and you may be using a particular programme to help them. That will be successful in the medium to long term; in the here and now of lessons, you want to prevent arithmetical insecurity being a barrier to progress and achievement. This is the purpose of the **Number Hack tables** at the back of Student Book.

Using the Number Hack Tables

Prompts in the Student Book to use the Number Hack tables are phrased in terms of 'checking' rather than 'helping'. This is to avoid undermining students' pride. Students with low prior attainment have often had negative prior experiences of mathematics; their enjoyment of and attainment in the subject have drained away in unison. Suggesting to secondary students they need *help* with calculations, which they know are from the primary curriculum, is unlikely to be well received. Explaining to them that the tables are there so they can *check* their calculations is a much more positive invitation.

The tables are for quick reference in the middle of a calculation. When students working through a multi-step calculation, for example, need to know the value of 7×8, they can turn to the multiplication table, *hack* the answer, and go back to the question.

The tables enable students to calculate quickly:

- a sum 'within 20' i.e. of two integers where $a + b \leq 20$
- a difference 'within 20' i.e. of two integers where $0 < a - b < 20$
- a multiplication up to 20×20
- a division with dividend ≤ 400 and divisor ≤ 20.

Throughout the Student Book, reference is made to the Number Hacks at points where lack of arithmetical fluency might hinder students' development of the core concept being studied, for example, equivalent fractions or ratios.

Addition and Subtraction Within 20

Successful implementation of the standard 'column method' of addition and subtraction requires confident addition of one-digit numbers and subtraction of one-digit numbers from a 'teen' number. For example, in Chapter 1 page 10:

In the column method, align the two numbers in columns by their place values. Add the digits in each column from right to left and regroup as shown below.

>
> **REMARK**
>
> You can use the addition table on page 358 to check that $8 + 7 = 15$.

238	8 ones + 7 ones = 15 ones = 1 ten + 5 ones.
+ 167	3 tens + 6 tens + 1 ten = 10 tens = 1 hundred.
405	2 hundreds + 1 hundred + 1 hundred = 4 hundreds.
1 1	Regrouping digits.

If students are not confident that $8 + 7 = 15$, or they are working out the sum by counting on in ones from 8 (saying '9, 10, 11, 12, 13, 14, 15'), they can instead use the addition table on page 358 to:

- *hack* the value of $8 + 7 = 15$
- then go back to $3 + 6 + 1 = 9$ (also *hacked* from the table) $+ 1 = 10$.

If students do not know that $9 + 1 = 10$, or the other whole number pairs that sum to 10 (i.e. their number bonds to 10), these are represented using images similar to number rods on page 362.

Later in Chapter 1, on page 15:

>
> **REMARK**
>
> You can check the answer to subtractions of numbers under twenty with the subtraction table, on page 358.

4 11 1	To subtract 8 ones from 4 ones, regroup the tens and ones.
524	14 ones − 8 ones = 6 ones.
− 378	To subtract 7 tens from 1 ten, regroup the hundreds and tens.
	11 tens − 7 tens = 4 tens.
146	4 hundreds − 3 hundreds = 1 hundred.

students can

- *hack* the values of 14 − 8 and 11 − 7, and even 4 − 3 if needed
- then go back and complete 524 − 378 = 146.

Multiplication and Division Tables

Confident multiplicative reasoning is essential for success in secondary maths because it underpins so many contexts. For example, in Chapter 11 page 304:

REMARK

You can use the multiplication table on page 359 to check these calculations.

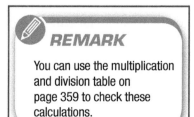

Try It! 8 An empty shoe box is in the shape of a cuboid. What is the volume of the shoe box?

12cm
15cm
30cm

To calculate the volume, a student needs to calculate $30 \times 15 \times 12$. Strategically, a good way to do this is to:

- *hack* the value of $12 \times 15 = 180$ from the table on page 359
- then go back and reason 180×30

  $= 18 \times 10 \times 3 \times 10$

  $= 18 \times 3 \times 10 \times 10$

  $= 54$ (also *hacked* from the table) $\times 100$

  $= 5400.$

Asking for calculation 'by hand' rather than using a calculator enables you to assess and develop students' conceptual understanding of multiplication. Here the students are using the commutativity and, in the separation and re-combination of the factors of 10, the associativity of multiplication.

Similarly, in Chapter 6 page 155, if a student is uncertain that $28 \div 4 = 7$, this value can be *hacked* from the multiplication table on page 359: the multiplication table is also, of course, a division table.

REMARK

You can use the multiplication and division table on page 359 to check these calculations.

Example 7 Convert each decimal to a mixed number in its simplest form.

(a) 13.28   (b) 9.625

Solution (a) $13.28 = 13 + \dfrac{28}{100}$ $13.28 = 13 + 0.28$

$= 13 + \dfrac{28 \div 4}{100 \div 4}$ Simplify the fraction.

$= 13 + \dfrac{7}{25}$

$= 13\dfrac{7}{25}$ Express as a mixed number.

The Number Hack multiplication table on page 359 will be especially supportive in Chapter 5 (Understanding Fractions) and Chapter 7 (Introduction to Ratio). Embedded within a multiplication table are equivalent fractions and ratios:

REMARK

You can use the multiplication table on page 359. 56 and 96 are both in the column that starts at 8. 84 and 144 are both in the column that starts at 12. Read across the rows to the left.

(c) 8 is a common factor of 56 and 96.

$\dfrac{56}{96} = \dfrac{56 \div 8}{96 \div 8}$

$= \dfrac{7}{12}$

12 is a common factor of 84 and 144.

$\dfrac{84}{144} = \dfrac{84 \div 12}{144 \div 12}$

$= \dfrac{7}{12}$

Both fractions reduce to the same fraction $\dfrac{7}{12}$ in their lowest terms.

$\therefore \dfrac{56}{96}$ and $\dfrac{84}{144}$ are equivalent fractions.

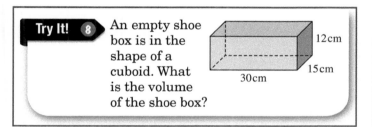

6	6	12	18	24	30	36	42	48	54	60	66	72	78
7	14	21	28	35	42	49	56	63	70	77	84	91
8	8	16	24	32	40	48	56	64	72	80	88	96	104
9	9	18	27	36	45	54	63	72	81	90	99	108	117
10	10	20	30	40	50	60	70	80	90	100	110	120	130
11	11	22	33	44	55	66	77	88	99	110	121	132	143
12	12	24	36	48	60	72	84	96	108	120	132	144	156
13	13	26	39	52	65	78	91	104	117	130	143	156	169

- 56 and 84 are in the '7-row' because $56 = 7 \times 8$ and $84 = 7 \times 12$.
- $96 = 12 \times 8$ and $144 = 12 \times 12$ so 96 and 144 are in the '12-row'.
- 56 and 96 are in the '8-column' as they are both multiples of 8.
- Likewise, 84 and 144 are both multiples of 12 and so are both in the '12-column'.
- The 'corners of a rectangle' alignment, as shown in the table, means that the fractions $\frac{56}{96}$ and $\frac{84}{144}$ are both equivalent to $\frac{7}{12}$, and the ratios $56 : 84$ and $96 : 144$ are both equivalent to $8 : 12$.

Number Bonds to 10

Number rods are the inspiration for the images on page 362. If you have a set of these your students can make these images concretely in the classroom as well as see them in the Student Book. Number bonds to 10 are represented, but take time to ensure that your students develop the fluency and understanding that these tell them bonds to *any* multiple of 10:

- 'I know that $3 + 7 = 10$ so I know that $13 + 7$ and $3 + 17$ both equal 10 more than 10, i.e. 20'
- 'I know that $4 + 6 = 10$ so I know that $54 + 6$ equals 10 more than 50, i.e. 60, and that $94 + 6$ equals 10 more than 90, i.e. 100'
- 'I know that $2 + 8 = 10$ so I know that $32 + 48$ equals 10 more than 30 and 40, i.e. 80'

The related images of bonds to 1 and percentages (that is, bonds to 100) are useful in their own right, but they also make clear the identical pattern of these three sets of bonds. The segment 0–100 is an enlargement (scale factor 10) of the segment 0–10, which in turn is an enlargement of the segment 0–1, and so on.

Teaching for Mastery with the Number Hack Tables

The Number Hack tables have been included in the Student Book to improve *procedural fluency*. However, when you show students how to use them, you should allow time to explore, identify and explain some of the many relationships within the tables, to improve their *conceptual understanding*. For example, ask students to identify and explain patterns between the values in the columns of the multiplication table that start (in the top row of numbers in the blue squares) with

- 2, 4, 8 and 16
- 4, 8 and 12
- 4, 6 and 10
- 6, 10 and 16
- 20, 19 and 18.

The reasoning they develop here will support them with calculation strategies in the main text of the Student Book, such as the distributive law of multiplication over addition and subtraction covered on page 83.

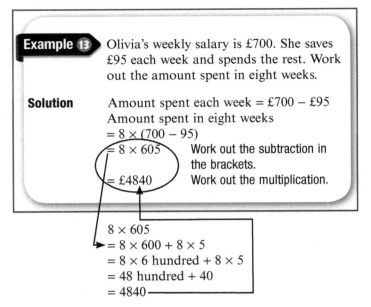

Example 13 Olivia's weekly salary is £700. She saves £95 each week and spends the rest. Work out the amount spent in eight weeks.

Solution

Amount spent each week = £700 − £95
Amount spent in eight weeks
$= 8 \times (700 − 95)$
$= 8 \times 605$ Work out the subtraction in the brackets.
$= £4840$ Work out the multiplication.

8×605
$= 8 \times 600 + 8 \times 5$
$= 8 \times 6 \text{ hundred} + 8 \times 5$
$= 48 \text{ hundred} + 40$
$= 4840$

A particularly fruitful question to consider with the support of the Number Hack tables is 'what's the same, what's different?' about sets of related calculations. For example:

- $5 + 8$, $4 + 9$, $3 + 10$ and so on
- $14 − 6$, $15 − 7$, $16 − 8$ and so on
- 3×16, 6×8, 12×4
- 3×16, 6×16, 12×16
- 4×18, 8×9, 12×6
- 8×9, 16×9, 8×18, 16×18
- $200 \div 20$, $100 \div 10$, $50 \div 5$
- $400 \div 20$, $200 \div 20$, $100 \div 20$
- $90 \div 5$, $90 \div 10$, $90 \div 15$

In each of these sets of calculations, carefully chosen variation enables you to isolate the effect (or not) that changes to the components of an addition, subtraction, multiplication or division calculation make to the overall answer. Knowing this is of practical value, not just theoretical interest. In each of the following, the last calculation is substantially easier than the first:

- $1000 − 562 = 999 − 561$
- $537 + 256 = 540 + 253 = 500 + 293$
- $15 \times 22 = 5 \times 66 = 10 \times 33$
- $240 \div 5 = 480 \div 10$

The Number Hack tables are a starting point for many rich discussions: for whole-class teaching, for pair work and partner talk, for small group support and for closing the gap interventions. Time spent in Key Stage 3 exploring the tables and making secure your students' Key Stage 2 knowledge, fluencies and understanding will bring them substantial rewards in Key Stage 4.

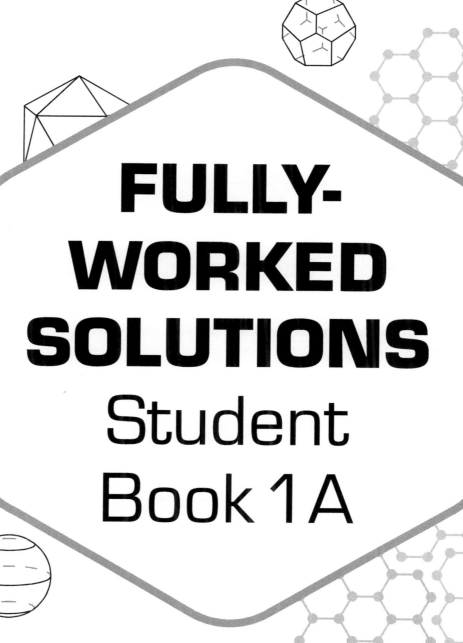

FULLY-WORKED SOLUTIONS

Student Book 1A

Adding and Subtracting Whole Numbers

Class Activity 1

Objective: To write an inequality between two numbers using a number line.

1. (a) Copy this number line. Complete the missing numbers.

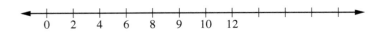

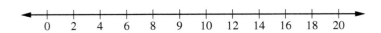

(b) Which number, 4 or 12, is greater? Explain your answer.

On the number line, a number is greater than any number to its left. Therefore, 12 is greater than 4.

(c) Name a number on the line that is greater than 10.

On a number line, a number is less than any number to its right. Therefore, 12, 14, 16, etc. are all greater than 10.

2. (a) Copy this number line. Complete the missing numbers.

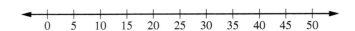

(b) Which number, 15 and 40, is smaller? Explain your answer.

On the number line, a number is less than any number to its right. Therefore, 15 is smaller than 40.

(c) Name a number on the line that is smaller than 25.

On the number line, a number is greater than any number to its left. Therefore, 10, 15, 20, etc. are all smaller than 25.

3. (a) In a car boot sale, book A costs 15p and book B costs 48p. Which book has the lower price?

Book A has the lower price.

(b) Copy the number line and plot the points representing the numbers 15 and 48.

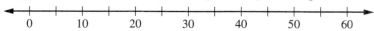

On the number line, the points represent the numbers 15 and 48.

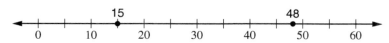

(c) Copy and complete 15 ☐ 48 using the inequality sign '<' or '>'.

15 $\boxed{<}$ 48

---

4. (a) A bottle of milk is 280 ml. A cup of coffee is 125 ml. Which drink has the larger volume?

The bottle of milk has the larger volume.

(b) Copy the number line and plot the points representing the numbers 125 and 280.

On the number line, the points represent the numbers 125 and 280.

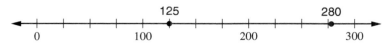

(c) Copy and complete 280 ☐ 125 using the inequality sign '<' or '>'.

280 $\boxed{>}$ 125

Class Activity 2

Objective: To develop knowledge of addition

1. Work out the sum 48 + 75 using
   (a) place value counters,

	Hundreds	Tens	Ones
48		10 10 10 10	1 1 1 1 1 1 1 1
75		10 10 10 10 10 10 10	1 1 1 1 1
48 + 75	100	10 10	1 1 1
Regroup	100	10	

∴ 48 + 75 = 123

(b) the column method.

$$\begin{array}{r} 48 \\ +75 \\ \hline 123 \\ \hline {\scriptstyle 1\,1} \end{array}$$

∴ 48 + 75 = 123

2. Work out the sum 216 + 397 using
   (a) place value counters,

	Hundreds	Tens	Ones
216	100 100	10	1 1 1 1 1 1
397	100 100 100	10 10 10 10 10 10 10 10 10	1 1 1 1 1 1 1
216 + 397	100 100 100 100 100 100	10	1 1 1
Regroup	100	10	

∴ 216 + 397 = 613

(b) the column method.

$$\begin{array}{r} 397 \\ +216 \\ \hline 613 \\ \hline {\scriptstyle 1\,1} \end{array}$$

∴ 216 + 397 = 613

3. Which method is easier to understand? What's the same and what's different between the two?

Both methods use columns to align numbers by their place values. The digits in each column are then added together and regrouped in tens from right to left. Although both methods are similar, the place counter method is easier to visualise.

Class Activity 3

Objective: To develop knowledge of subtraction.

1. Calculate 82 − 65 using
   (a) place value counters,

	Tens	Ones
Regroup		1 1 1 1 X / 1 1 1 X X
82	X X X 10 10 / X X X	X X
65	10 10 10 10 10 / 10	1 1 1 1 / 1
82 − 65	10	1 1 1 1 / 1 1 1

∴ 82 − 65 = 17

(b) the column method.

$$\begin{array}{r} {\scriptstyle 7\ 1} \\ 8\,2 \\ -\ 6\,5 \\ \hline 1\,7 \end{array}$$

$\therefore\ 82 - 65 = 17$

2. Calculate $435 - 179$ using
   (a) place value counters,

	Hundreds	Tens	Ones
Regroup		10 10 10 10 10 ~~10~~ ~~10~~ ~~10~~ ~~10~~ ~~10~~	1 1 1 ~~1~~ ~~1~~ 1 1 1 ~~1~~ ~~1~~
435	100 100 1~~00~~ ~~100~~	~~10~~ ~~10~~ ~~10~~	~~1~~ ~~1~~ ~~1~~ ~~1~~ ~~1~~
179	100	10 10 10 10 10 10 10	1 1 1 1 1 1 1 1 1
435 − 179	100 100	10 10 10 10 10	1 1 1 1 1 1

$\therefore\ 435 - 179 = 256$

(b) the column method.

$$\begin{array}{r} {\scriptstyle 3\ 12\ 1} \\ 4\,3\,5 \\ -1\,7\,9 \\ \hline 2\,5\,6 \end{array}$$

$\therefore\ 435 - 179 = 256$

3. Which method is easier to understand? What's the same and what's different about the methods?

   Both methods use columns to align numbers by their place values. The digits in each column are then subtracted and regrouped in tens from right to left. Although both methods are similar, the place counter method is easier to visualise.

Class Activity 4

Objective: To recognise the inverse relationship between addition and subtraction.
Your teacher will give you resources to work with in this Class Activity.

1. Find the values of these expressions.
   (a) $5 + 8$

   $5 + 8 = 13$

   (b) $13 - 5$

   $13 - 5 = 8$

(c) $13 - 8$

$13 - 8 = 5$

2. Find the values of these expressions.
   (a) $24 + 67$

   $24 + 67 = 91$

   (b) $91 - 24$

   $91 - 24 = 67$

   (c) $91 - 67$

   $91 - 67 = 24$

3. Find the values of these expressions.
   (a) $147 + 55$

   $147 + 55 = 202$

   (b) $202 - 147$

   $202 - 147 = 55$

   (c) $202 - 55$

   $202 - 55 = 147$

4. Find the values of these expressions.
   (a) $213 + 546$

   $213 + 546 = 759$

   (b) $759 - 213$

   $759 - 213 = 546$

   (c) $759 - 546$

   $759 - 546 = 213$

5. By looking at the above results, if number 1 + number 2 = sum, what is
   (a) sum − number 1,

   sum − number 1 = number 2

   (b) sum − number 2?

   sum − number 2 = number 1

Class Activity 5

Objective: To explore some properties of addition.

1. Find the value of these sums.
    (a) 34 + 18

    34 + 18 = 52

    (b) 18 + 34

    18 + 34 = 52

    (c) 56 + 79

    56 + 79 = 135

    (d) 79 + 56

    79 + 56 = 135

2. What do you observe from the results in Question **1**? Suggest one property of addition from the results.

    The results in Question **1** show that numbers can be added in any order. It suggests the following property of addition:

    number 1 + number 2 = number 2 + number 1

3. Work out the sum within the brackets first and then work out the value of the whole calculation.
    (a) (3 + 7) + 8

    (3 + 7) + 8
    = 10 + 8
    = 18

    (b) 3 + (7 + 8)

    3 + (7 + 8)
    = 3 + 15
    = 18

    (c) (25 + 39) + 41

    (25 + 39) + 41
    = 64 + 41
    = 105

    (d) 25 + (39 + 41)

    25 + (39 + 41)
    = 25 + 80
    = 105

4. What do you observe from the results in Question **3**? Suggest one property of addition from the results.

    The results in Question **2** show that numbers can be arranged and added in any order. It suggests the following property of addition:

    (number 1 + number 2) + number 3 = number 1 + (number 2 + number 3)

Try It!

Section 1.1

1. (a) Write the number 28 054 in expanded form.
    (b) What is the place value of the digit 8?
    (c) What value does the digit 8 represent?

    Solution
    (a) $28\,054 = 2 \times 10\,000 + 8 \times 1000 + 5 \times 10 + 4 \times 1$

    (b) The place value of the digit 8 is thousands.

    (c) The digit 8 represents the value 8000.

2. Look at the number 6238.
    (a) Which digit represents the highest value? What is this value?
    (b) Which digit represents the lowest value? What is this value?

    Solution
    (a) The digit 6 represents the highest value. The value of the digit 6 in this number is 6000.

    (b) The digit 8 represents the lowest value. The value of the digit 8 in this number is 8.

3. Copy and fill in each blank with the inequality sign '<' or '>'. Explain your reasoning in full sentences.

    (a) 731 ☐ 4265

    (b) 95 387 ☐ 95 360

    Solution
    (a) 4 in 4265 represents the value 4000. 7 in 731 represents the value 700. As 700 is less than 4000, this means:

    731 $\boxed{<}$ 4265

    (b) The digit 9 in both numbers represents 90 000. The digit 5 in both numbers represents 5000. The digit 3 in both numbers represents 300. The fourth highest value digit of 95 387 represents 80, whilst the fourth highest value digit of 95 360 represents 60. 80 is greater than 60, which means:

    95 387 $\boxed{>}$ 95 360

Section 1.2

4. Calculate 86 + 954.

    Solution
    $$\begin{array}{r} 86 \\ + \ 954 \\ \hline 1040 \\ \hline {}_{1 \ 1} \end{array}$$

    $\therefore 86 + 954 = 1040$

5. Tom's scores in two computer games are 1387 and 2594. Find his total score for the two games.

    Solution
    Total score for the two games
    $= 1387 + 2594$
    $= 3981$

    $$\begin{array}{r} 1387 \\ + 2594 \\ \hline 3981 \\ \hline {}_{1 \ 1} \end{array}$$

6. A recipe uses 140 g of beef, 165 g of potato and 250 g of tomato. Find the total mass of these ingredients.

    Solution
    Total mass of ingredients
    $= 140 + 165 + 250$
    $= 555 \, \text{g}$

    $$\begin{array}{r} 140 \\ 165 \\ + 250 \\ \hline 555 \\ \hline {}_{1} \end{array}$$

    Alternatively,
    $140 + 165 + 250$
    $= 305 + 250$
    $= 555 \, \text{g}$

Section 1.3

7. Calculate 7026 − 849.

    Solution

    $$\begin{array}{r} {}^{6\ 9\ 11\ 1} \\ 7026 \\ - \ \ 849 \\ \hline 6177 \end{array}$$

    $\therefore 7026 - 849 = 6177$

8. Find the missing number in each expression.

    (a) 56 + ☐ = 88   (b) 75 − ☐ = 26

    Solution
    (a) 56 + ☐ = 88

    From the inverse relationship, the missing number
    ☐ = 88 − 56
    = 32

    $$\begin{array}{r} 88 \\ - 56 \\ \hline 32 \end{array}$$

    (b) 75 − ☐ = 26
    The missing number
    ☐ = 75 − 26
    = 49

    $$\begin{array}{r} {}^{6\ 1} \\ 75 \\ - 26 \\ \hline 49 \end{array}$$

9. Alyssa has £746 in her savings account. She withdraws £250 from the account. She then pays a bill of £318 using the account. How much is left of her savings?

Solution

The bar model for this situation is shown below.

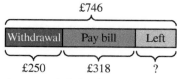

£746

Withdrawal	Pay bill	Left

£250   £318   ?

Amount left in the account
= original amount in the account − withdrawal −
pay bill
= £746 − £250 − £318
= £496 − £318
= £178

$$\begin{array}{r} {}^6{}^1 \\ 7\,4\,6 \\ -2\,5\,0 \\ \hline 4\,9\,6 \end{array} \qquad \begin{array}{r} {}^8{}^1 \\ 4\,9\,6 \\ -3\,1\,8 \\ \hline 1\,7\,8 \end{array}$$

10. A lift is 97 m above the ground. It moves up 84 m and then moves down 126 m. How many metres from the ground is the lift in its final position?

Solution

Height of the lift from the ground in its final position
= 97 + 84 − 126
= 55 m

$$\begin{array}{r} 9\,7 \\ +\ 8\,4 \\ \hline 1\,8\,1 \\ {}_1 \end{array} \qquad \begin{array}{r} {}^7{}^1 \\ 1\,8\,1 \\ -1\,2\,6 \\ \hline 5\,5 \end{array}$$

Section 1.4

11. Calculate these sums by reordering the numbers first to make the addition easier.
   (a) 39 + 42 + 21
   (b) 256 + 145 + 55 + 324

Solution
   (a) 39 + 42 + 21
   = 39 + 21 + 42
   = 60 + 42
   = 102

   (b) 256 + 145 + 55 + 324
   = 256 + 324 + 145 + 55
   = 580 + 200
   = 780

12. Calculate these sums by reordering the numbers first to make the addition easier.
   (a) 92 − 25 − 62   (b) 754 − 315 − 254

Solution
   (a) 92 − 25 − 62
   = 92 − 62 − 25
   = 30 − 25
   = 5

   (b) 754 − 315 − 254
   = 754 − 254 − 315
   = 500 − 315
   = 185

13. Calculate the following expressions by first using methods to make them easier.
   (a) 74 + 18
   (b) 265 + 346
   (c) 8497 − 2534

Solution
   (a) 74 + 18
   = 74 + 10 + 8
   = 84 + 8
   = 92

   (b) 265 + 346
   = 265 + 300 + 40 + 6
   = 565 + 40 + 6
   = 605 + 6
   = 611

   (c) 8497 − 2534
   = 8497 − 2000 − 500 − 30 − 4
   = 6497 − 500 − 30 − 4
   = 5967 − 4
   = 5963

14. Work out these expressions by first replacing values with near numbers.
   (a) 512 + 89
   (b) 625 − 497

Solution
   (a) 512 + 89
   = 512 + 90 − 1
   = 602 − 1
   = 601

   (b) 625 − 497
   = 625 − 500 + 3
   = 125 + 3
   = 128

15. A rope is 150 cm long. A length of 56 cm and a length of 68 cm are cut from the rope. Find the remaining length of the rope.

Solution
150 − 56 − 68
= 150 − 50 − 6 − 70 + 2
= 100 − 6 − 70 + 2
= 94 − 70 + 2
= 24 + 2
= 26
The remaining length of the rope is 26 cm.

Practice 1.1

1. Put these numbers in a place value table using counters. Then write the numbers out in expanded form.
   (a) 328   (b) 3280
   (c) 32 800   (d) 30 028

Solution

(a)

	Hundreds	Tens	Ones
328	100 100 100	10 10	1 1 1 1 1 1 1 1

$328 = 3 \times 100 + 2 \times 10 + 8 \times 1$

(b)

	Thousands	Hundreds	Tens	Ones
3280	1000 1000 1000	100 100	10 10 10 10 10 10 10 10	

$3280 = 3 \times 1000 + 2 \times 100 + 8 \times 10$

(c)

	Ten thousands	Thousands	Hundreds	Tens	Ones
32 800	10000 10000 10000	1000 1000	100 100 100 100 100 100 100 100		

$32 800 = 3 \times 10 000 + 2 \times 1000 + 8 \times 100$

(d)

	Ten thousands	Thousands	Hundreds	Tens	Ones
30 028	10000 10000 10000			10 10	1 1 1 1 1 1 1 1

$30 028 = 3 \times 10 000 + 2 \times 10 + 8 \times 1$

2. Write down the value represented by the digit 3 in each number. Use place value counters to help you.
   (a) 937   (b) 9703
   (c) 37 900   (d) 73 090

Solution

(a) The value represented by the digit 3 in the number 937 is 30.

(b) The value represented by the digit 3 in the number 9703 is 3.

(c) The value represented by the digit 3 in the number 37 900 is 30 000.

(d) The value represented by the digit 3 in the number 73 090 is 3000.

3. Make and draw these numbers on a place value table. Which of the numbers represents seven thousand and four?
   704   7400   7004   7040

Solution
7004 is seven thousand and four.

4. Here is a list of numbers:
   6023,   8416,   162,   61 999,   35 679.
   (a) In which number does the digit 6 represent the lowest value? What is this value?
   (b) In which number does the digit 6 represent the highest value? What is this value?

Solution
(a) In 8416, the digit 6 represents the lowest value. This value is 6.

(b) In 61 999, the digit 6 represents the highest value. This value is 60 000.

5. Copy and fill in each blank with '<' or '>'. Use a place value table or draw a number line for each part to help you.
   (a) 138 ☐ 38   (b) 7326 ☐ 7845
   (c) 4607 ☐ 4670   (d) 29 731 ☐ 29 751

Solution
(a) 138 ⊐>⊏ 38   (b) 7326 ⊐<⊏ 7845

(c) 4607 ⊐<⊏ 4670   (d) 29 731 ⊐<⊏ 29 751

6. Here is a list of numbers:
   30 007,   38 970,   38 030,   30 907,
   30 070,   38 709.
   Write down the numbers that are
   (a) less than 30 709,   (b) less than 37 000,
   (c) greater than 35 000,   (d) greater than 38 500.

Solution
(a) 30 007 and 30 070 are less than 30 709.

(b) 30 007, 30 907 and 30 070 are less than 37 000.

(c) 38 970, 38 030 and 38 709 are greater than 35 000.

(d) 38 970 and 38 709 are greater than 38 500.

7. The floor area of Buckingham Palace is 77 000 m².
   (a) Write 77 000 in expanded form.
   (b) What is the value represented by the first digit 7?

Solution

(a) $77\,000 = 7 \times 10\,000 + 7 \times 1000$

(b) The value represented by the first digit 7 is $70\,000$.

8. The price of a car is £25 639.
   (a) State the digit which represents the greatest value.
   (b) What is the value of this digit?

Solution

(a) The digit 2 represents the greatest value.

(b) The value represented by the digit 2 in 25 639 is 20 000.

9. Isaac is 175 cm tall, Ben is 164 cm tall and Karim is 173 cm tall. Write the names of the boys in order from the shortest to the tallest.

Solution

As 164 cm < 173 cm < 175 cm, the names of the boys in order from the shortest to the tallest are Ben, Karim, Isaac.

10. Write down a 5-digit number such that the values of two of its digits represent 80 000 and 20.

Solution

Some possible 5-digit numbers are
80 020, 80 320, 80 325, 87 020, 87 320, 87 325.

Practice 1.2

Level 1   GCSE Grade **1 / 1⁺**

1. Use place value counters to represent these calculations. Then copy and complete them using the column method.

   (a) $\begin{array}{r} 423 \\ +\ 389 \\ \hline \end{array}$
   (b) $\begin{array}{r} 423 \\ +\ 589 \\ \hline \end{array}$

   (c) $\begin{array}{r} 489 \\ +\ 523 \\ \hline \end{array}$
   (d) $\begin{array}{r} 483 \\ +\ 529 \\ \hline \end{array}$

Solution

(a) $\begin{array}{r} 423 \\ +389 \\ \hline 812 \\ \hline {\scriptstyle 1\ 1} \end{array}$
(b) $\begin{array}{r} 423 \\ +\ 589 \\ \hline 1012 \\ \hline {\scriptstyle 1\ 1} \end{array}$

(c) $\begin{array}{r} 489 \\ +\ 523 \\ \hline 1012 \\ \hline {\scriptstyle 1\ 1} \end{array}$
(d) $\begin{array}{r} 483 \\ +\ 529 \\ \hline 1012 \\ \hline {\scriptstyle 1\ 1} \end{array}$

2. Evaluate (that is, work out the values of) these expressions.
   (a) $1432 + 81$ **(b)** $1432 + 781$
   (c) $625 + 2564$ **(d)** $61\,438 + 7295$

Solution

(a) $\begin{array}{r} 1432 \\ +\quad 81 \\ \hline 1513 \\ \hline {\scriptstyle 1} \end{array}$
(b) $\begin{array}{r} 1432 \\ +\ 781 \\ \hline 2213 \\ \hline {\scriptstyle 1\ 1} \end{array}$

(c) $\begin{array}{r} 625 \\ +2564 \\ \hline 3189 \\ \hline {\scriptstyle 1} \end{array}$
(d) $\begin{array}{r} 61438 \\ +\ 7295 \\ \hline 68733 \\ \hline {\scriptstyle 1\ 1} \end{array}$

3. Calculate these sums.
   (a) $23 + 50 + 19$ **(b)** $47 + 83 + 145$
   (c) $328 + 67 + 512$ **(d)** $426 + 201 + 534$

Solution

(a) $\begin{array}{r} 23 \\ 50 \\ +19 \\ \hline 92 \\ \hline {\scriptstyle 1} \end{array}$

$\therefore 23 + 50 + 19 = 92$

Alternatively,
$23 + 50 + 19$
$= 73 + 19$
$= 92$

$\begin{array}{r} 23 \\ +\ 50 \\ \hline 73 \end{array}$ $\begin{array}{r} 73 \\ +19 \\ \hline 92 \\ \hline {\scriptstyle 1} \end{array}$

(b) $\begin{array}{r} 47 \\ 83 \\ +145 \\ \hline 275 \\ \hline {\scriptstyle 1\ 1} \end{array}$

$\therefore 47 + 83 + 145 = 275$

(c) $\begin{array}{r} 328 \\ 67 \\ +512 \\ \hline 907 \\ \hline {\scriptstyle 1\ 1} \end{array}$

$\therefore 328 + 67 + 512 = 907$

(d) $\begin{array}{r} 426 \\ 201 \\ +\ 534 \\ \hline 1161 \\ \hline {\scriptstyle 1} \end{array}$

$\therefore 426 + 201 + 534 = 1161$

4. The bar model shows the masses of two fish. Find the total mass of these two fish.

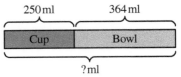

Solution

Total mass of the two fish
= 446 + 385
= 831 g

```
  446
+ 385
  831
  1 1
```

Level 2  **GCSE Grade 2⁻**

5. The capacity of a cup is 250 ml. The capacity of a bowl is 364 ml. Draw a bar model and find the total capacity of the cup and the bowl.

Solution

The bar model to show this case is drawn below.

Total capacity of the cup and the bowl
= 250 + 364
= 614 ml

```
  250
+ 364
  614
  1
```

6. Mr Singh earns £3480 a month. Mrs Singh earns £3720 a month. What is their total income in a month?

Solution

Total income of the couple in a month
= £3480 + £3720
= £7200

```
  3480
+ 3720
  7200
  1 1
```

7. A red ribbon is 187 cm long. A white ribbon is 64 cm long. A blue ribbon is 239 cm long. Draw a bar model and find the total length of
(a) the red ribbon and the white ribbon,
(b) all three ribbons.

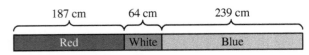

Solution

(a) The bar model to show this case is drawn below.
Total length of the red and white ribbons
= 187 + 64
= 251 cm

```
  187
+  64
  251
   1 1
```

(b) Total length of all three ribbons
= 187 + 64 + 239
= 251 + 239
= 490 cm

```
  251
+ 239
  490
   1
```

8. (a) Create two 4-digit numbers such that their sum is 8888.
(b) Create one 4-digit number and one 3-digit number such that their sum is 8888.
(c) Create one 4-digit number and one 2-digit number such that their sum is 8888.

Solution

There are many possible answers. Three are suggested for each part.
(a) 4800 + 4088 = 8888
5000 + 3888 = 8888
2222 + 6666 = 8888

(b) 8000 + 888 = 8888
8088 + 800 = 8888
8333 + 555 = 8888

(c) 8800 + 88 = 8888
8850 + 38 = 8888
8815 + 73 = 8888

9. (a) What errors have these students made when adding?

Student A	Student B
19621	19621
+ 379	+ 379
19990	23411

For each student, write a sentence starting with 'Be careful _____'.
Explain what mistake they should avoid when adding.
(b) Calculate the correct answer to the sum of 19 621 and 379.

Solution

(a) Student A has not regrouped his numbers. In the sum of ones,
1 one + 9 ones = 10 ones
= 1 ten + 0 ones
Student A should have put 1 ten in the Tens column and 0 in the Ones column. Next, to work out the sum of tens, student A should have
2 tens + 7 tens + 1 ten (from above)
= 10 tens
= 1 hundred + 0 tens

Student A should regroup 10 tens and put 1 in the Hundreds column and 0 in the Tens column.
The same applies for the sum of hundreds and thousands.

For student A:
Be careful that each column can only have up to 9 units. Regroup when you have more than 9.

Student B has not aligned the two numbers being added in columns by their place values.

For student B:
Be careful when aligning the numbers in columns by their place values. Add the digits in each column from right to left.

(b)
$$\begin{array}{r} 19621 \\ +\quad 379 \\ \hline 20000 \\ \hline {\scriptstyle 1\ 1\ 1\ 1} \end{array}$$

$$\therefore 19621 + 379 = 20\,000$$

10. Find the missing digits to complete this addition.

$$\begin{array}{r} 3\ \square\ 4\ \square \\ +\ 2\ 6\ \square\ 9 \\ \hline \square\ 2\ 3\ 6 \end{array}$$

Solution

$$\begin{array}{r} 3\ \boxed{5}\ 4\ \boxed{7} \\ +\ 2\ 6\ \boxed{8}\ 9 \\ \hline \boxed{6}\ 2\ 3\ 6 \end{array}$$

Practice 1.3

Level 1 | GCSE Grade **1** / **1**⁺ |

1. Use place value counters to represent these calculations. Then copy and complete them.

(a)
$$\begin{array}{r} 84 \\ -35 \end{array}$$

(b)
$$\begin{array}{r} 684 \\ -\ 35 \end{array}$$

(c)
$$\begin{array}{r} 684 \\ -235 \end{array}$$

(d)
$$\begin{array}{r} 687 \\ -238 \end{array}$$

Solution

(a)
$$\begin{array}{r} {\scriptstyle 7\ 1} \\ 84 \\ -35 \\ \hline 49 \end{array}$$

(b)
$$\begin{array}{r} {\scriptstyle 7\ 1} \\ 684 \\ -\ 35 \\ \hline 649 \end{array}$$

(c)
$$\begin{array}{r} {\scriptstyle 7\ 1} \\ 684 \\ -235 \\ \hline 449 \end{array}$$

(d)
$$\begin{array}{r} {\scriptstyle 7\ 1} \\ 687 \\ -238 \\ \hline 449 \end{array}$$

2. Evaluate these expressions.
(a) $534 - 310$ **(b)** $534 - 390$
(c) $4382 - 2170$ **(d)** $36\,540 - 12\,782$

Solution

(a)
$$\begin{array}{r} 534 \\ -310 \\ \hline 224 \end{array}$$

$$\therefore 534 - 310 = 224$$

(b)
$$\begin{array}{r} {\scriptstyle 4\ 1} \\ 534 \\ -390 \\ \hline 144 \end{array}$$

$$\therefore 534 - 390 = 144$$

(c)
$$\begin{array}{r} 4382 \\ -2170 \\ \hline 2212 \end{array}$$

$$\therefore 4382 - 2170 = 2212$$

(d)
$$\begin{array}{r} {\scriptstyle 5\ 14\ 13\ 1} \\ 36540 \\ -12782 \\ \hline 23758 \end{array}$$

$$\therefore 36\,540 - 12\,782 = 23\,758$$

3. Work out these values.
(a) $78 - 23 - 18$ **(b)** $431 - 86 - 134$
(c) $342 + 256 - 428$ **(d)** $630 - 418 + 253$

Solution

(a) $78 - 23 - 18$
$= 55 - 18$
$= 37$

$$\begin{array}{r} 78 \\ -23 \\ \hline 55 \end{array} \qquad \begin{array}{r} {\scriptstyle 4\ 1} \\ 55 \\ -18 \\ \hline 37 \end{array}$$

(b) $431 - 86 - 134$
$= 345 - 134$
$= 211$

$$\begin{array}{r} {\scriptstyle 3\ 12\ 1} \\ 431 \\ -\ 86 \\ \hline 345 \end{array} \qquad \begin{array}{r} 345 \\ -134 \\ \hline 211 \end{array}$$

(c) $342 + 256 - 428$
$= 598 - 428$
$= 170$

$$\begin{array}{r} 342 \\ +256 \\ \hline 598 \end{array} \qquad \begin{array}{r} 598 \\ -428 \\ \hline 170 \end{array}$$

(d) $630 - 418 + 253$
$= 212 + 253$
$= 465$

$$\begin{array}{r} {\scriptstyle 2\ 1} \\ 630 \\ -418 \\ \hline 212 \\ +253 \\ \hline 465 \end{array}$$

4. Find the missing number in each expression.
(a) $34 + \boxed{} = 87$
(b) $\boxed{} + 432 = 710$
(c) $2689 - \boxed{} = 245$
(d) $\boxed{} - 4836 = 13\,590$

Solution

(a) $34 + \boxed{} = 87$

From the inverse relationship, the missing number

$\boxed{} = 87 - 34$
$\phantom{\boxed{}} = 53$

$\begin{array}{r} 87 \\ -34 \\ \hline 53 \end{array}$

(b) $\boxed{} + 432 = 710$

The missing number

$\boxed{} = 710 - 432$
$\phantom{\boxed{}} = 278$

$\begin{array}{r} {}^{6}\,{}^{10}\,{}^{1} \\ 7\,1\,0 \\ -4\,3\,2 \\ \hline 2\,7\,8 \end{array}$

(c) $2689 - \boxed{} = 245$

The missing number

$\boxed{} = 2689 - 245$
$\phantom{\boxed{}} = 2444$

$\begin{array}{r} 2689 \\ -\ \ 245 \\ \hline 2444 \end{array}$

(d) $\boxed{} - 4836 = 13\,590$

The missing number

$\boxed{} = 13\,590 + 4836$
$\phantom{\boxed{}} = 18\,426$

$\begin{array}{r} 13590 \\ +\ 4836 \\ \hline 18426 \\ {}_{1\ 1} \end{array}$

5. The bar model shows the number of sweets in a full packet and the number of sweets that have been eaten. Find the number of sweets left.

Full packet
67

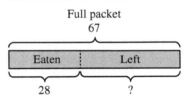

Eaten	Left
28	?

Solution

Number of sweets that are left
$= 67 - 28$
$= 39$

$\begin{array}{r} {}^{5}\,{}^{1} \\ 67 \\ -28 \\ \hline 39 \end{array}$

Level 2   GCSE Grade 2^-

6. A metal rod is 176 cm long. 89 cm is cut from it. Draw a bar model to represent the information. Find the length of the remaining rod.

Solution

The bar model to represent the information is shown.

176 cm

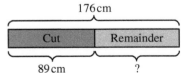

Cut	Remainder
89 cm	?

Length of the remaining rod
$= 176 - 89$
$= 87$ cm

$\begin{array}{r} {}^{0}\,{}^{16}\,{}^{1} \\ 1\,7\,6 \\ -\ \ 8\,9 \\ \hline 8\,7 \end{array}$

7. The longest river in the UK is the Severn. It is 354 km long. The second longest is the Thames. It is 346 km long. Find

(a) the total length of these two rivers,

(b) the difference in length between these two rivers.

Solution

(a) Total length of the two rivers
$= 354 + 346$
$= 700$ km

$\begin{array}{r} 354 \\ +346 \\ \hline 700 \\ {}_{1\ 1} \end{array}$

(b) Difference in their lengths
$= 354 - 346$
$= 8$ km

$\begin{array}{r} {}^{4}\,{}^{1} \\ 354 \\ -346 \\ \hline 8 \end{array}$

8. The price of a necklace is £217. The price of a ring is £154.

(a) Find the total price of the necklace and the ring.

(b) Jo has £400 and buys both items. How much money is left?

Solution

(a) Total price of the two items
$= £217 + £154$
$= £371$

$\begin{array}{r} 217 \\ +154 \\ \hline 371 \\ {}_{1} \end{array}$

(b) Amount of money left
$= £400 - £371$
$= £29$

$\begin{array}{r} {}^{3}\,{}^{9}\,{}^{1} \\ 400 \\ -371 \\ \hline 29 \end{array}$

9. **(a)** What errors have these students made when subtracting?

Student A	Student B
83752	83752
$-\ \ 6104$	-6104
87658	22712

For each student, write a sentence starting with 'Be careful _____'.
Explain what mistake they should avoid when subtracting.

(b) Calculate the correct answer to $83\,752 - 6104$.

Solution

(a) Student A has not regrouped digits. In the Ones column, 4 ones cannot be subtracted from 2 ones. So, student A needs to regroup 1 ten from the first number to 10 ones.

1 ten + 2 ones − 4 ones
$= 12$ ones − 4 ones
$= 8$ ones

Thus, student A is left with 4 tens in the Tens column.

4 tens − 0 tens = 4 tens (not 5 tens)

The next column is correct but a similar mistake is also made in the following column.

For student A:
Be careful to regroup the digits in the next place value correctly when subtracting.

Student B has not aligned the two numbers in columns by their place values.

For student B:
Be careful when using the column method for subtraction that you have aligned the numbers by their place values in columns.

(b)

$$\begin{array}{r} {}^{7\,1}{}^{4\,1} \\ 8\,3\,7\,5\,2 \\ -\ \ 6\,1\,0\,4 \\ \hline 7\,7\,6\,4\,8 \end{array}$$

$\therefore 83\,752 - 6104 = 77\,648$

10. Write an expression with two 4-digit whole numbers where the result is 1500 when the smaller number is subtracted from the larger number.

Solution
Second number – first number = 1500
Three possible sets of two 4-digit whole numbers are suggested.

first number	second number	
1000	2500	i.e. 2500 − 1000 = 1500
1500	3000	i.e. 3000 − 1500 = 1500
2000	3500	i.e. 3500 − 2000 = 1500

Practice 1.4

In this exercise, choose the best method for each question to make the calculation easier.

Level 1   GCSE Grade **1 / 1⁺**

1. Calculate these sums.
  (a) 52 + 28   **(b)** 52 + 31
  (c) 52 + 47 + 28   **(d)** 31 + 52 + 89

Solution
(a) 52 + 28
  = 52 + 20 + 8
  = 72 + 8
  = 80
(b) 52 + 31
  = 52 + 30 + 1
  = 82 + 1
  = 83
(c) 52 + 47 + 28
  = 52 + 28 + 47
  = 80 + 47
  = 127
(d) 31 + 52 + 89
  = 31 + 89 + 52

  = 31 + 9 + 80 + 52
  = 40 + 80 + 52
  = 120 + 52
  = 172

2. Calculate these expressions.
  (a) 78 − 26 − 18   **(b)** 22 + 15 + 38
  (c) 362 + 215 − 142   **(d)** 126 + 233 + 134

Solution
(a) 78 − 26 − 18
  = 78 − 18 − 20 − 6
  = 60 − 20 − 6
  = 40 − 6
  = 34

(b) 22 + 15 + 38
  = 22 + 38 + 15
  = 60 + 15
  = 75

(c) 362 + 215 − 142
  = 362 − 142 + 215
  = 362 − 100 − 42 + 215
  = 262 − 42 + 215
  = 220 + 200 + 15
  = 420 + 15
  = 435

(d) 126 + 233 + 134
  = 126 + 134 + 233
  = 126 + 100 + 34 + 233
  = 226 + 34 + 233
  = 260 + 200 + 33
  = 460 + 33
  = 493

3. Work out these values.
  (a) 432 + 199   **(b)** 360 − 238
  (c) 236 + 317   **(d)** 180 − 139 − 21

Solution
(a) 432 + 199
  = 432 + 200 − 1
  = 632 − 1
  = 631

(b) 360 − 238
  = 360 − 200 − 30 − 8
  = 160 − 30 − 8
  = 130 − 8
  = 122

(c) 236 + 317
  = 236 + 300 + 17
  = 536 + 4 + 13
  = 540 + 13
  = 553

(d) 180 − 139 − 21
  = 180 − 130 − 9 − 21
  = 50 − 9 − 21
  = 41 − 21
  = 20

4. Evaluate these expressions.

(a) 254 + 347   (b) 254 + 387

(c) 4570 − 2346   (d) 4570 − 2386

Solution

(a)   254 + 347

= 254 + 300 + 47

= 554 + 46 + 1

= 600 + 1

= 601

(b)   254 + 387

= 254 + 300 + 87

= 554 + 46 + 41

= 600 + 41

= 641

(c)   4570 − 2346

= 4570 − 2000 − 300 − 46

= 2570 − 300 − 46

= 2270 − 46

= 2270 − 50 + 4

= 2220 + 4

= 2224

(d)   4570 − 2386

= 4570 − 2000 − 300 − 86

= 2570 − 300 − 86

= 2270 − 70 − 16

= 2200 − 10 − 6

= 2190 − 6

= 2184

5. Work out these expressions.

(a) 34 + 32 + 28 + 46

(b) 47 + 66 − 37 − 26

(c) 314 − 205 + 131 − 45

(d) 625 − 199 − 238 − 147

Solution

(a)   34 + 32 + 28 + 46

= 34 + 46 + 32 + 28

= 80 + 60

= 140

(b)   47 + 66 − 37 − 26

= 47 − 37 + 66 − 26

= 10 + 40

= 50

(c)   314 − 205 + 131 − 45

= 314 + 131 − 205 − 45

= 445 − 45 − 205

= 400 − 205

= 400 − 200 − 5

= 200 − 5

= 195

(d)   625 − 199 − 238 − 147

= 625 − 200 + 1 − 200 − 38 − 100 − 47

= 625 − 200 − 200 − 100 − 38 − 47 + 1

= 625 − 500 − 38 − 47 + 1

= 125 − 25 − 13 − 47 + 1

= 100 − 13 − 47 + 1

= 87 − 47 + 1

= 40 + 1

= 41

Level 2   **GCSE Grade 2⁻**

6. Find the missing number in each of these calculations using the inverse relationship between addition and subtraction.

(a) 38 + ☐ = 67   (b) ☐ + 59 = 88

(c) ☐ − 239 = 416   (d) 381 − ☐ = 245

Solution

(a)   38 + ☐ = 67

From the inverse relationship, the missing number

☐ = 67 − 38

= 67 − 40 + 2

= 27 + 2

= 29

(b)   ☐ + 59 = 88

☐ = 88 − 59

= 88 − 60 + 1

= 28 + 1

= 29

(c)   ☐ − 239 = 416

☐ = 416 + 239

= 416 + 200 + 39

= 616 + 40 − 1

= 656 − 1

= 655

(d)   381 − ☐ = 245

☐ = 381 − 245

= 381 − 200 − 45

= 181 − 50 + 5

= 131 + 5

= 136

7. 960 ml of purple paint is made by mixing 346 ml of red paint with 314 ml of blue paint and some white paint. Find the volume of white paint used.

Solution

Volume of white paint used

= 960 − 346 − 314

= 960 − 300 − 40 − 6 − 314

= 660 − 40 − 6 − 314

= 620 − 6 − 314

= 614 − 314

= 300 ml

8. The diagram is a 4 by 4 magic square. It is 'magic' because the numbers in each row, each column and each diagonal have the same total. One of the numbers is wrong. Find and correct it.

19	16	13	26
14	25	20	15
24	11	18	21
17	22	24	12

Solution

One most direct method to solve this problem is to find the sum of the numbers in each row (R), each column (C) and each diagonal to check which of them have a different total. The wrong number can then be identified and corrected.

	C1	C2	C3	C4	Sum
R1	19	16	13	26	74
R2	14	25	20	15	74
R3	24	11	18	21	74
R4	17	22	24	12	(75)
Sum	74	74	(75)	74	

Sum of diagonal = 74
Sum of diagonal = 74

All rows , except R4, have a total of 74 and all columns, except C3, have totals of 74. The numbers on the two diagonals also add to a total of 74. Hence, the number '24' at the intersection of R4 and C3 is wrong. To get a total of 74 instead of 75, the number should be reduced from 24 to 23. Thus, the correct number is 23.

9. Match each calculation to one of the methods A to D
   (a) 678 + 41   (b) 678 − 39
   (c) 678 − 41   (d) 678 + 39

   A   + 40 − 1   B   + 40 + 1
   C   − 40 − 1   D   − 40 + 1

   Solution
   (a) B   (b) D
   (c) C   (d) A

10. Create a calculation with four whole numbers for a friend. Write your calculation so that your friend will need to reorder the numbers to make it easier to work out. Ask your friend to calculate the answer and then discuss the method used.

   Solution
   Student's calculations

Challenge 1

Your classmate Max has a 4-digit combination lock for a bicycle.
You are challenged to work out the number that will unlock it using these statements.

1. The first digit is the hundreds digit of the year of Max's birth.
2. The second digit is the tens digit of the sum of 6789 and 9876.
3. The third digit is the ones digit of the whole number that is greater than 6789 but less than 6791.
4. The fourth digit is the digit representing the highest value in the answer to 9876 − 6789.

What number will unlock Max's bicycle?

Solution
1. The hundreds digit of the year of birth is 0, so the first digit of the bicycle lock is 0.
2. The tens digit of the sum of 6789 and 9876 is 6. Thus, the second digit of the lock is 6.

3. 6789 < 6790 < 6791
   The ones digit of 6790 is 0. Thus, the third digit of the lock is 0.
4. 9876 − 6789 = 3087
   The digit that represents the highest value in 3087 is 3.

Thus, the number that will unlock Max's bicycle is 0603.

Revision Exercise 1

1. (a) Write the expanded form of the number 30 947.
   (b) State the value of the digit which represents the highest value.

   Solution
   (a) $30\,947 = 3 \times 10\,000 + 9 \times 100 + 4 \times 10 + 7 \times 1$
   (b) The digit 3 represents the highest value. The value is 30 000.

2. The mass of a car is 1478 kg.
   (a) What is the place value of the digit 8?
   (b) What is the value represented by the digit 4?

   Solution
   (a) The place value of the digit 8 is ones.
   (b) The value represented by the digit 4 is 400.

3. Copy and complete each statement using '<' or '>'.
   (a) 458 ☐ 1309   (b) 73 256 ☐ 73 265

   Solution
   (a) 458 < 1309
   (b) 73 256 < 73 265

4. Work out these values.

(a) 345 + 2679   **(b)** 36 709 + 25 418

(c) 8325 − 2678   **(d)** 93 560 − 9356

Solution

(a)
```
   345
 +2679
  3024
  1 1 1
```
∴ 345 + 2679 = 3024

(b)
```
  36709
 +25418
  62127
  1 1  1
```
∴ 36 709 + 25 418 = 62 127

(c)
```
 7 12 11 1
  8 3 2 5
 −2 6 7 8
  5 6 4 7
```
∴ 8325 − 2678 = 5647

(d)
```
 8 1   5 1
  93560
 − 9356
  84204
```
∴ 93 560 − 9356 = 84 204

5. Calculate these expressions, by first using methods to make the calculations easier.

(a) 53 + 48 + 17 + 52   **(b)** 836 + 104 − 236

(c) 625 + 87   **(d)** 1564 − 889

Solution

(a) 53 + 48 + 17 + 52
= 53 + 17 + 48 + 52
= 70 + 100
= 170

(b) 836 + 104 − 236
= 836 − 236 + 104
= 600 + 104
= 704

(c) 625 + 87
= 620 + 5 + 80 + 7
= 620 + 80 + 5 + 7
= 700 + 12
= 712

(d) 1564 − 889
= 1564 − 800 − 89
= 764 − 64 − 25
= 700 − 25
= 675

6. The price of a sofa set is £2859 in Shop Budget and £2895 in Shop Value.

(a) Which shop's price is lower?

(b) How much cheaper is it?

Solution

(a) As £2859 < £2895, Shop Budget offers the lower price.

(b)
```
   8 1
  2895
 −2859
    36
```
The sofa set is cheaper by £36 in Shop Budget than in Shop Value.

7. Look at the numbers 8031, 3081, 1038, 8310 and 3180. Find the sum of the numbers that are less than 3180.

Solution

The numbers that are less than 3180 are 3081 and 1038.

The sum is
3081 + 1038
= 4119

```
  3081
 +1038
  4119
     1
```

8. A burger provides 2125 kJ of energy. Four chicken nuggets provide 722 kJ. Three fish fingers provide 813 kJ. What is the total energy provided by all these food items?

Solution

Total energy provided
= 2125 + 722 + 813
= 3660 kJ

```
  2125
   722
 + 813
  3660
   1 1
```

9. Alana scores 7863 marks in a computer game. Oli scores 1295 fewer marks than Alana. What is their total score?

Solution

Oli scores 7863 − 1295
= 6568

```
  7 15 1
  7 8 6 3
 −1 2 9 5
  6 5 6 8
```

Their total score
= 7863 + 6568
= 14 431

```
  7863
 + 6568
  14431
  1 1 1
```

10. Copy and complete the circle diagram with the numbers 212, 213, 214, 215, 216, 217 and 218. You can use each number only once. Each line of numbers should give the same total.

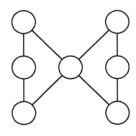

Solution

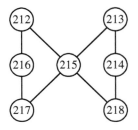

2 Multiplying and Dividing Whole Numbers

Class Activity 1

Objective: To explore multiplication patterns using a multiplication table and a calculator.

×	1	2	3	4	5	6	7	8	9	10	11	12
1	1	2	3	4	5	6	7	8	9	10	11	12
2	2	4	6	8	10	12	14	16	18	20	22	24
3	3	6	9	12	15	18	21	24	27	30	33	36
4	4	8	12	16	20	24	28	32	36	40	44	48
5	5	10	15	20	25	30	35	40	45	50	55	60
6	6	12	18	24	30	36	42	48	54	60	66	72
7	7	14	21	28	35	42	49	56	63	70	77	84
8	8	16	24	32	40	48	56	64	72	80	88	96
9	9	18	27	36	45	54	63	72	81	90	99	108
10	10	20	30	40	50	60	70	80	90	100	110	120
11	11	22	33	44	55	66	77	88	99	110	121	132
12	12	24	36	48	60	72	84	96	108	120	132	144

This is a multiplication table. It shows the product of any two numbers from 1 to 12.
For example, $4 \times 5 = 20$ (the highlighted number). Use this table for this activity.

1. **(a)** State these products.
   (i) 3×8 and 8×3

   $3 \times 8 = 24$
   $8 \times 3 = 24$

   (ii) 6×7 and 7×6

   $6 \times 7 = 42$
   $7 \times 6 = 42$

   (iii) 4×11 and 11×4

   $4 \times 11 = 44$
   $11 \times 4 = 44$

   (iv) 9×12 and 12×9

   $9 \times 12 = 108$
   $12 \times 9 = 108$

   (b) What do you notice?

   The results in (a) show that numbers can be multiplied in any order.

   number 1 × number 2 = number 2 × number 1

2. **(a)** State these products.
   (i) 1×5 and 2×5

   $1 \times 5 = 5$
   $2 \times 5 = 10$

   (ii) 3×7 and 6×7

   $3 \times 7 = 21$
   $6 \times 7 = 42$

   (iii) 4×9 and 8×9

   $4 \times 9 = 36$
   $8 \times 9 = 72$

   (iv) 6×4 and 12×4

   $6 \times 4 = 24$
   $12 \times 4 = 48$

(b) What pattern do you notice?

The results in (a) show that when one number being multiplied is doubled, the resulting product will be double the original product.

If number 1 × number 2 = number 3, then (twice number 1) × number 2 = twice number 3.

(c) If 2 × a number = 12, what is the value of 4 × the number? Explain your answer.

If 2 × a number = 12, then
4 × the number = 2 × 2 × the number
$\qquad\qquad$ = 2 × 12
$\qquad\qquad$ = 24

3. (a) Write down the values in this list.
1 × 10, 2 × 10, 3 × 10, 4 × 10, 5 × 10, 6 × 10, 7 × 10, 8 × 10, …

10, 20, 30, 40, 50, 60, 70, 80, …

(b) Using place value counters, find the next four numbers in the list. Copy the table and complete the values.

Number	Place value counters	Value
9 × 10	10 10 10 10 10 10 10 10 10	90
10 × 10	10 10 10 10 10 10 10 10 10 10	100
11 × 10	10 10 10 10 10 10 10 10 10 10 10	110
12 × 10	10 10 10 10 10 10 10 10 10 10 10 10	120

(c) What do you notice?

When a number is multiplied by 10, each digit moves one place to the left.

4. (a) Using place value counters, find the values of 2 × 100, 3 × 100, 4 × 100, 5 × 100. Copy the table and complete the values.

Number	Place value counters	Value
2 × 100	100 100	200
3 × 100	100 100 100	300
4 × 100	100 100 100 100	400
5 × 100	100 100 100 100 100	500

(b) What do you notice?

When a number is multiplied by 100, each digit moves two places to the left.

5. (a) Using place value counters, find the values of 4 × 9, 4 × 90 and 4 × 900.
Hint: Use regrouping if necessary.

×	9
4	① ① ① ① ① ① ① ① ①
4	① ① ① ① ① ① ① ① ①
4	① ① ① ① ① ① ① ① ①
4	① ① ① ① ① ① ① ① ①
4 × 9	36

×	90
4	⑩ ⑩ ⑩ ⑩ ⑩ ⑩ ⑩ ⑩ ⑩
4	⑩ ⑩ ⑩ ⑩ ⑩ ⑩ ⑩ ⑩ ⑩
4	⑩ ⑩ ⑩ ⑩ ⑩ ⑩ ⑩ ⑩ ⑩
4	⑩ ⑩ ⑩ ⑩ ⑩ ⑩ ⑩ ⑩ ⑩
4 × 90	360

×	900
4	⑩⑩ ⑩⑩ ⑩⑩ ⑩⑩ ⑩⑩ ⑩⑩ ⑩⑩ ⑩⑩ ⑩⑩
4	⑩⑩ ⑩⑩ ⑩⑩ ⑩⑩ ⑩⑩ ⑩⑩ ⑩⑩ ⑩⑩ ⑩⑩
4	⑩⑩ ⑩⑩ ⑩⑩ ⑩⑩ ⑩⑩ ⑩⑩ ⑩⑩ ⑩⑩ ⑩⑩
4	⑩⑩ ⑩⑩ ⑩⑩ ⑩⑩ ⑩⑩ ⑩⑩ ⑩⑩ ⑩⑩ ⑩⑩
4 × 900	3600

(b) What do you notice?

Each digit in the product moves to the left by a number of places depending on the number of zeros in the multiple of 10.

6. (a) Using the above results, copy and complete this place value table.

Number	Thousands	Hundreds	Tens	Ones
4				4
4 × 10			4	0
4 × 100		4	0	0
4 × 9			3	6
4 × 90		3	6	0
4 × 900	3	6	0	0

(b) If a number is multiplied by 10, what can you say about the position of its digit in the place value table?

If a number is multiplied by 10, its digit moves into the tens column.

(c) If a number is multiplied by 100, what can you say about its digit in the place value table?

If a number is multipled by 100, its digit moves into the hundreds column.

Class Activity 2

Objective: To explore the relationship between multiplication and division.

1. Calculate these values.
   (a) 2×3

   $2 \times 3 = 6$

   (b) $6 \div 2$

   $6 \div 2 = 3$

   (c) $6 \div 3$

   $6 \div 3 = 2$

2. Calculate these values.
   (a) 2×5

   $2 \times 5 = 10$

   (b) $10 \div 2$

   $10 \div 2 = 5$

   (c) $10 \div 5$

   $10 \div 5 = 2$

3. Calculate these values.
   (a) 3×7

   $3 \times 7 = 21$

   (b) $21 \div 3$

   $21 \div 3 = 7$

   (c) $21 \div 7$

   $21 \div 7 = 3$

4. Calculate these values.
   (a) 4×6

   $4 \times 6 = 24$

   (b) $24 \div 4$

   $24 \div 4 = 6$

   (c) $24 \div 6$

   $24 \div 6 = 4$

5. Observe the above results. If number 1 × number 2 = number 3, what is
   (a) number 3 ÷ number 1,

   number 3 ÷ number 1 = number 2

   (b) number 3 ÷ number 2?

   number 3 ÷ number 2 = number 1

Try It!

Section 2.1

1. (a) 37×4 **(b)** 137×4

Solution

(a) 37×4

Grid method:

×	30	7
4	120	28

```
  120
+  28
-----
  148
```

$\therefore 37 \times 4 = 148$

Column method:

```
  37
×  4
----
 148
  2
```

$\therefore 37 \times 4 = 148$

(b) 137×4

Grid method:

×	100	30	7
4	400	120	28

```
  400
  120
+  28
-----
  548
```

$\therefore 137 \times 4 = 548$

Column method:

```
 137
×  4
----
 548
 1 2
```

$\therefore 137 \times 4 = 548$

2. Calculate 5829×6.

Solution

5829×6

Grid method:

×	5000	800	20	9
6	30000	4800	120	54

```
  30000
   4800
    120
+    54
-------
  34974
```

$\therefore 5829 \times 6 = 34974$

Column method:

```
  5829
×    6
------
 34974
 4 1 5
```

$\therefore 5829 \times 6 = 34974$

3. (a) Use the grid method to work out 47×65.
(b) Use the column method to calculate these products.
     (i) 47×5 **(ii)** 47×60 **(iii)** 47×65

Solution

(a) 47×65

×	40	7
60	2400	420
5	200	35

```
  2400
   420
   200
+   35
------
  3055
   1
```

$\therefore 47 \times 65 = 3055$

(b) (i)
```
   47
×   5
-----
  235
   3
```

$\therefore 47 \times 5 = 235$

(ii)
```
    47
×   60
------
  2820
   4
```

$\therefore 47 \times 60 = 2820$

(iii)
```
    47
×   65
------
   235
  2820
------
  3055
   1
```

$\therefore 47 \times 65 = 3055$

4. Evaluate 219×61 using
  (a) the grid method,
  (b) the column method.

Solution
(a) 219×61

×	200	10	9
60	12 000	600	540
1	200	10	9

Sum of the products in the first row:

```
  12 0 0 0
     6 0 0
+    5 4 0
─────────
  1 3 1 4 0
       1
```

Sum of the products in the second row
$= 200 + 10 + 9$
$= 219$

```
  1 3 1 4 0
+     2 1 9
─────────
  1 3 3 5 9
```

$\therefore 219 \times 61 = 13\,359$

(b)
```
      2 1 9
  ×     6 1
  ─────────
      2 1 9
  1 3 1 4 0
  ─────────
  1 3 3 5 9
```

$\therefore 219 \times 61 = 13\,359$

5. George has 256 photos on his mobile phone. Peter has three times as many photos as George. How many photos does Peter have?

Solution

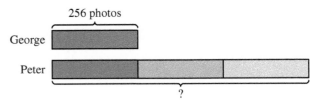

George

Peter

256 photos

?

Number of photos Peter has
$= 256 \times 3$
$= 768$

```
    2 5 6
  ×   3
  ───────
    7 6 8
    1 1
```

6. A school has 24 classes. Each class has 30 students. For a fundraising day, each student donates £5. How much do they donate in total?

Solution
Total number of students in the school
$= 24 \times 30$
$= 720$

```
      2 4
  ×   3 0
  ───────
    7 2 0
        1
```

Total amount of money donated by the students of the school
$= 720 \times 5$
$= £3600$

```
    7 2 0
  ×     5
  ───────
  3 6 0 0
        1
```

7. Calculate these values.
  (a) 14^2 (b) 8^3

Solution

(a) $14^2 = 14 \times 14$
            $= 196$
```
      1 4
  ×   1 4
  ───────
      5 6
    1 4 0
  ───────
    1 9 6
```

(b) $8^3 = 8 \times 8 \times 8$
         $= 64 \times 8$
         $= 512$
```
      6 4
  ×     8
  ───────
    5 1 2
        3
```

Section 2.2

8. Calculate these quotients.
  (a) $48 \div 2$ (b) $50 \div 3$

Solution
(a)
```
     2 4
  2) 4 8
     4
     ─
     8
     8
     ─
     0
```

$\therefore 48 \div 2 = 24$

(b)
```
      1 6 r 2
  3) 5 0
     3
     ──
     2 0
     1 8
     ──
      2
```

$\therefore 50 \div 3 = 16 \text{ r } 2$

9. Find each quotient and remainder.

(a) $\frac{534}{3}$ **(b)** $\frac{5034}{8}$

Solution

(a)

$$\begin{array}{r} 178 \\ 3\overline{)534} \\ \underline{3} \\ 23 \\ \underline{21} \\ 24 \\ \underline{24} \\ 0 \end{array}$$

Hence, $\frac{534}{3} = 178$.

∴ the quotient = 178 and the remainder = 0.

(b)

$$\begin{array}{r} 629\text{ r }2 \\ 8\overline{)5034} \\ \underline{48} \\ 23 \\ \underline{16} \\ 74 \\ \underline{72} \\ 2 \end{array}$$

Hence, $\frac{5034}{8} = 629$ r 2.

∴ the quotient = 629 and the remainder = 2.

10. Find the missing numbers.

(a) 208 ÷ ☐ = 8

(b) ☐ ÷ 15 = 22

Solution

(a) 208 ÷ ☐ = 8

☐ = 208 ÷ 8
= 26

$$\begin{array}{r} 26 \\ 8\overline{)208} \\ \underline{16} \\ 48 \\ \underline{48} \\ 0 \end{array}$$

(b) ☐ ÷ 15 = 22

☐ = 15 × 22
= 330

$$\begin{array}{r} 15 \\ \underline{\times 22} \\ 30 \\ \underline{300} \\ 330 \end{array}$$

11. In a woodland, 1080 trees are planted in nine equal rows. How many trees are in each row?

Solution

Number of trees in each row
= 1080 ÷ 9
= 120

$$\begin{array}{r} 120 \\ 9\overline{)1080} \\ \underline{9} \\ 18 \\ \underline{18} \\ 00 \\ \underline{0} \\ 0 \end{array}$$

12. There are 200 ml of medicine in a bottle. How many full spoons can be filled and how much is left in the bottle if each spoon can hold 18 ml?

Solution

200 ÷ 18
= 11 r 2

$$\begin{array}{r} 11\text{ r }2 \\ 18\overline{)200} \\ \underline{18} \\ 20 \\ \underline{18} \\ 2 \end{array}$$

Hence, 11 spoons can be filled, and there is 2 ml of medicine left in the bottle..

Section 2.3

13. Calculate these products by first reordering to make them easier.

(a) 2 × 47 × 5
(b) 50 × 68 × 2

Solution

(a) 2 × 47 × 5
= 2 × 5 × 47
= 10 × 47
= 470

(b) 50 × 68 × 2
= 50 × 2 × 68
= 100 × 68
= 6800

14. Work these out by first doubling or halving one of the numbers

(a) 152 × 4 **(b)** 256 ÷ 8

Solution

(a) 152 × 4
= 152 × 2 × 2
= 304 × 2
= 608

(b) 256 ÷ 8
= 256 ÷ 2 ÷ 2 ÷ 2
= 128 ÷ 2 ÷ 2
= 64 ÷ 2
= 32

15. Work these out using a method to make them easier.

(a) 217 × 5
(b) 148 × 20
(c) 86 × 25

Solution

(a) 217 × 5
= 217 × 10 ÷ 2
= 2170 ÷ 2
= 1085

(b) 148 × 20
= 148 × 2 × 10
= 296 × 10
= 2960

(c) 86 × 25
= 86 × 100 ÷ 4
= 8600 ÷ 2 ÷ 2
= 4300 ÷ 2
= 2150

16. Calculate these products by partitioning first.
- **(a)** 257×3
- **(b)** 634×9
- **(c)** 185×102

Solution

(a) 257×3
$$= (200 + 50 + 7) \times 3$$
$$= 200 \times 3 + 50 \times 3 + 7 \times 3$$
$$= 600 + 150 + 21$$
$$= 771$$

(b) 634×9
$$= 634 \times (10 - 1)$$
$$= 634 \times 10 - 634 \times 1$$
$$= 6340 - 634$$
$$= 6300 + 40 - 600 - 34$$
$$= 6300 - 600 + 40 - 34$$
$$= 5700 + 6$$
$$= 5706$$

(c) 185×102
$$= 185 \times (100 + 2)$$
$$= 185 \times 100 + 185 \times 2$$
$$= 18\,500 + 370$$
$$= 18\,500 + 300 + 70$$
$$= 18\,800 + 70$$
$$= 18\,870$$

17. Work these out by first applying techniques to make them easier.
- **(a)** $553 \div 7$
- **(b)** $432 \div 18$

Solution

(a) $553 \div 7$
$$= (490 + 63) \div 7$$
$$= 490 \div 7 + 63 \div 7$$
$$= 70 + 9$$
$$= 79$$

(b) $432 \div 18$
$$= 432 \div 2 \div 9$$
$$= 216 \div 9$$
$$= 216 \div 3 \div 3$$
$$= 72 \div 3$$
$$= 24$$

18. Each spider has eight legs. Find the total number of legs on 198 spiders.

Solution
Total number of legs
$$= 198 \times 8$$
$$= (200 - 2) \times 8$$
$$= 200 \times 8 - 2 \times 8$$
$$= 1600 - 16$$
$$= 1580 + 20 - 16$$
$$= 1580 + 4$$
$$= 1584$$

Section 2.4

19. List all the whole number factors of 18.

Solution
$$18 = 1 \times 18$$
$$= 2 \times 9$$
$$= 3 \times 6$$
$\therefore$ the whole number factors of 18 are 1, 2, 3, 6, 9 and 18.

20. **(a)** Find the common whole number factors of the numbers 20 and 25.
   (b) State the HCF of the numbers 20 and 25.

Solution

(a) $20 = 1 \times 20$ $\qquad$ $25 = 1 \times 25$
   $\quad = 2 \times 10$ $\qquad\qquad\quad = 5 \times 5$
   $\quad = 4 \times 5$

The whole number factors of 20 are 1, 2, 4, 5, 10 and 20.

The whole number factors of 25 are 1, 5 and 25.

Hence, the common whole number factors of 20 and 25 are 1 and 5.

(b) The HCF of 20 and 25 is 5.

21. List the first six whole number multiples of 7.

Solution
The first six whole number multiples of 7 are 1×7, 2×7, 3×7, 4×7, 5×7 and 6×7.

i.e. 7, 14, 21, 28, 35 and 42.

22. **(a)** List the first ten whole number multiples of the numbers 3 and 9.
   (b) Write down the first three common whole number multiples of 3 and 9.
   (c) State the LCM of 3 and 9.

Solution

(a) The first ten whole number multiples of 3 are 3, 6, 9, 12, 15, 18, 21, 24, 27 and 30.

The first ten whole number multiples of 9 are 9, 18, 27, 36, 45, 54, 63, 72, 81 and 90.

(b) The first three common whole number multiples of 3 and 9 are 9, 18 and 27.

(c) The LCM of 3 and 9 is 9.

23. List the prime numbers that are more than 15 and less than 20.

Solution
List the factors of the numbers 16 to 19.

Number	Factors
16	1, 2, 4, 8, 16
17	1, 17
18	1, 2, 3, 6, 9, 18
19	1, 19

The numbers with only two factors each are 17 and 19.
Hence, the prime numbers are 17 and 19.

24. Express 90 as a product of prime factors.

Solution

$90 = 2 \times 45$
$\quad = 2 \times 9 \times 5$
$\quad = 2 \times 3 \times 3 \times 5$

Thus, 90 as a product of prime factors is $2 \times 3 \times 3 \times 5$.

Practice 2.1
Level 1   GCSE Grade **1** / **1⁺**

1. Copy and complete these calculations.

(a) $28 + 28 + 28 =$ ☐ $\times 28$

    $=$ ☐

(b) $47 + 47 + 47 + 47 =$ ☐ $\times 47$

    $=$ ☐

(c) $51 + 51 + 51 + 51 + 51 =$ ☐ $\times$ ☐

(d)   ☐ $+$ ☐ $+$ ☐ $=$ ☐ $\times 79$

Solution

(a) $28 + 28 + 28 =$ 3 $\times 28$

    $=$ 84

(b) $47 + 47 + 47 + 47 =$ 4 $\times 47$

    $=$ 188

(c) $51 + 51 + 51 + 51 + 51 =$ 5 $\times$ 51

(d)   79 $+$ 79 $+$ 79 $=$ 3 $\times 79$

2. (a) Copy and complete the grids and calculate these products.

(i) 53×2

×	50	3
2		

(ii) 4×53

×	4
50	
3	

(iii) 218×3

×	200	10	8
3			

(iv) 218×5

×	200	10	8
5			

(b) What is the relationship between 53×2 and 4×53?

Solution

(a)   (i) 53×2

×	50	3
2	100	6

$100 + 6 = 106$
$\therefore 53 \times 2 = 106$

(ii) 4×53

×	4
50	200
3	12

$200 + 12 = 212$
$\therefore 4 \times 53 = 212$

(iii) 218×3

×	200	10	8
3	600	30	24

$\therefore 218 \times 3 = 654$

```
   600
    30
 +  24
   654
```

(iv) 218×5

×	200	10	8
5	1000	50	40

$1000 + 50 + 40 = 1090$
$\therefore \quad 218 \times 5 = 1090$

(b) $4 \times 53 = 2 \times 2 \times 53 = 2 \times 53 \times 2$
Therefore, 4×53 has a value twice as large as 53×2.

3. (a)   Find these values, using the column method.
(i) 603×8 (ii) 6003×8
(iii) 235×10 (iv) 235×50
(b)   What is the relationship between 235×10 and 235×50?

Solution

(a)   (i)
```
    603
 ×    8
   4824
     2
```
$\therefore 603 \times 8 = 4824$

(ii)

$$\begin{array}{r} 6\,0\,0\,3 \\ \times \quad\ 8 \\ \hline 4\,8\,0\,2\,4 \\ \scriptstyle 2 \end{array}$$

$$\therefore\ 6003 \times 8 = 48\,024$$

(iii)

$$\begin{array}{r} 2\,3\,5 \\ \times \quad 1\,0 \\ \hline 2\,3\,5\,0 \end{array}$$

$$\therefore\ 235 \times 10 = 2350$$

(iv)

$$\begin{array}{r} 2\,3\,5 \\ \times \quad\ 5\,0 \\ \hline 1\,1\,7\,5\,0 \\ \scriptstyle 1\ 2 \end{array}$$

$$\therefore\ 235 \times 50 = 11\,750$$

(b) $235 \times 50 = 235 \times 10 \times 5$
Therefore, 235×50 has a value five times as large as 235×10.

4. (a) Work out these products.
    (i) 16×21 **(ii)** 21×17
    (iii) 829×13 **(iv)** 25×617

(b) What is the relationship between 16×21 and 21×17?

(c) Without calculating it, what do you predict the value of 830×13 to be? Calculate the answer to check your prediction.

Solution

(a) (i) 16×21
Grid method:

×	10	6
20	200	120
1	10	6

$200 + 120 + 10 + 6$
$= 320 + 16$
$= 336$
$\therefore\ 16 \times 21 = 336$

Column method:

$$\begin{array}{r} 1\,6 \\ \times \quad 2\,1 \\ \hline 1\,6 \\ +\,3\,2\,0 \\ \hline 3\,3\,6 \end{array}$$

$$\therefore\ 16 \times 21 = 336$$

(ii) 21×17
Grid method:

×	20	1
10	200	10
7	140	7

$200 + 10 + 140 + 7$
$= 210 + 147$
$= 357$
$\therefore\ 21 \times 17 = 357$

Column method:

$$\begin{array}{r} 2\,1 \\ \times\,1\,7 \\ \hline 1\,4\,7 \\ +\,2\,1\,0 \\ \hline 3\,5\,7 \end{array}$$

$$\therefore\ 21 \times 17 = 357$$

(iii) 829×13
Grid method:

×	800	20	9
10	8000	200	90
3	2400	60	27

Sum of the products in the first row
$= 8000 + 200 + 90$
$= 8290$

Sum of the products in the second row
$= 2400 + 60 + 27$
$= 2487$

$$\begin{array}{r} 8\,2\,9\,0 \\ +\ \ 2\,4\,8\,7 \\ \hline 1\,0\,7\,7\,7 \\ \scriptstyle 1 \end{array}$$

$$\therefore\ 829 \times 13 = 10\,777$$

Column method:

$$\begin{array}{r} 8\,2\,9 \\ \times \quad 1\,3 \\ \hline 2\,4\,8\,7 \\ +\ \ 8\,2\,9\,0 \\ \hline 1\,0\,7\,7\,7 \\ \scriptstyle 1 \end{array}$$

$$\therefore\ 829 \times 13 = 10\,777$$

(iv) 25×617
Grid method:

×	20	5
600	12 000	3000
10	200	50
7	140	35

1st row: $12\,000 + 3000 = 15\,000$
2nd row: $200 + 50 = 250$
3rd row: $140 + 35 = 175$

$$\begin{array}{r} 1\,5\,0\,0\,0 \\ 2\,5\,0 \\ +\ \ \ 1\,7\,5 \\ \hline 1\,5\,4\,2\,5 \\ \scriptstyle 1 \end{array}$$

$$\therefore\ 25 \times 617 = 15\,425$$

Column method:

$$
\begin{array}{r}
25 \\
\times\ 617 \\
\hline
175 \\
250 \\
+15000 \\
\hline
15425 \\
\scriptstyle 1
\end{array}
$$

∴ 25 × 617 = 15 425

(b) 21 × 17 = 21 × 16 + 21 = 16 × 21 + 21
Therefore, 21 × 17 has a value 21 units higher than 16 × 21.

(c) 830 × 13 would be 13 units higher than 829 × 13. that is, 10 777 + 13 = 10 777 + 10 + 3
= 10 787 + 3
= 10 790
Calculating this fully by any method gives the same answer.

5. Find these values.
    (a) 10^2 **(b)** 15^2
    (c) 6^3 **(d)** 9^3

Solution
(a) $10^2 = 10 \times 10$
        $= 100$

(b) $15^2 = 15 \times 15$
         $= 225$

$$
\begin{array}{r}
15 \\
\times 15 \\
\hline
75 \\
150 \\
\hline
225
\end{array}
$$

(c) $6^3 = 6 \times 6 \times 6$
      $= 36 \times 6$
      $= 216$

$$
\begin{array}{r}
36 \\
\times\ 6 \\
\hline
216 \\
\scriptstyle 3
\end{array}
$$

(d) $9^3 = 9 \times 9 \times 9$
      $= 81 \times 9$
      $= 729$

$$
\begin{array}{r}
81 \\
\times\ 9 \\
\hline
729
\end{array}
$$

Level 2   **GCSE Grade 2⁻**

6. Mr Taylor's electricity bill is twice as much as Mr Smith's electricity bill. This information is shown using a bar model. How much is Mr Taylor's electricity bill?

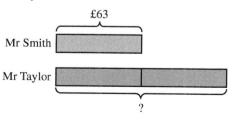

Solution
Mr Taylor's electricity bill
= £63 × 2
= £126

$$
\begin{array}{r}
63 \\
\times\ 2 \\
\hline
126
\end{array}
$$

7. Anita is four times as old as her daughter. The information is shown using a bar model. Find Anita's age.

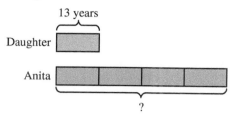

Solution
Anita's age
= 13 × 4
= 52 years

$$
\begin{array}{r}
13 \\
\times 4 \\
\hline
52 \\
\scriptstyle 1
\end{array}
$$

8. The price of a chair is £187. The price of a table is three times as much as the price of the chair. Draw a bar model to represent the information. Find the price of the table.

Solution
The information is shown in the bar model.

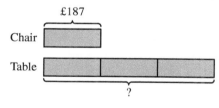

Price of the table
= £187 × 3
= £561

$$
\begin{array}{r}
187 \\
\times\ 3 \\
\hline
561 \\
\scriptstyle 2\ 2
\end{array}
$$

9. A technician prepares 230 ml of a solution in each of 26 flasks. What is the total volume of the solution?

Solution
Total volume of the solution
= 230 × 26
= 5980 ml

$$
\begin{array}{r}
230 \\
\times\ 26 \\
\hline
1380 \\
+4600 \\
\hline
5980
\end{array}
$$

10. A multi-storey car park has six levels. On each level there are seven rows of 12 spaces. How many spaces are there altogether in the car park?

Solution

Number of spaces on each level of the car park
$= 12 \times 7$
$= 84$

Total number of spaces on the six levels of the car park
$= 84 \times 6$
$= 504$

$$
\begin{array}{r}
8\,4 \\
\times\ 6 \\
\hline
5\,0\,4 \\
{\scriptstyle 2}
\end{array}
$$

Practice 2.2
Level 1   GCSE Grade $1^+ / 2^-$

1. **(a)** Calculate these quotients. You may use place value counters to help you.
 (i) $75 \div 3$ **(ii)** $75 \div 5$
 (iii) $896 \div 7$ **(iv)** $896 \div 8$
 (b) Without working it out, which would be greater, $3696 \div 7$ or $3696 \div 8$? Explain your answer.

Solution

(a) **(i)**
$$
\begin{array}{r}
25 \\
3\overline{)75} \\
6 \\
\hline
15 \\
15 \\
\hline
0
\end{array}
$$
$\therefore 75 \div 3 = 25$

(ii)
$$
\begin{array}{r}
15 \\
5\overline{)75} \\
5 \\
\hline
25 \\
25 \\
\hline
0
\end{array}
$$
$\therefore 75 \div 5 = 15$

(iii)
$$
\begin{array}{r}
128 \\
7\overline{)896} \\
7 \\
\hline
19 \\
14 \\
\hline
56 \\
56 \\
\hline
0
\end{array}
$$
$\therefore 896 \div 7 = 128$

(iv)
$$
\begin{array}{r}
112 \\
8\overline{)896} \\
8 \\
\hline
09 \\
8 \\
\hline
16 \\
16 \\
\hline
0
\end{array}
$$
$\therefore 896 \div 8 = 112$

(b) $3696 \div 7$ is greater because 3696 is being divided into fewer equal parts than $3696 \div 8$.

2. Work out these values.
 (a) $108 \div 9$ **(b)** $1008 \div 9$
 (c) $143 \div 13$ **(d)** $651 \div 21$

Solution

(a)
$$
\begin{array}{r}
12 \\
9\overline{)108} \\
9 \\
\hline
18 \\
18 \\
\hline
0
\end{array}
$$
$\therefore 108 \div 9 = 12$

(b)
$$
\begin{array}{r}
112 \\
9\overline{)1008} \\
9 \\
\hline
10 \\
9 \\
\hline
18 \\
18 \\
\hline
0
\end{array}
$$
$\therefore 1008 \div 9 = 112$

(c)
$$
\begin{array}{r}
11 \\
13\overline{)143} \\
13 \\
\hline
13 \\
13 \\
\hline
0
\end{array}
$$
$\therefore 143 \div 13 = 11$

(d)
$$
\begin{array}{r}
31 \\
21\overline{)651} \\
63 \\
\hline
21 \\
21 \\
\hline
0
\end{array}
$$
$\therefore 651 \div 21 = 31$

3. Find these quotients and remainders. You may use place value counters to help you.
 (a) $58 \div 4$ **(b)** $905 \div 6$
 (c) $\dfrac{123}{10}$ **(d)** $\dfrac{870}{15}$

Solution

(a)
$$
\begin{array}{r}
14\ r\ 2 \\
4\overline{)58} \\
4 \\
\hline
18 \\
16 \\
\hline
2
\end{array}
$$
Hence, $58 \div 4 = 14$ r 2.
$\therefore$ the quotient = 14 and the remainder = 2.

(b)
$$
\begin{array}{r}
150\ r\ 5 \\
6\overline{)905} \\
6 \\
\hline
30 \\
30 \\
\hline
05 \\
0 \\
\hline
5
\end{array}
$$
Hence, $905 \div 6 = 150$ r 5.
$\therefore$ the quotient = 150 and the remainder = 5.

(c)
$$
\begin{array}{r}
12\ r\ 3 \\
10\overline{)123} \\
10 \\
\hline
23 \\
20 \\
\hline
3
\end{array}
$$
Hence, $\dfrac{123}{10} = 12$ r 3.
$\therefore$ the quotient = 12 and the remainder = 3.

(d)
$$
\begin{array}{r}
58 \\
15\overline{)870} \\
75 \\
\hline
120 \\
120 \\
\hline
0
\end{array}
$$
Hence, $\dfrac{870}{15} = 58$.
$\therefore$ the quotient = 58 and the remainder = 0

4. Find the missing numbers. Explain your answers.

(a) $153 \div \boxed{} = 9$

(b) $\boxed{} \div 7 = 26$

(c) $23 \times \boxed{} = 414$

(d) $\boxed{} \times 11 = 715$

Solution

(a) $153 \div \boxed{} = 9$

By the inverse relationship,

$$\boxed{} = 153 \div 9$$
$$= 17$$

$$\begin{array}{r} 17 \\ 9\overline{)153} \\ 9 \\ \hline 63 \\ 63 \\ \hline 0 \end{array}$$

(b) $\boxed{} \div 7 = 26$

$$\boxed{} = 26 \times 7$$
$$= 182$$

$$\begin{array}{r} 2\,6 \\ \times\ 7 \\ \hline 1\,8\,2 \\ {}_{4} \end{array}$$

(c) $23 \times \boxed{} = 414$

$$\boxed{} = 414 \div 23$$
$$= 18$$

$$\begin{array}{r} 18 \\ 23\overline{)414} \\ 23 \\ \hline 184 \\ 184 \\ \hline 0 \end{array}$$

(d) $\boxed{} \times 11 = 715$

$$\boxed{} = 715 \div 11$$
$$= 65$$

$$\begin{array}{r} 65 \\ 11\overline{)715} \\ 66 \\ \hline 55 \\ 55 \\ \hline 0 \end{array}$$

5. The bar model shows jelly beans shared equally among five children. How many jelly beans does each child get?

320

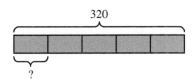

?

Solution

Number of jelly beans that each child gets
$= 320 \div 5$
$= 64$

$$\begin{array}{r} 64 \\ 5\overline{)320} \\ 30 \\ \hline 20 \\ 20 \\ \hline 0 \end{array}$$

6. Given that $325 \times 79 = 25\,675$, state the value of

(a) $25\,675 \div 79$,   (b) $25\,675 \div 325$.

(c) $256\,750 \div 79$

Solution

As $325 \times 79 = 25\,675$,

(a) $25\,675 \div 79 = 325$

(b) $25\,675 \div 325 = 79$

(c) $256\,750 \div 79 = 25\,675 \times 10 \div 79$
$$= 325 \times 10$$
$$= 3250$$

7. A ribbon is 216 cm long. It is cut into four equal parts. Draw a bar model to show this. Find the length of each part.

Solution

The bar model shows the four equal parts cut from the ribbon.

216 cm

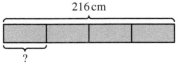

?

Length of each part
$= 216 \div 4$
$= 54$ cm

$$\begin{array}{r} 54 \\ 4\overline{)216} \\ 20 \\ \hline 16 \\ 16 \\ \hline 0 \end{array}$$

8. A farmer has 651 eggs. They are packed into boxes of 12 for sale.

(a) How many boxes are filled?

(b) How many eggs are left after all the boxes have been packed?

Solution

$651 \div 12 = 54$ r 3

$$\begin{array}{r} 54 \text{ r } 3 \\ 12\overline{)651} \\ 60 \\ \hline 51 \\ 48 \\ \hline 3 \end{array}$$

(a) 54 boxes are filled.

(b) 3 eggs are left after packing.

9. A school hires some buses for a school trip. A total of 428 students and staff go on the trip. Each bus can take 54 passengers and the cost of each bus is £310.
   (a) How many buses are needed?
   (b) What is the total cost?

Solution
(a) First find the value of $428 \div 54$.
$428 \div 54 = 7 \text{ r } 50$

$$\begin{array}{r} 7 \\ 54\overline{)428} \\ 378 \\ \hline 50 \end{array}$$

If 7 buses are hired, 50 students and staff will be left behind.
Hence, the number of buses needed is $7 + 1 = 8$.

(b) The total cost of hiring 8 buses
$= £310 \times 8$
$= £2480$

$$\begin{array}{r} 310 \\ \times \quad 8 \\ \hline 2480 \end{array}$$

10. Find the digits represented by ▲, ● and ▇ in this multiplication.

$$\begin{array}{r} 5▲ \\ \times \quad ●4 \\ \hline 212 \\ ▇240 \\ \hline ▇452 \end{array}$$

Solution

$$\begin{array}{r} 5\boxed{3} \\ \times\boxed{8}4 \\ \hline 212 \\ \boxed{4}240 \\ \hline \boxed{4}452 \end{array}$$

$212 \div 4 = 53$

Hence, ▲ is digit 3, ● is digit 8 and ▇ is digit 4.

Practice 2.3

For each question in this exercise, choose the best method to make the calculation easier.

Level 1   **GCSE Grade** $\boxed{1^-/1^+}$

1. Calculate these products.
   (a) $2 \times 78 \times 5$
   (b) $50 \times 29 \times 2$
   (c) 2×90
   (d) 59×4

Solution
(a) $2 \times 78 \times 5$
$= 2 \times 5 \times 78$
$= 10 \times 78$
$= 780$

(b) $50 \times 29 \times 2$
$= 50 \times 2 \times 29$
$= 100 \times 29$
$= 2900$

(c) 2×90
$= 2 \times 9 \times 10$
$= 18 \times 10$
$= 180$

(d) 59×4
$= (60 - 1) \times 4$
$= 60 \times 4 - 1 \times 4$
$= 240 - 4$
$= 236$

2. Evaluate these expressions.
   (a) $86 \div 2$
   (b) $4 \times 31 \times 5$
   (c) 65×8
   (d) 237×8

Solution
(a) $86 \div 2$
$= (80 + 6) \div 2$
$= 80 \div 2 + 6 \div 2$
$= 40 + 3$
$= 43$

(b) $4 \times 31 \times 5$
$= 4 \times 5 \times 31$
$= 20 \times 31$
$= 10 \times 2 \times 31$
$= 10 \times 62$
$= 620$

(c) 65×8
$= 65 \times 2 \times 2 \times 2$
$= 130 \times 2 \times 2$
$= 260 \times 2$
$= 520$

(d) 237×8
$= (200 + 30 + 7) \times 8$
$= 200 \times 8 + 30 \times 8 + 7 \times 8$
$= 1600 + 240 + 56$
$= 1840 + 56$
$= 1896$

3. Work out these values.
   (a) 132×5
   (b) $96 \div 4$
   (c) 568×9
   (d) $342 \div 18$

Solution
(a) 132×5
$= 132 \times 10 \div 2$
$= 1320 \div 2$
$= 660$

(b) $96 \div 4$
$= 96 \div 2 \div 2$
$= 48 \div 2$
$= 24$

(c) 568×9
$= 568 \times (10 - 1)$
$= 568 \times 10 - 568 \times 1$
$= 5680 - 568$
$= 5680 - 500 - 60 - 8$
$= 5180 - 60 - 8$
$= 5120 - 8$
$= 5112$

(d) $342 \div 18$
$= 342 \div 2 \div 9$
$= 171 \div 9$
$= 171 \div 3 \div 3$
$= 57 \div 3$
$= 19$

4. Work out these values.

(a) $368 \div 4$ (b) $1000 \div 8$

(c) 67×25 (d) 214×25

Solution

(a) $368 \div 4$

$= 368 \div 2 \div 2$

$= 184 \div 2$

$= 92$

(b) $1000 \div 8$

$= 1000 \div 2 \div 2 \div 2$

$= 500 \div 2 \div 2$

$= 250 \div 2$

$= 125$

(c) 67×25

$= 67 \times 100 \div 4$

$= 6700 \div 4$

$= 6700 \div 2 \div 2$

$= 3350 \div 2$

$= 1675$

(d) 214×25

$= (200 + 10 + 4) \times 25$

$= 200 \times 25 + 10 \times 25 + 4 \times 25$

$= 5000 + 250 + 100$

$= 5250 + 100$

$= 5350$

5. Compute these expressions. Explain your method.

(a) 926×20 (b) 762×11

(c) $680 \div 20$ (d) 65×102

Solution

(a) 926×20

$= 926 \times 10 \times 2$

$= 9260 \times 2$

$= (9000 + 200 + 60) \times 2$

$= 9000 \times 2 + 200 \times 2 + 60 \times 2$

$= 18\,000 + 400 + 120$

$= 18\,400 + 120$

$= 18\,520$

(b) 762×11

$= 762 \times (10 + 1)$

$= 762 \times 10 + 762 \times 1$

$= 7620 + 762$

$= 7620 + 400 + 362$

$= 8020 + 300 + 62$

$= 8320 + 62$

$= 8382$

(c) $680 \div 20$

$= 680 \div 10 \div 2$

$= 68 \div 2$

$= 34$

(d) 65×102

$= 65 \times (100 + 2)$

$= 65 \times 100 + 65 \times 2$

$= 6500 + 130$

$= 6630$

6. Evaluate these expressions. Explain your method.

(a) $936 \div 8$ (b) 315×8

(c) 875×99 (d) $315 \div 21$

Solution

(a) $936 \div 8$

$= (960 - 24) \div 8$

$= 960 \div 8 - 24 \div 8$

$= 120 - 3$

$= 117$

(b) 315×8

$= 315 \times 2 \times 2 \times 2$

$= 630 \times 2 \times 2$

$= 1260 \times 2$

$= (1200 + 60) \times 2$

$= 1200 \times 2 + 60 \times 2$

$= 2400 + 120$

$= 2520$

(c) 875×99

$= 875 \times (100 - 1)$

$= 875 \times 100 - 875 \times 1$

$= 87\,500 - 875$

$= 86\,500 + 1000 - 875$

$= 86\,500 + 100 + 900 - 875$

$= 86\,600 + 25$

$= 86\,625$

(d) $315 \div 21$

$= 315 \div 3 \div 7$

$= 105 \div 7$

$= 15$

Level 2   **GCSE Grade** $\boxed{2^-}$

7. The weekly salary of a clerk in a company is £735. There are nine clerks. What is their total weekly salary?

Solution

Total weekly salary of 9 clerks

$= £735 \times 9$

$= 735 \times (10 - 1)$

$= 735 \times 10 - 735 \times 1$

$= 7350 - 735$

$= 7350 - 300 - 435$

$= 7050 - 435$

$= 7050 - 400 - 35$

$= 6650 - 35$

$= £6615$

8. A scholarship of £5096 is shared equally among eight students. How much does each student get?

Solution
Scholarship for each student
$= £5096 \div 8$
$= 5096 \div 2 \div 2 \div 2$
$= 2548 \div 2 \div 2$
$= 1274 \div 2$
$= £637$

9. The price of a Big Ben souvenir is £25. A shop sells 234 of these souvenirs. How much does the shop receive from the sales?

Solution
Amount received from the sales
$= 234 \times 25$
$= 234 \times 100 \div 4$
$= 23\,400 \div 4$
$= 23\,400 \div 2 \div 2$
$= 11\,700 \div 2$
$= £5850$

10. Describe a real-life situation where you can use multiplication or division to work out a solution. For this situation, write three examples of a calculation you may have to do without a calculator. Explain your method for calculating the answers efficiently.

Solution
Student's own answer

Practice 2.4

Level 1   GCSE Grade **1⁺ / 2⁻**

1. List all the whole number factors of each number.
   (a) 10 **(b)** 27 **(c)** 36 **(d)** 40

Solution
(a) $10 = 1 \times 10$
        $= 2 \times 5$
    ∴ the whole number factors of 10 are 1, 2, 5 and 10.

(b) $27 = 1 \times 27$
        $= 3 \times 9$
    ∴ the whole number factors of 27 are 1, 3, 9 and 27.

(c) $36 = 1 \times 36$
        $= 2 \times 18$
        $= 3 \times 12$
        $= 4 \times 9$
        $= 6 \times 6$
    ∴ the whole number factors of 36 are 1, 2, 3, 4, 6, 9, 12, 18 and 36.

(d) $40 = 1 \times 40$
        $= 2 \times 20$
        $= 4 \times 10$
        $= 5 \times 8$
    ∴ the whole number factors of 40 are 1, 2, 4, 5, 8, 10, 20 and 40.

2. List the first six whole number multiples of each number.
   (a) 3 **(b)** 10 **(c)** 11 **(d)** 20

Solution
(a) The first six whole number multiples of 3 are
    $1 \times 3, 2 \times 3, 3 \times 3, 4 \times 3, 5 \times 3$ and 6×3
    $= 3, 6, 9, 12, 15$ and 18.

(b) The first six whole number multiples of 10 are
    $1 \times 10, 2 \times 10, 3 \times 10, 4 \times 10, 5 \times 10$ and 6×10
    $= 10, 20, 30, 40, 50$ and 60.

(c) The first six whole number multiples of 11 are
    $1 \times 11, 2 \times 11, 3 \times 11, 4 \times 11, 5 \times 11$ and 6×11
    $= 11, 22, 33, 44, 55$ and 66.

(d) The first six whole number multiples of 20 are
    $1 \times 20, 2 \times 20, 3 \times 20, 4 \times 20, 5 \times 20$ and 6×20
    $= 20, 40, 60, 80, 100$ and 120.

3. Determine which of these numbers are prime numbers.
   (a) 30 **(b)** 31 **(c)** 47 **(d)** 53

Solution
(a) $30 = 1 \times 30$
        $= 2 \times 15$
        $= 3 \times 10$
        $= 5 \times 6$
    Since 30 has more than two whole number factors, 30 is not a prime number.

(b) The whole number factors of 31 are 1 and 31. Since 31 has only two whole number factors, 31 is a prime number.

(c) The whole number factors of 47 are 1 and 47. Since 47 has only two whole number factors, 47 is a prime number.

(d) The whole number factors of 53 are 1 and 53. Since 53 has only two whole number factors, 53 is a prime number.

4. Which of these numbers below would you consider the odd one out? Explain your answer.
21, 31, 36, 81

Solution
31 is different from the other numbers as it is a prime number (only divisible by 1 and 31). All of the other numbers can be divided by 3 so they cannot be prime.

Level 2   **GCSE Grade 2 / 3**

5. (a) List the whole number factors of the numbers 10 and 15.
   (b) List the common whole number factors of 10 and 15.
   (c) State the HCF of 10 and 15.

Solution
(a) $10 = 1 \times 10$ $15 = 1 \times 15$
        $ = 2 \times 5$ $ = 3 \times 5$

   The whole number factors of 10 are 1, 2, 5, 10.
   The whole number factors of 15 are 1, 3, 5, 15.

(b) Hence, the common whole number factors of 10 and 15 are 1 and 5.

(c) The HCF of 10 and 15 is 5.

6. (a) List the first 10 whole number multiples of each of the numbers 4 and 6.
   (b) Write down the first three common whole number multiples of the numbers 4 and 6.
   (c) State the LCM of 4 and 6.

Solution
(a) The first ten whole number multiples of 4 are 4, 8, 12, 16, 20, 24, 28, 32, 36 and 40.
    The first ten whole number multiples of 6 are 6, 12, 18, 24, 30, 36, 42, 48, 54 and 60.

(b) The first three common whole number multiples of 4 and 6 are 12, 24 and 36.

(c) The LCM of 4 and 6 is 12.

7. Express each number as a product of its prime factors.
   (a) 42   (b) 105
   (c) 24   (d) 99

Solution
(a) $42 = 2 \times 21$
        $ = 2 \times 3 \times 7$

(b) $105 = 3 \times 35$
        $ = 3 \times 5 \times 7$

(c) $24 = 2 \times 12$
        $ = 2 \times 2 \times 6$
        $ = 2 \times 2 \times 2 \times 3$

(d) $99 = 3 \times 33$
        $ = 3 \times 3 \times 11$

8. A model kit has red rods of length 12 cm and blue rods of length 15 cm.
   Some red rods are joined in a straight line to form a long red stick. Some blue rods are joined in a straight line to form a long blue stick. If the red stick and the blue stick have the same length, what is the minimum length of the red stick?

Solution
Since the red stick and the blue stick are the same length, to find the minimum length of the blue stick we must find the lowest common multiple of the length of the red rod and the length of the blue rod, 12 cm and 15 cm.
The first five whole number multiples of 12 are 12, 24, 36, 48, 60.
The first five whole number multiples of 15 are 15, 30, 45, 60, 75.
Therefore, the lowest common multiple of 12 cm and 15 cm is 60 cm.
The minimum length of the red stick is 60 cm.

9. (a) Pick the multiples of 3 from this list.
       42   96   101   135
   (b) For each multiple of 3 in part (a), add up the digits. Is the sum of the digits also a multiple of 3? Does this work for any multiple of 3?

Solution
(a) 42, 96 and 135 are multiples of 3.

(b) Sum of the digits in 42
    $= 4 + 2$
    $= 6$
    Sum of the digits in 96
    $= 9 + 6$
    $= 15$
    Sum of digits in 135
    $= 1 + 3 + 5$
    $= 9$
    For each multiple of 3 in part (a) the sum of its digits is a multiple of 3.
    This works for any multiple of 3.

Challenge 2

Here are four digits: 2, 3, 6 and 8. Use these digits to make two whole numbers. You can only use each digit once. What is the greatest possible product of the two whole numbers you can make?

Hint: The products you can make are 23 × 68, 362 × 8, etc.

Solution

To get the greatest possible product of the two whole numbers formed using the digits 2, 3, 6 and 8, the two whole numbers should be as large as possible.

The two possible whole numbers whose products you should consider and determine which is the greatest include 632 × 8, 832 × 6, 82 × 63 and 83 × 62.

632 × 8 = 5056
832 × 6 = 4992
82 × 63 = 5166
83 × 62 = 5146

The two whole numbers 63 and 82 give the greatest possible product 5166.

Revision Exercise 2

1. Calculate these products.

(a) 235 × 6
(b) 418 × 7
(c) 9 × 306
(d) 5 × 1209

Solution

(a)
$$\begin{array}{r} 235 \\ \times\ \ \ 6 \\ \hline 1410 \\ {\scriptstyle 2\ 3} \end{array}$$

∴ 235 × 6 = 1410

(b)
$$\begin{array}{r} 418 \\ \times\ \ \ 7 \\ \hline 2926 \\ {\scriptstyle 1\ 5} \end{array}$$

∴ 418 × 7 = 2926

(c)
$$\begin{array}{r} 306 \\ \times\ \ \ 9 \\ \hline 2754 \\ {\scriptstyle 5} \end{array}$$

9 × 306 = 306 × 9
= 2754

(d)
$$\begin{array}{r} 1209 \\ \times\ \ \ 5 \\ \hline 6045 \\ {\scriptstyle 1\ \ 4} \end{array}$$

5 × 1209 = 1209 × 5
= 6045

2. Find these values.

(a) 34 × 11
(b) 25 × 64
(c) 408 × 13
(d) 38 × 157

Solution

(a)
$$\begin{array}{r} 34 \\ \times 11 \\ \hline 374 \\ {\scriptstyle 4} \end{array}$$

∴ 34 × 11 = 374

(b) 25 × 64

Grid method:

×	20	5
60	1200	300
4	80	20

1200 + 300 + 80 + 20
= 1500 + 100
= 1600
∴ 25 × 64 = 1600

Column method:

$$\begin{array}{r} 25 \\ \times\ \ 64 \\ \hline 100 \\ +1500 \\ \hline 1600 \end{array}$$

∴ 25 × 64 = 1600

(c) 408 × 13

Grid method:

×	400	8
10	4000	80
3	1200	24

4000 + 80 + 1200 + 24
= 4080 + 1224
= 5304
∴ 408 × 13 = 5304

Column method:

$$\begin{array}{r} 408 \\ \times\ \ 13 \\ \hline 1224 \\ +4080 \\ \hline 5304 \\ {\scriptstyle 1} \end{array}$$

∴ 408 × 13 = 5304

(d) 38×157

Grid method:

×	30	8
100	3000	800
50	1500	400
7	210	56

$3000 + 800 + 1500 + 400 + 210 + 56$
$= 3800 + 1900 + 266$
$= 5966$

$\therefore 38 \times 157 = 5966$

Column method:

$$
\begin{array}{r}
38 \\
\times 157 \\
\hline
266 \\
1900 \\
+3800 \\
\hline
5966 \\
\hline
{\scriptstyle 1}
\end{array}
$$

$\therefore 38 \times 157 = 5966$

3. **(a)** You are told that $369 \times 258 = 95\,202$. State the value of

    (i) $95\,202 \div 369$,   **(ii)** $95\,202 \div 258$.

(b) Find the missing number in $518 \div$ $= 14$.

Solution

(a) As $369 \times 258 = 95\,202$,
    (i) $95\,202 \div 369 = 258$
    (ii) $95\,202 \div 258 = 369$

(b) $518 \div \boxed{} = 14$

    $\boxed{} = 518 \div 14$
    $= 37$

$$
\begin{array}{r}
37 \\
14\overline{)518} \\
42 \\
\hline
98 \\
98 \\
\hline
0
\end{array}
$$

4. Find each quotient and remainder.

(a) $\dfrac{536}{4}$ **(b)** $\dfrac{1289}{3}$

(c) $562 \div 11$ **(d)** $2458 \div 23$

Solution

(a)
$$
\begin{array}{r}
134 \\
4\overline{)536} \\
4 \\
\hline
13 \\
12 \\
\hline
16 \\
16 \\
\hline
0
\end{array}
$$

Hence, $\dfrac{536}{4} = 134$.

$\therefore$ the quotient $= 134$ and the remainder $= 0$.

(b)
$$
\begin{array}{r}
429 \text{ r } 2 \\
3\overline{)1289} \\
12 \\
\hline
08 \\
6 \\
\hline
29 \\
27 \\
\hline
2
\end{array}
$$

Hence, $\dfrac{1289}{3} = 429 \text{ r } 2$.

$\therefore$ the quotient $= 429$ and the remainder $= 2$.

(c)
$$
\begin{array}{r}
51 \text{ r } 1 \\
11\overline{)562} \\
55 \\
\hline
12 \\
11 \\
\hline
1
\end{array}
$$

Hence, $562 \div 11 = 51 \text{ r } 1$.

$\therefore$ the quotient $= 51$ and the remainder $= 1$.

(d)
$$
\begin{array}{r}
106 \text{ r } 20 \\
23\overline{)2458} \\
23 \\
\hline
15 \\
0 \\
\hline
158 \\
138 \\
\hline
20
\end{array}
$$

Hence, $2458 \div 23 = 106 \text{ r } 20$.

$\therefore$ the quotient $= 106$ and the remainder $= 20$.

5. Work out these expressions by first using methods to make the calculations easier. Explain your steps.

(a) $5 \times 167 \times 2$ **(b)** $384 \div 8$
(c) 625×101 **(d)** 73×499

Solution

(a) $5 \times 167 \times 2$
    $= 5 \times 2 \times 167$
    $= 10 \times 167$
    $= 1670$

(b) $384 \div 8$
    $= 384 \div 2 \div 2 \div 2$
    $= 192 \div 2 \div 2$
    $= 96 \div 2$
    $= 48$

(c) 625×101
    $= 625 \times (100 + 1)$
    $= 625 \times 100 + 625 \times 1$
    $= 62\,500 + 625$
    $= 62\,500 + 500 + 125$
    $= 63\,000 + 125$
    $= 63\,125$

(d) 73 × 499
$$= 73 \times (500 - 1)$$
$$= 73 \times 500 - 73 \times 1$$
$$= 36\,500 - 73$$
$$= 36\,400 + 100 - 73$$
$$= 36\,400 + 27$$
$$= 36\,427$$

6. **(a)** Write down the whole number factors of 36 and 45.

(b) Find the common whole number factors of 36 and 45.

(c) State the HCF of 36 and 45.

Solution

(a)
1 × 36 = 36	1 × 45 = 45
2 × 18 = 36	3 × 15 = 45
3 × 12 = 36	5 × 9 = 45
4 × 9 = 36	
6 × 6 = 36	

The whole number factors of 36 are 1, 2, 3, 4, 6, 9, 12, 18 and 36.
The whole number factors of 45 are 1, 3, 5, 9, 15, 45.

(b) The common whole number factors of 36 and 45 are 1, 3 and 9.

(c) The HCF of 36 and 45 is 9.

7. **(a)** Write down the first ten whole number multiples of 10 and 15.

(b) Write down the first three common whole number multiples of 10 and 15.

(c) State the LCM of 10 and 15.

(d) List the factors of the LCM of 10 and 15 that are prime numbers.

Solution

(a) The first ten whole number multiples of 10 are 10, 20, 30, 40, 50, 60, 70, 80, 90 and 100.
The first ten whole number multiples of 15 are 15, 30, 45, 60, 75, 90, 105, 120, 135 and 150.

(b) The first three common whole number multiples of 10 and 15 are 30, 60 and 90.

(c) The LCM of 10 and 15 is 30.

(d)
$$30 = 2 \times 15$$
$$= 2 \times 3 \times 5$$
The prime factors of 30 are 2, 3 and 5.

8. A bakery has two trays of muffins. Each tray has five rows and each row has 18 muffins. Find the total number of muffins on the two trays.

Solution

Number of muffins on one tray = 5 × 18
Total number of muffins on two trays
$$= 2 \times 5 \times 18$$
$$= 10 \times 18$$
$$= 180$$

9. There are 254 guests attending a dinner party. Each table at the party has seats for eight guests. How many tables are needed for the party?

Solution

First find the value of 254 ÷ 8
254 ÷ 8 = 31 r 6
6 guests will be left without a table
if 31 tables are arranged.
Hence, the number of tables needed
for the party = 31 + 1
           = 32

```
     31
 8 )254
     24
     14
      8
      6
```

10. A school has 1086 students. Each student donates £5. The total donation is shared equally among three charities. How much is the donation to each charity?

Solution

Total donation from the school
$$= 1086 \times 5$$
$$= £5430$$

```
  1 0 8 6
 ×     5
  5 4 3 0
   4 3
```

Donation given to each charity
$$= £5430 \div 3$$
$$= £1810$$

```
      1810
   3 )5430
      3
      24
      24
      03
       3
      00
       0
       0
```

3 Calculation

Class Activity 1

Objective: To round numbers to the nearest 10, 100, 1000 and 10 000.

1.

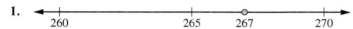

As you can see from the number line, 267 is between 260 and 270.

(a) Which is 267 closer to: 260 or 270?

267 is closer to 270 than 260.

(b) Which number, 260 or 270, would you use as an approximation of 267? Explain your answer.

I would use 270 as an approximation of 267 as 267 is closer to 270.

2.

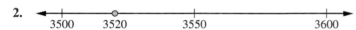

As you can see from the number line, 3520 is between 3500 and 3600.

(a) Which is 3520 closer to: 3500 or 3600?

3520 is closer to 3500 than 3600.

(b) Which number, 3500 or 3600, would you use as an approximation of 3520? Explain your answer.

I would use 3500 as an approximation of 3520 as 3520 is closer to 3500.

3.

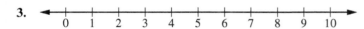

The number line above shows the digits from 0 to 10. If you were rounding to the nearest 10,

(a) which whole numbers would you round to 0,

I would round numbers 1, 2, 3 and 4 to 0.

(b) which whole numbers would you round to 10?

I would round numbers 5, 6, 7, 8 and 9 to 10.

4.

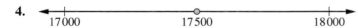

The number line above counts up in thousands. 17 500 is between 17 000 and 18 000.

(a) Which is 17 500 closer to: 17 000 or 18 000?

17 500 is midway between 17 000 and 18 000.

(b) Which number, 17 000 or 18 000, would you use as an approximation of 17 500? Explain your answer.

I would use 18 000 as an approximation of 17 500 for the reason as in (a).

5.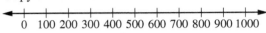

10000   15000   17500   20000

As you can see from the number line, 17500 is between 10000 and 20000.

(a) Which is 17500 closer to: 10000 or 20000?

17500 is closer to 20000 than 10000.

(b) Which number, 10000 or 20000, would you use as an approximation of 17500? Explain your answer.

I would use 20000 as an approximation of 17500 as 17500 is closer to 20000.

6. Copy the three number lines shown.

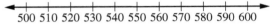

0 100 200 300 400 500 600 700 800 900 1000

500 510 520 530 540 550 560 570 580 590 600

510 511 512 513 514 515 516 517 518 519 520

(a) Add a circle to each number line to represent the number 513.

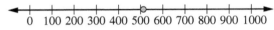

0 100 200 300 400 500 600 700 800 900 1000

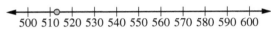

500 510 520 530 540 550 560 570 580 590 600

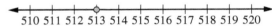

510 511 512 513 514 515 516 517 518 519 520

(b) Round 513 to the nearest 10, 100 and 1000.

513 is 510 to the nearest 10.

513 is 500 to the nearest 100.

513 is 1000 to the nearest 1000.

Class Activity 2

Objective: To estimate the total cost of buying two items.

Mrs Roberts wants to buy a vase that costs £68.90 and a teapot that costs £31.30. She has £100 in her purse. Two of her grandchildren, Leanne and William, estimate the total price of the two items for her.

1. Leanne rounds each price to the nearest £10 and then finds the sum of the two rounded numbers. What is her estimate?

£68.90 is approximately £70 and £31.30 is approximately £30.

Leanne's estimated total price = £70 + £30

                            = £100

2. William rounds up each price to the nearest £10 and then finds the sum of the two rounded numbers. What is his estimate?

£68.90 is rounded up to £70 and £31.30 is rounded up to £40

William's estimated total price = £70 + £40

                            = £110

3. Whose estimate, Leanne's or William's, will guarantee that Mrs Roberts has or hasn't got enough money for these two items? Explain your answer.

William's estimate guarantees that Mrs Roberts hasn't got enough money for these

two items. This is because both items have been rounded up and the answer is

an overestimate. Leanne's estimate does not guarantee that Mrs Roberts has

enough money for the two items. This is because one item is rounded up, and the

other item is rounded down. The actual answer is £68.90 + £31.30 = £100.20, so

Leanne's estimate is an underestimate.

Class Activity 3

Objective: To explore the order of operations.

Work in pairs. Using the digits 1, 2, 3 and 4 , in that order, in a row, insert some operation signs (+, − , ×, ÷) and brackets. Can you create thirteen calculations that have the answers 0 to 12?

For example, $(1 + 2) \times 3 - 4 = 5$,
$$12 \div 3 + 4 = 8,$$
$$1 + 2 + 3 + 4 = 10.$$

Compare your answers with other classmates.

What do you notice about the order you carry out the operations on the numbers?

Student's answers

Try It!

Section 3.1

1. The volume of milk in a jug is 1827 ml. Round the volume to
    (a) the nearest 10 ml,
    (b) the nearest 100 ml.

    Solution
    (a) Volume of milk = 1827 ml
    $$= 1830 \text{ ml (to the nearest 10 ml)}$$

    (b) Volume of milk = 1827 ml
    $$= 1800 \text{ ml (to the nearest 100 ml)}$$

2. The number of people taking part in a charity run is 2497. Each participant pays a £6 entry fee. Find the total entry fee, giving your answer to the nearest £1000.

    Solution
    Total entry fee = £6 × 2497
    $$= £14 982$$
    $$= £15 000 \text{ (to the nearest £1000)}$$

Section 3.2

3. Estimate these calculations by first rounding the numbers to the nearest 10.
    (a) 58 + 91   **(b)** 97 − 34
    (c) 273 × 92   **(d)** 416 ÷ 68

Solution
(a) $58 + 91 \approx 60 + 90$ Each number is rounded
$$= 150$$ to the nearest ten.

(b) $97 - 34 \approx 100 - 30$ Each number is rounded
$$= 70$$ to the nearest ten.

(c) $273 \times 92 \approx 270 \times 90$ Each number is rounded
$$= 24 300$$ to the nearest ten.

(d) $416 \div 68 \approx 420 \div 70$ Each number is rounded
$$= 6$$ to the nearest ten.

4. Estimate 395 − 217 by first rounding each number to
    (a) the nearest 100,
    (b) the nearest 10.

    Solution
    (a) $395 - 217 \approx 400 - 200$ Each number is rounded
    $$= 200$$ to the nearest hundred.

    (b) $395 - 217 \approx 400 - 220$ Each number is rounded
    $$= 180$$ to the nearest ten.

5. Simon wants to paint some of the rooms in his house. He needs 12 litres of paint for the bathrooms, 13 litres for the bedrooms and 9 litres for the hall. Estimate the total amount of paint he needs. Is the estimated amount an under-estimate or an over-estimate of the actual amount needed?

Solution

12 litres ≈ 10 litres

13 litres ≈ 10 litres

9 litres ≈ 10 litres

Total estimated amount of paint needed

≈ 10 + 10 + 10

= 30 litres.

Since the actual amount of paint needed is
12 + 13 + 9 = 34 litres, the estimated amount is
an under-estimate of the actual amount needed.

6. Mrs Simpson wants to buy two pots that cost £159
each and 16 plates that cost £12 each. She estimates
that she needs £610 in total. Use estimation to
check whether her estimate is reasonable.

Solution

$2 \times £159 + 16 \times £12$

$\approx 2 \times £160 + 16 \times £10$ Each cost is rounded to

$= £320 + £160$ the nearest £10.

$= £480$

The total estimated cost of the items is £480.

The actual cost $2 \times £159 + 16 \times £12 = £510$

If Mrs Simpson estimates that she needs £610 in
total, she has made a large over-estimate. Thus, her
estimate is not reasonable.

Section 3.3

7. Calculate
   (a) $84 \div 7 + 16 \times 3$,
   (b) $67 + 9 \times 4 \div 3 - 71$.

Solution

(a) $84 \div 7 + 16 \times 3$

$= 12 + 48$

$= 60$

(b) $67 + 9 \times 4 \div 3 - 71$

$= 67 + 36 \div 3 - 71$

$= 67 + 12 - 71$

$= 79 - 71$

$= 8$

8. Calculate
   (a) $6^3 + 5^2 \times 4$,
   (b) $4^3 - 3^2 \times 5 + 63 \div 9$.

Solution

(a) $6^3 + 5^2 \times 4$

$= 6 \times 6 \times 6 + 5 \times 5 \times 4$

$= 216 + 25 \times 4$

$= 216 + 100$

$= 316$

(b) $4^3 - 3^2 \times 5 + 63 \div 9$

$= 64 - 9 \times 5 + 63 \div 9$

$= 64 - 45 + 7$

$= 19 + 7$

$= 26$

9. Calculate the following.
   (a) $85 - (41 - 23)$
   (b) $(85 - 41) - 23$

Solution

(a) $85 - (41 - 23)$

$= 85 - 18$

$= 67$

(b) $(85 - 41) - 23$

$= 44 - 23$

$= 21$

10. Calculate the following.
    (a) $12 \times (9 + 8)$
    (b) $(324 - 168) \div 13$

Solution

(a) $12 \times (9 + 8)$

$= 12 \times 17$

$= 204$

(b) $(324 - 168) \div 13$

$= 156 \div 13$

$= 12$

11. Calculate the following.
    (a) $(17 - 12) \times 18 - 15 \div (29 - 26)$
    (b) $17 - 12 \times (18 - 15) \div (29 - 26)$

Solution

(a) $(17 - 12) \times 18 - 15 \div (29 - 26)$

$= 5 \times 18 - 15 \div 3$

$= 90 - 5$

$= 85$

(b) $17 - 12 \times (18 - 15) \div (29 - 26)$

$= 17 - 12 \times 3 \div 3$

$= 17 - 12 \times 1$

$= 5$

12. Work out $4^3 \div (5 - 3) + 15 \times 5 - 7^2 \times 2$.

Solution

$4^3 \div (5 - 3) + 15 \times 5 - 7^2 \times 2$

$= 64 \div 2 + 15 \times 5 - 49 \times 2$

$= 32 + 75 - 98$

$= 107 - 98$

$= 9$

13. Chocolate bars are delivered in boxes containing
    12 bars. In each box, three bars have nuts. Find the
    total number of chocolate bars without nuts in five
    boxes.

Solution

Number of chocolate bars without nuts

$= 5 \times (12 - 3)$

$= 5 \times 9$

$= 45$

14. At a charity event, Sarah walks 8 miles, Akira walks 10 miles, Leah walks 11 miles and Evie walks 7 miles. Find the mean distance that the four girls walk.

Solution
Mean distance that the girls walk
$= (8 + 10 + 11 + 7) \div 4$
$= 36 \div 4$
$= 9$ miles

Section 3.4

15. Calculate the following.
    (a) $8395 \div 23 - 18^2$
    (b) $476 + 21^3 \times 59$
    (c) $(3851 - 2701) \div 25$

Solution
(a) $8395 \div 23 - 18^2$
    $= 41$

    Checking:
    $8395 \div 23 - 18^2$
    $\approx 8400 \div 20 - 20^2$
    $= 20$

    As the answer and the estimate both have the same place value, the answer is in a reasonable range.

(b) $476 + 21^3 \times 59$
    $= 546875$

    Checking $476 + 21^3 \times 59$
    $\approx 480 + 20^3 \times 60$
    $= 480480$
    Both numbers are 6-digit. The answer is in a reasonable range.

(c) $(3851 - 2701) \div 25$
    $= 46$

    Checking:
    $(3851 - 2701) \div 25$
    $\approx (3900 - 2700) \div 30$
    $= 40$

    The answer is in a reasonable range.

16. Find the quotient and remainder when
    (a) 17 is divided by 3,
    (b) 473 is divided by 12.

Solution
(a) $17 \div 3 = 5$ r 2
    The quotient is 5 and the remainder is 2.

(b) $473 \div 12 = 39$ r 5
    The quotient is 39 and the remainder is 5.

17. A lab technician mixes 8432 ml of one chemical with 7243 ml of another chemical to form a substance that will be used by students in a chemistry experiment. If each student requires 190 ml of the substance, how many students will be able to perform this experiment?

Solution
Total volume of the substance
$= 8432 + 7243 = 15\,675$ ml
Number of 190 ml portions
$= 15\,675 \div 190$
$= 82$ r 95

i.e. 82 students can complete the experiment and 95 ml of substance remains (not enough to complete an experiment).

18. The mean daily sales in a shop over three days is £1830. The sales on the first two days are £2061 and £1647. Find the value of the sales on the third day.

Solution
Value of the sales on the third day
$= 1830 \times 3 - (2061 + 1647)$
$= 5490 - 3708$
$= 1782$
The value of sales on the third day is £1782.

Practice 3.1

Level 1   **GCSE Grade** $1^+ / 2^-$

1. The number 1384 is rounded to the nearest 10. Which of these gives the correct answer?
    A   1380   **B**   1390
    C   1400   **D**   1300

Solution
A   1380 gives the correct answer

2. **(a)** Draw each number on a number line. Then use that to round the number to the nearest 10.
        (i)   927   **(ii)**   451
    (b) Round each number to the nearest 10, explaining your reasoning.
        (i)   1689   **(ii)**   3925

Solution
(a) **(i)**

920 921 922 923 924 925 926 927 928 929 930

        927 rounds to 930 (to the nearest 10)

    (ii)

450 451 452 453 454 455 456 457 458 459 460

        451 rounds to 450 (to the nearest 10)

(b) **(i)** 1689 = 1690 (to the nearest 10)
    (ii) 3925 = 3930 (to the nearest 10)

3. **(a)** Draw each number on a number line. Then use that to round the number to the nearest 100.
    (i) 369   **(ii)** 447
 (b) Round each number to the nearest 100, explaining your reasoning.
    (i) 2455   **(ii)** 36 308

Solution
(a) **(i)**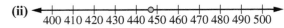

    369 rounds to 400 (to the nearest 100)

    (ii)

    447 rounds to 400 (to the nearest 100)

(b) **(i)** 2455 = 2500 (to the nearest 100)
    (ii) 36 308 = 36 300 (to the nearest 100)

4. **(a)** Round each number to the nearest 1000.
    (i) 4561   **(ii)** 3295
    (iii) 26 718   **(iv)** 63 039
 (b) Round each number to the nearest 10 000.
    (i) 30 912   **(ii)** 7 123
    (iii) 844 596   **(iv)** 96 712

Solution
(a) **(i)** 4561 = 5000 (to the nearest 1000)
    (ii) 3295 = 3000 (to the nearest 1000)
    (iii) 26 718 = 27 000 (to the nearest 1000)
    (iv) 63 039 = 63 000 (to the nearest 1000)

(b) **(i)** 30 912 = 30 000 (to the nearest 10 000)
    (ii) 7 123 = 10 000 (to the nearest 10 000)
    (iii) 844 596 = 840 000 (to the nearest 10 000)
    (iv) 96 712 = 100 000 (to the nearest 10 000)

5. Which of the following numbers rounds to 4800, when rounding to the nearest 100? (There may be more than one number)
  A 4700   **B** 4750
  C 4825   **D** 4775

Solution
B, C and D (4750, 4825 and 4775) round to 4800, to the nearest 100.

Level 2   GCSE Grade **2**

6. The volume of juice in a carton is 405 ml. Round the volume to the nearest 10 ml.

Solution
Volume of the juice
= 405 ml
= 410 ml (to the nearest 10 ml)

7. The highest mountain in the UK is Ben Nevis. Its height is 1344 m. Round the height to the nearest 100 m.

Solution
Height of Ben Nevis
= 1344 m
= 1300 m (to the nearest 100 m)

8. The price of a necklace is £3450. Find the total price of three such necklaces, giving your answer to the nearest £1000.

Solution
Total price of three such necklaces
= £3450 × 3
= £10 350
= £10 000 (to the nearest £1000)

9. Mrs Thomas's annual income is £53 278.
Mr Thomas's annual income is £64 914.
 (a) Find the total annual income of Mr and Mrs Thomas.
 (b) Round the answer in **(a)** to the nearest £10 000.
 (c) Find the total annual income of Mr and Mrs Thomas by rounding each of their annual incomes to the nearest £10 000 first. Compare this answer with the answer in **(b)**.

Solution
(a) Total annual income
    = £53 278 + £64 914
    = £118 192

(b) Rounding the answer in **(a)** to the nearest £10 000, their total income is £120 000.

(c) 53 278 = 50 000 (to the nearest 10 000)
    64 914 = 60 000 (to the nearest 10 000)
    Thus their total annual income after rounding each income = £50 000 + £60 000
                      = £110 000
    The value obtained in **(b)** is closer to the value in **(a)** than it is to this answer.

10. Alice thinks of a number and rounds it. She says her number is 38 000 to the nearest 1000. Write a possible value of Alice's number which is
 (a) smaller than 38 000,
 (b) greater than 38 000.

Solution
(a) Possible numbers which are smaller than 38 000 that will be 38 000 when rounded to the nearest 1000 include 37 500, 37 602 and 37 914.

(b) Possible numbers which are greater than 38 000 that will be 38 000 when rounded to the nearest 1000 include 38 499, 38 456 and 38 098.
    Note: 37 500 ≤ Alice's number < 38 500.

Practice 3.2

Level 1   GCSE Grade $1^+/2^-$

1. Four students are asked to estimate the calculation $75 + 291$ by rounding to the nearest 10.
   Which student has written the correct calculation?
   Student A $80 + 300$ **Student B** $70 + 290$
   Student C $80 + 290$ **Student D** $70 + 300$

   Solution
   Student C ($80 + 290$) is correct.

2. Estimate these calculations by first rounding the numbers to the nearest 10.
   (a) $12 + 68$ (b) $569 - 46$
   (c) 42×31 (d) $704 \div 65$

   Solution
   (a) $12 + 68 \approx 10 + 70$
                  $= 80$

   (b) $569 - 46 \approx 570 - 50$ Each number is rounded
                 $= 520$ to the nearest ten.

   (c) $42 \times 31 \approx 40 \times 30$ Each number is rounded
                $= 1200$ to the nearest ten.

   (d) $704 \div 65 \approx 700 \div 70$ Each number is rounded
                $= 10$ to the nearest ten.

3. Estimate these calculations by first rounding the numbers to the nearest 100.
   (a) $350 + 634$ (b) $7413 - 483$
   (c) 53×9112 (d) $2974 \div 503$

   Solution
   (a) $350 + 634 \approx 400 + 600$ Each number is rounded
                 $= 1000$ to the nearest hundred.

   (b) $7413 - 483 \approx 7400 - 500$ Each number is
                $= 6900$ rounded to the nearest hundred.

   (c) $53 \times 9112 \approx 100 \times 9100$ Each number is
               $= 910\,000$ rounded to the nearest hundred.

   (d) $2974 \div 503 \approx 3000 \div 500$ Each number is
                $= 6$ rounded to the nearest hundred.

4. Estimate these calculations by first rounding the numbers to the nearest 10.
   (a) $67 + 15 - 22$ (b) $96 - 78 + 20$
   (c) $216 + 49 + 113$ (d) $398 - 214 - 67$

   Solution
   (a) $67 + 15 - 22 \approx 70 + 20 - 20$ Each number is
                 $= 90 - 20$ rounded to the
                 $= 70$ nearest ten.

   (b) $96 - 78 + 20 \approx 100 - 80 + 20$ Each number is
                 $= 120 - 80$ rounded to the
                 $= 40$ nearest ten.

   (c) $216 + 49 + 113 \approx 220 + 50 + 110$ Each number is
                 $= 380$ rounded to the nearest ten.

   (d) $398 - 214 - 67 \approx 400 - 210 - 70$ Each number is
                 $= 400 - 280$ rounded to the
                 $= 120$ nearest ten.

Level 2   GCSE Grade $2/2^+$

5. Estimate these calculations by first rounding the numbers to the nearest 100.
   (a) $168 - 215 + 23$ (b) $5618 + 3480 - 219$
   (c) $5671 - 206 - 1598$ (d) $1192 + 72 + 368$

   Solution
   (a) $168 - 215 + 23 \approx 200 - 200 + 0$ Each number is rounded to the nearest hundred.
                 $= 0$

   (b) $5618 + 3480 - 219 \approx 5600 +$ Each number is rounded to the nearest hundred.
              $3500 - 200 = 8900$

   (c) $5671 - 206 - 1598 \approx 5700 - 200 - 1600$ Each number is rounded to the nearest hundred.
                 $= 5500 - 1600$
                 $= 3900$

   (d) $1192 + 72 + 368 \approx 1200 + 100 + 400$ Each number is rounded to the nearest hundred.
                 $= 1300 + 400$
                 $= 1700$

6. A student estimates a calculation by rounding to the nearest 100. They write $1200 - 800$.
   Which of these was the original calculation?
   A $1255 - 750$ **B** $1150 - 755$
   C $1200 - 855$ **D** $1155 - 850$

   Solution
   Calculation B ($1150 - 755$)

7. Mr Watkins has £450 in his wallet. He buys three items at £23, £85 and £208. Estimate the amount of money he has left by rounding each amount spent to the nearest £100. Is this an under-estimate or an over-estimate?

Solution

£23 + £85 + £208   Each amount is rounded to the
≈ 0 + 100 + 200   nearest hundred.
= 300

Hence, the total estimated amount of money spent is £300.

∴ the estimated amount of money left
= £450 − £300
= £150

The actual amount of money spent
= £23 + £85 + £208
= £316

The actual amount of money left
= £450 − £316
= £134

Comparing the estimated amount £150 with the actual amount £134, the estimated amount is an over-estimate of the actual amount.

8. A builder requires 123 kg of cement and 277 kg of sand for a job. He estimates that the amount of material needed is 500 kg in total. Use estimation by rounding each given quantity to the nearest 10 kg to check whether the builder's estimate is reasonable. Has he made an under-estimate or an over-estimate?

Solution

123 + 277
≈ 120 + 280   Each amount is rounded to the
= 400   nearest ten.

i.e. the estimated total amount of material needed is 400 kg.
The actual amount = 123 + 277 = 400 kg

If the builder estimates that he needs 500 kg in total, his calculation is not reasonable. He has made an over-estimate.

9. In the stands at a football match there are 9874 fans supporting one team and 7573 fans supporting the other team.
    (a) Estimate the total number of fans attending the match by
        (i) rounding each number to the nearest 1000,
        (ii) rounding each number to the nearest 100.
    (b) Compare the two estimates in (a).

Solution

(a) (i) 9874 + 7573
        ≈ 10 000 + 8000 Each number is rounded
        = 18 000   to the nearest thousand.
    (ii) 9874 + 7573
        ≈ 9900 + 7600   Each number is rounded
        = 17 500   to the nearest hundred.

The total number of fans estimated by first rounding each number to the nearest thousand is 18 000 and by first rounding each number to the nearest hundred is 17 500.

Actual total number of fans = 9874 + 7573
                            = 17 447

Both totals in part (a) have been over-estimated. If you first rounded each number to the nearest hundred before adding, you get a closer estimate to the actual total.

10. Emma and Luke estimate the sum of the volumes of juice in two cartons of drinks. One carton contains 337 ml and one contains 275 ml. Emma estimates the answer by rounding the volumes to the nearest 10 ml. Luke estimates the answer by rounding the volumes to the nearest 100 ml. Whose estimation is closer to the actual value?

Solution

Emma's estimation of 337 + 275 ≈ 340 + 280
                                = 620 ml
Luke's estimation of 337 + 275 ≈ 300 + 300
                                = 600 ml
Actual volume = 337 + 275
              = 612 ml
Emma's estimation is 620 − 612 = 8 ml from the actual value. Luke's estimation is 612 − 600 = 12 ml from the actual value.
Hence, Emma's estimation is closer to the actual value.

Practice 3.3

Level 1   GCSE Grade 1⁺ / 2

1. Calculate these expressions.
    (a) 6 + 7 × 3   (b) 20 − 8 × 2
    (c) 19 + 42 ÷ 6   (d) 88 − 96 ÷ 8

Solution

(a) 6 + 7 × 3   (b) 20 − 8 × 2
    = 6 + 21   = 20 − 16
    = 27   = 4

(c) 19 + 42 ÷ 6   (d) 88 − 96 ÷ 8
    = 19 + 7   = 88 − 12
    = 26   = 76

2. The value of each of these expressions can be changed by adding brackets. Copy each expression then add brackets so that its value changes. (You don't need to work out the answers.)
    (a) 8 × 3 + 2 × 9   (b) 160 ÷ 40 − 32 ÷ 8
    (c) 84 ÷ 12 − 6 × 2   (d) 81 + 15 ÷ 3 × 4

Solution

(a) $8 \times (3 + 2) \times 9$

(b) $160 \div (40 - 32) \div 8$

(c) $84 \div (12 - 6) \times 2$

(d) $(81 + 15) \div 3 \times 4$

3. James buys two 6-packs of juice cartons, then gives 2 cartons to a friend. Which of these calculations represents how many cartons James has left?

   A $2 \times 6 - 2$ B $2 \div 6 - 2$

   C $2 \times (6 - 2)$ D $2 \div (6 - 2)$

Solution

Calculation A: $2 \times 6 - 2$

4. Evaluate these expressions.

   (a) 2×5^2 (b) 5×2^3

   (c) $5 \times 4 + 8^2$ (d) $100 - 8^3 \div 16$

Solution

(a) 2×5^2
    $= 2 \times 25$
    $= 50$

(b) 5×2^3
    $= 5 \times 8$
    $= 40$

(c) $5 \times 4 + 8^2$
    $= 5 \times 4 + 64$
    $= 20 + 64$
    $= 84$

(d) $100 - 8^3 \div 16$
    $= 100 - 512 \div 16$
    $= 100 - 32$
    $= 68$

5. Work out these values.

   (a) $28 - (17 - 5)$ (b) $(23 - 12) \times 8$

   (c) $26 \div (15 - 2)$ (d) $(21 + 3) \times (4 + 6)$

Solution

(a) $28 - (17 - 5)$
    $= 28 - 12$
    $= 16$

(b) $(23 - 12) \times 8$
    $= 11 \times 8$
    $= 88$

(c) $26 \div (15 - 2)$
    $= 26 \div 13$
    $= 2$

(d) $(21 + 3) \times (4 + 6)$
    $= 24 \times 10$
    $= 240$

Level 2   **GCSE Grade** $2^+ / 3^-$

6. Calculate these expressions.

   (a) $(20 + 7) \times 4 - 3$ (b) $(20 + 7) \times (4 - 3)$

   (c) $(20 + 7 \times 4) - 3$ (d) $20 + 7 \times (4 - 3)$

   (e) $(2^3 + 11) \times 3$ (f) $2^3 + 11 \times 3$

   (g) $(200 - 5^3) \div 25$ (h) $3 \times 3^3 \div (4^2 - 7)$

Solution

(a) $(20 + 7) \times 4 - 3$
    $= 27 \times 4 - 3$
    $= 108 - 3$
    $= 105$

(b) $(20 + 7) \times (4 - 3)$
    $= 27 \times 1$
    $= 27$

(c) $(20 + 7 \times 4) - 3$
    $= (20 + 28) - 3$
    $= 48 - 3$
    $= 45$

(d) $20 + 7 \times (4 - 3)$
    $= 20 + 7 \times 1$
    $= 20 + 7$
    $= 27$

(e) $(2^3 + 11) \times 3$
    $= (8 + 11) \times 3$
    $= 19 \times 3$
    $= 57$

(f) $2^3 + 11 \times 3$
    $= 8 + 33$
    $= 41$

(g) $(200 - 5^3) \div 25$
    $= (200 - 125) \div 25$
    $= 75 \div 25$
    $= 3$

(h) $3 \times 3^3 \div (4^2 - 7)$
    $= 3 \times 27 \div (16 - 7)$
    $= 3 \times 27 \div 9$
    $= 81 \div 9$
    $= 9$

7. Work out these values.

   (a) $7 \times 5 + (9^2 - 6) \times 3$

   (b) $7 \times 5 + (9^2 - 6 \times 3)$

   (c) $416 \div (2^3 - 4) + 3 \times 7$

   (d) $416 \div 2^3 - (4 + 3) \times 7$

Solution

(a) $7 \times 5 + (9^2 - 6) \times 3$
    $= 7 \times 5 + (81 - 6) \times 3$
    $= 7 \times 5 + 75 \times 3$
    $= 35 + 225$
    $= 260$

(b) $7 \times 5 + (9^2 - 6 \times 3)$
    $= 7 \times 5 + (81 - 6 \times 3)$
    $= 7 \times 5 + (81 - 18)$
    $= 35 + 63$
    $= 98$

(c) $416 \div (2^3 - 4) + 3 \times 7$
    $= 416 \div (8 - 4) + 3 \times 7$
    $= 416 \div 4 + 21$
    $= 104 + 21$
    $= 125$

(d) $416 \div 2^3 - (4 + 3) \times 7$
    $= 416 \div 8 - (4 + 3) \times 7$
    $= 416 \div 8 - 7 \times 7$
    $= 52 - 49$
    $= 3$

8. Calculate each pair of expressions, working from left to right when there are no brackets, and compare the results. Can you describe a pattern or a rule?

   (a) $85 + (47 - 46)$ and $85 + 47 - 46$

   (b) $263 - (53 + 47)$ and $263 - 53 + 47$

   (c) $9 \times (8 \div 4)$ and $9 \times 8 \div 4$

   (d) $12 \div (6 \times 2)$ and $12 \div 6 \times 2$

Solution

(a) $85 + (47 - 46)$
$= 85 + 1$
$= 86$

$85 + 47 - 46$
$= 86$
The results are the same.

(b) $263 - (53 + 47)$
$= 263 - 100$
$= 163$

$263 - 53 + 47$
$= 210 + 47$
$= 257$
The results are different because subtraction comes before addition in the second expression.

(c) $9 \times (8 \div 4)$
$= 9 \times 2$
$= 18$

$9 \times 8 \div 4$
$= 72 \div 4$
$= 18$
The results are the same.

(d) $12 \div (6 \times 2)$
$= 12 \div 12$
$= 1$

$12 \div 6 \times 2$
$= 2 \times 2$
$= 4$
The results are different because division comes before multiplication in the second expression.

9. In an experiment, $100 \, \text{cm}^3$ of water is added to $250 \, \text{cm}^3$ of vinegar. The mixture is poured equally into ten test tubes. What is the volume of the mixture in each test tube?

Solution
Total volume of the mixture $= (100 + 250) \, \text{cm}^3$
$\therefore$ volume of the mixture in each test tube
$= (100 + 250) \div 10$
$= 350 \div 10$
$= 35 \, \text{cm}^3$

10. Ava donates $470 \, \text{ml}$ of blood. Ben donates $456 \, \text{ml}$. Cathy donates $466 \, \text{ml}$. Find the mean volume of their blood donations.

Solution
Mean volume of their blood donations
$= (470 + 456 + 466) \div 3$
$= 1392 \div 3$
$= 464 \, \text{ml}$

Practice 3.4

You should check your answers using estimation.

Level 1   **GCSE Grade** $1^+ / 2^-$

1. Calculate these expressions.
  (a) $3156 + 478$
  (b) $98\,370 - 56\,142$
  (c) 937×56
  (d) $31\,590 \div 78$
  (e) 451^2
  (f) 47^3

Solution

(a) $3156 + 478 = 3634$
  Checking: $3156 + 478$
  $\approx 3200 + 500$
  $= 3700$

As the answer and the estimate both have the same place value, the answer is in a reasonable range.

(b) $98\,370 - 56\,142 = 42\,228$
  Checking: $98\,370 - 56\,142$
  $\approx 98\,000 - 56\,000$
  $= 42\,000$

The answer is in a reasonable range.

(c) $937 \times 56 = 52\,472$
  Checking: 937×56
  $\approx 940 \times 60$
  $= 56\,400$

The answer is in a reasonable range.

(d) $31\,590 \div 78 = 405$
  Checking: $31\,590 \div 78$
  $\approx 32\,000 \div 80$
  $= 400$

The answer is in a reasonable range.

(e) $451^2 = 203\,401$
  Checking: 451^2
  $\approx 500^2$
  $= 250\,000$

The answer is in a reasonable range.

(f) $47^3 = 103\,823$
  Checking: $47^3 \approx 50^3$
  $= 125\,000$

The answer is in a reasonable range.

2. Find the quotient and the remainder.
  (a) $451 \div 7$
  (b) $4398 \div 23$
  (c) $3840 \div 15$
  (d) $52\,639 \div 624$

Solution

(a) $451 \div 7 = 64 \text{ r } 3$
  i.e. the quotient is 64 and the remainder is 3.
  Checking: $450 \div 10 = 45$
  The answer is in a reasonable range.

(b) $4398 \div 23 = 191 \text{ r } 5$
  The quotient is 191 and the remainder is 5.
  Checking: $4400 \div 20 = 220$
  The answer is in a reasonable range.

(c) $3840 \div 15 = 256$

The quotient is 256 and the remainder is 0.

Checking: $4000 \div 20 = 200$

The answer is in a reasonable range.

(d) $52\,639 \div 624$

$= 84 \text{ r } 223$

The quotient is 84 and the remainder is 223.

Checking: $52\,000 \div 600 \approx 90$

The answer is in a reasonable range.

3. Work out these expressions.
   (a) $3872 - 1298 + 4561$ **(b)** $145 \times 324 \div 36$
   (c) $987 + 56 \times 4^3$ **(d)** $67^2 - 14\,445 \div 45$

Solution

(a) $3872 - 1298 + 4561 = 7135$

Checking: Rounding to the nearest hundred,

$$3872 - 1298 + 4561$$
$$\approx 3900 - 1300 + 4600$$
$$= 7200$$

The answer is in a reasonable range.

(b) $145 \times 324 \div 36 = 1305$

Checking: Rounding to the nearest ten,

$$145 \times 324 \div 36$$
$$\approx 150 \times 320 \div 40$$
$$= 1200$$

As the answer and the estimate both have the same place value, the answer is in a reasonable range.

(c) $987 + 56 \times 4^3 = 4571$

Checking: $987 + 56 \times 4^3$
$$= 987 + 56 \times 64$$
$$\approx 990 + 60 \times 60$$
$$= 4590$$

The answer is in a reasonable range.

(d) $67^2 - 14\,445 \div 45 = 4168$

Checking: $67^2 - 14\,445 \div 45$
$$\approx 70^2 - 14\,400 \div 50$$
$$= 4612$$

The answer is in a reasonable range.

4. Evaluate these expressions.
   (a) $987 \times (675 - 301)$
   (b) $(2875 + 5189) \div 12^2$
   (c) $43 + (9871 - 16^3) \div 55$
   (d) $4717 \div 53 + 5^3 \times (264 - 189)$

Solution

(a) $987 \times (675 - 301) = 369\,138$

Checking: $987 \times (675 - 301)$
$$\approx 1000 \times (700 - 300)$$
$$= 400\,000$$

The answer is in a reasonable range.

(b) $(2875 + 5189) \div 12^2 = 56$

Checking: $(2875 + 5189) \div 12^2$
$$\approx (2900 + 5200) \div 100$$
$$= 81$$

The answer is in a reasonable range.

(c) $43 + (9871 - 16^3) \div 55 = 148$

Checking: $43 + (9871 - 16^3) \div 55$
$$\approx 40 + (9870 - 4100) \div 60$$
$$= 40 + 5770 \div 60$$
$$= 40 + 96$$
$$= 136$$

The answer is in a reasonable range.

(d) $4717 \div 53 + 5^3 \times (264 - 189) = 9464$

Checking: $4717 \div 53 + 53 \times (264 - 189)$
$$\approx 4720 \div 50 + 130 \times (260 - 190)$$
$$= 4720 \div 50 + 130 \times 70$$
$$= 4720 \div 50 + 130 \times 70$$
$$= 94 + 9100$$
$$= 9194$$

The answer is in a reasonable range.

Level 2   **GCSE Grade 2 / 2$^+$**

5. Georgia goes to a gym 19 times in a month. She pays £5 each time. How much does she spend on the gym in a year?

Solution

Amount that Georgia spends on the gym in one month $= £19 \times 5$

Amount that she spends in a year
$$= £19 \times 5 \times 12$$
$$= £1140$$

6. A train has 578 passengers. At the next station, 124 people get off and 236 people get on the train. Find the number of passengers on the train now.

Solution

Number of passengers on the train now
$$= 578 - 124 + 236$$
$$= 690$$

7. The heights of five basketball players are 209 cm, 198 cm, 187 cm, 205 cm and 196 cm. Find the mean height of these players.

Solution

Mean height of these players
$$= (209 + 198 + 187 + 205 + 196) \div 5$$
$$= 199 \text{ cm}$$

8. There are some boxes each containing 750 grams of cornflakes. Each serving of cornflakes is 30 grams. A family has four members. Each member has one serving of cornflakes every morning. How many boxes of cornflakes should be bought for 30 days?

Solution
Number of servings of cornflakes needed by the family in one day = 4
Thus, the number of servings needed for 30 days
= 30 × 4
= 120

Amount of cornflakes needed for 30 days
= 30 × 120 = 3600 grams

To find the number of boxes that should be bought, you first find the value of 3600 ÷ 750 = 4.8

Since you do not buy a portion of a box, the number of boxes of cornflakes that should be bought for 30 days is 5 (round up 4.8).

9. Ava, Ben, Chloe and David do the same assignment. The mean time taken by them to complete the assignment is 43 minutes. Ava takes 45 minutes. Ben takes 38 minutes. Chloe takes 40 minutes. What is the time taken by David?

Solution
Since the mean time taken by the 4 students is 43 minutes, the total time taken by them
= 43 × 4 = 172 minutes

The total time taken by Ava, Ben and Chloe
= 45 + 38 + 40 = 123 minutes

Hence the time taken by the fourth person, David,
= 172 − 123
= 49 minutes

Challenge 3

Write a calculation using all the digits 5, 6, 7 and 8 once only with some of the operators +, −, ×, ÷ and brackets.

(a) What is the smallest non-zero whole number result you can get?
(b) What is the greatest whole number result you can get?

Hint: Here are a few examples of calculations:
$5 × 678 \quad 85 × 76(8 − 6) + 5 − 7 \quad 8 − 5 ÷ (7 − 6)$

Solution
(a) The smallest non-zero whole number result you can get is 1 using $(8 − 6) ÷ (7 − 5)$
(b) The greatest whole number result you can get is 6460 using $85 × 76$

Revision Exercise 3

1. Round these numbers to the given degree of accuracy.

   (a) 328, to the nearest 10
   (b) 3125, to the nearest 100
   (c) 9504, to the nearest 1000
   (d) 51 978, to the nearest 10 000

Solution
   (a) 328 = 330 (to the nearest 10)
   (b) 3125 = 3100 (to the nearest 100)
   (c) 9504 = 10 000 (to the nearest 1000)
   (d) 51 978 = 50 000 (to the nearest 10 000)

2. Which of these numbers can be rounded to 61 700 to the nearest 100?

   61 734   61 783   61 649   61 659   61 650

Solution
61 734, 61 659 and 61 650 can be rounded to 61 700 to the nearest 100.

3. Estimate the values of these expressions by first rounding each number to the nearest 100.
   (a) 328 + 1745 − 34
   (b) 6178 − 2319 + 4753
   (c) 69 325 − 417 × 97
   (d) 249 + 35 350 ÷ 202

Solution
   (a) 328 + 1745 − 34
   ≈ 300 + 1700 − 0
   = 2000

   (b) 6178 − 2319 + 4753
   ≈ 6200 − 2300 + 4800
   = 8700

   (c) 69 325 − 417 × 97
   ≈ 69 300 − 400 × 100
   = 69 300 − 40 000
   = 29 300

   (d) 249 + 35 350 ÷ 202
   ≈ 200 + 35 400 ÷ 200
   ≈ 200 + 177 = 377

4. Use a calculator to work out these expressions.

   (a) 89 + 12 × 11
   (b) 84 − 162 ÷ 3²
   (c) 16 + (98 − 56) × 12
   (d) 4² × (70 − 57) − 5³

Solution
   (a) $89 + 12 × 11 = 221$
   (b) $84 − 162 ÷ 3^2 = 66$
   (c) $16 + (98 − 56) × 12 = 520$
   (d) $4^2 × (70 − 57) − 5^3 = 83$

5. Use a calculator to work out these expressions.

(a) $8713 - (2566 + 1704)$

(b) $45 \times 96 - 15^2 \div 45$

(c) $7326 + 13^3 \times (242 - 239)$

(d) $801 - (47 + 12) \times 7 + 19^2$

Solution

(a) $8713 - (2566 + 1704) = 4443$

(b) $45 \times 96 - 15^2 \div 45 = 4315$

(c) $7326 + 13^3 \times (242 - 239) = 13\,917$

(d) $801 - (47 + 12) \times 7 + 19^2 = 749$

6. The mass of a can of pineapple is 453 grams.

(a) Find the total mass of three cans of pineapple.

(b) Round your answer in (a) to the nearest 100 grams.

Solution

(a) Total mass of three cans of pineapple
$= 453 \times 3$
$= 1359$ grams

(b) 1359 grams = 1400 grams (to the nearest 100 grams)

7. A garden has an area of $345\,\text{m}^2$. Trees cover $109\,\text{m}^2$, and flowers cover $137\,\text{m}^2$. The rest is lawn.

(a) Find the area of the garden that is lawn.

(b) Round your answer in (a) to the nearest $10\,\text{m}^2$.

Solution

(a) Area of the garden that is lawn
$= 345 - 109 - 137$
$= 99\,\text{m}^2$

(b) $99 = 100\,\text{m}^2$ (to the nearest $10\,\text{m}^2$)

8. The Emirates Air Line is a cable car link across the River Thames in London. The maximum capacity of each cabin is ten people. 2374 people want to take a ride on the cable car.

(a) What is the smallest number of cabins required?

(b) Round your answer in (a) to the nearest 10 cabins.

Solution

(a) $2374 \div 10 = 237$ r 4

If 237 cabins are used, four people will not be able to take a ride on the cable car across the River Thames.

So in order to accommodate everyone, the smallest number of cabins required $= 237 + 1$
$= 238$

(b) $238 = 240$ (to the nearest 10)

9. A metal wire is 125 cm long. Four pieces each of length 20 cm are cut from the wire to form a square frame. The remaining length of the wire is cut into three equal pieces to form an equilateral triangle (all sides are the same length). What is the length of a side of the triangle?

Solution

Remaining length of the wire for the triangle
$= 125 - 20 \times 4$
$= 125 - 80$
$= 45\,\text{cm}$
$\therefore$ the length of a side of the triangle $= 45 \div 3$
$= 15\,\text{cm}$

10. The mass of a basketball is 623 grams. The mass of a football is 431 grams. The mass of a volleyball is 272 grams. Find the mean mass of these three balls.

Solution

Mean mass of these three balls
$= (623 + 431 + 272) \div 3$
$= 1326 \div 3$
$= 442$ grams

4 Use of Letters

Class Activity 1

Objective: To use letters to represent numbers and the relationship between numerical quantities.

Anne is 28 years older than her son Lucas. The relationship between their ages can be shown in a table.

Lucas's age (years)	Anne's age (years)
0	28
1	28 + 1 = 29
11	28 + 11 = 39
16	28 + __ = __
x	
	y

There are some blanks where information is missing.

1. Copy the table and fill in the blanks in the 4th row.

Lucas's age (years)	Anne's age (years)
0	28
1	28 + 1 = 29
11	28 + 11 = 39
16	28 + 16 = 44
x	
	y

2. Explain what the relationship is between the numbers on the same row but in different columns.

   Anne's age increases by the same number of years as Lucas's age. For example, when Lucas's age is 11, Anne is 11 years older than she was when Lucas was 0 years old.

3. If Lucas's age is x years, how can you represent Anne's age in terms of x?

   When Lucas is x years old, Anne is 28 + x years old.

4. If Anne's age is y years, how can you represent Lucas's age in terms of y?

   When Anne is y years old, Lucas is $y - 28$ years old.

5. Now, represent your reasoning from questions **3** and **4** to fill in the bottom two rows.

Lucas's age (years)	Anne's age (years)
0	28
1	28 + 1 = 29
11	28 + 11 = 39
16	28 + 16 = 44
x	28 + x
$y - 28$	y

Class Activity 2

Objective: To match algebraic expressions with the correct statements.

1. Match the statements on the left with the algebraic expressions on the right.
    An algebraic expression may be matched by more than one statement.

Hint: Remember x represents a value. If you are not sure about which statement matches which expression, give x a
value (a number) and see if this helps you decide which are the matching pairs.

Product of x and 5.	$5 + x$
Sum of 5 and x.	
Subtract x from 5.	$x \times 5$
x groups of 5.	$5 - x$
x more than 5.	$x - 5$
x less than 5.	
Divide 5 by x.	$\dfrac{5}{x}$

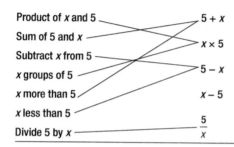

2. Can you write a statement that would match the unmatched expression, and compare with your classmates?

5 less than x or subtract 5 from x

Class Activity 3

Objective: To match expressions with values.

1. In this question, $m = 2$ and $n = 5$. Copy and evaluate each expression below, using the numbers in the circle. You
    may use each number more than once.

    (a) $m + 10 =$

    (b) $7 - m =$

    (c) $3m =$

    (d) $18 \div m =$

    (e) $2n + 2 =$

    (f) $4n - 13 =$

    (g) $\dfrac{6n}{10} =$

    (h) $m + n =$

    Circle contains: 5, 7, 6, 3, 12, 9

    (a) $m + 10 = 12$

    (b) $7 - m = 5$

    (c) $3m = 6$

    (d) $18 \div m = 9$

    (e) $2n + 2 = 12$

    (f) $4n - 13 = 7$

(g) $\frac{6n}{10} = 3$

(h) $m + n = 7$

2. Create an expression in x such that the expression has the value 14 when $x = 4$.

For example, $x + 10 = 14$, $18 - x = 14$, etc.

3. Create an expression in y such that the expression has the value 7 when $y = 3$, and the expression has the value 13 when $y = 6$. Discuss this with your classmates and compare your expressions with theirs. **Hint:** Your expression can contain more than one operation, like examples **(e)**, **(f)** and **(g)** in question **1**.

$2y + 1$

Try It!

Section 4.1

1. Write two possible statements, in words, for each algebraic expression.
   (a) $4 + p$ **(b)** $q - 8$
   (c) $r \times 13$ **(d)** $20 \div s$

   Solution
   Note: An algebraic expression may be expressed more than one way. Some possible statements are given for each algebraic expression below.
   (a) $4 + p$: sum of 4 and p,
   add p to 4,
   4 plus p,
   p more than 4.

   (b) $q - 8$: subtract 8 from q,
   take away 8 from q,
   q minus 8,
   8 less than q.

   (c) $r \times 13$: product of r and 13,
   multiply r by 13,
   r times 13,
   r groups of 13.

   (d) $20 \div s$: quotient of 20 divided by s,
   divide 20 by s,
   s divided into 20.

2. Aiden and Mason take the same test. Aiden scores seven marks more than Mason. Draw a bar model. Find Aiden's score if Mason's score is
   (a) 62 marks,
   (b) 89 marks,
   (c) p marks.

   Solution
   The bar model for this situation is:

   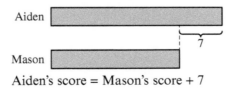

   Aiden's score = Mason's score + 7

(a) If Mason's score is 62 marks,
Aiden's score = 62 + 7
             = 69 marks

(b) If Mason's score is 89 marks,
Aiden's score = 89 + 7
             = 96 marks

(c) If Mason's score is p marks,
Aiden's score = $(p + 7)$ marks

3. The length of a nail is twice the length of a screw. Draw and label a bar model to represent the relationship between the variables. Find the length of the nail if the length of the screw is
   (a) 25 mm,   **(b)** 37 mm,   **(c)** d mm.

   Solution
   The bar model for this situation is:

   Nail [ ]

   Screw [ ]

   Length of the nail = 2 times the length of the screw
   (a) If the screw is 25 mm long, the length of the nail
   $= 2 \times 25$
   $= 50$ mm

   (b) If the screw is 37 mm long, the length of the nail
   $= 2 \times 37$
   $= 74$ mm

   (c) If the screw is d mm long, the length of the nail
   $= 2 \times d$
   $= 2d$ mm

4. A prize of £750 is shared equally among some winners. Draw bar models and find the amount that each winner gets if there are
   (a) 5 winners,
   (b) 15 winners,
   (c) W winners.

Solution

(a)

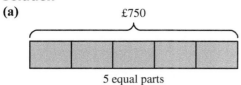

£750

5 equal parts

The amount that each winner gets = £750 ÷ 5
= £150

(b)

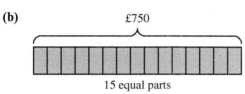

£750

15 equal parts

The amount that each winner gets = £750 ÷ 15
= £50

(c)

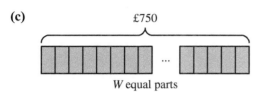

£750

W equal parts

The amount that each winner gets = £750 ÷ *W*
$$= £\left(\frac{750}{W}\right)$$

Section 4.2

5. Find the value of $t - 18$ when
   (a) $t = 29$,   **(b)** $t = 35$.

Solution

(a) When $t = 29$,   **(b)** When $t = 35$,
   $t - 18 = 29 - 18$ $t - 18 = 35 - 18$
   $= 11$ $= 17$

6. **(a)** Work out the value of $5q$ when $q = 6$.

   (b) Work out the value of $\frac{q}{2}$ when $q = 6$.

Solution

(a) When $q = 6$ **(b)** When $q = 6$,
   $5q = 5 \times 6$ $\frac{q}{2} = \frac{6}{2}$
   $= 30$ $= 3$

7. The number of fish oil pills in a bottle after y days is $54 - 3y$. Find the number of pills after
   (a) 0 days,
   (b) eight days.

Solution

Number of fish oil pills after y days = $54 - 3y$
(a) When $y = 0$,
   the number of pills after 0 days
   $= 54 - 3 \times 0$
   $= 54$

(b) When $y = 8$,
   the number of pills after 8 days
   $= 54 - 3 \times 8$
   $= 30$

Practice 4.1

Level 1

1. Write two possible statements, in words, for each algebraic expression.
   (a) $a + 9$ **(b)** $10 - b$
   (c) $8 \times c$ **(d)** $d \div 12$

Solution

(a) $a + 9$ is 'add 9 to a' or 'a plus 9'.

(b) $10 - b$ is 'subtract b from 10' or '10 minus b'.

(c) $8 \times c$ is 'multiply 8 by c' or '8 times c'.

(d) $d \div 12$ is 'divide d by 12' or '12 divided into d'.

2. In the diagram, m represents the value of B. Express the value of A in terms of m.

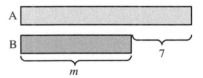

Solution

Value of A = $m + 7$

3. In the diagram, C is p units less than D. Express the value of C in terms of p.

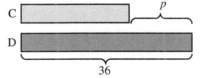

Solution

Value of C = $36 - p$

4. In the bar model, the value of F is q. Express the value of E in terms of q.

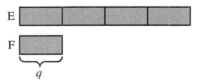

Solution

Value of E = $4q$

5. In the bar model, the value of H is W. Express the value of G in terms of W.

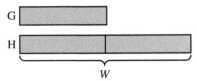

Solution

Value of $G = \frac{1}{2}W$ or $\frac{W}{2}$

Level 2 |GCSE Grade **2** / **2⁺**|

Draw and label bar models to help you with these questions if necessary.

6. A tank has seven fish. Find the total number of fish in the tank after
  (a) three fish are added to the tank,
  (b) eight fish are added to the tank,
  (c) n fish are added to the tank.

Solution

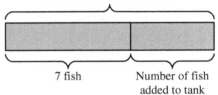

Total number of fish in tank

7 fish   Number of fish added to tank

Total number of fish in the tank = 7 + number of fish added to the tank

  (a) Total number = 7 + 3
                = 10

  (b) Total number = 7 + 8
                = 15

  (c) Total number = 7 + n

7. Emma is 5 cm shorter than John. Find Emma's height if John's height is
  (a) 176 cm,
  (b) 184 cm,
  (c) h cm.

Solution

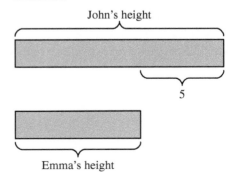

John's height

5

Emma's height

Emma's height = John's height − 5 cm

  (a) If John's height is 176 cm,
       Emma's height = 176 − 5
                = 171 cm

  (b) If John's height is 184 cm,
       Emma's height = 184 − 5
                = 179 cm

  (c) If John's height is h cm,
       Emma's height = $(h − 5)$ cm

8. One ant has six legs. Find the total number of legs on
  (a) five ants,
  (b) nine ants,
  (c) p ants.

Solution
  (a) Total number of legs on 5 ants = 6 × 5
                          = 30

  (b) Total number of legs on 9 ants = 6 × 9
                          = 54

  (c) Total number of legs on p ants = 6 × p
                          = 6p

9. 90 apples are shared equally among some families. How many apples does each family get if there are
  (a) 10 families,
  (b) 18 families,
  (c) M families?

Solution
  (a) The share of each family = 90 ÷ 10
                        = 9 apples

  (b) The share of each family = 90 ÷ 18
                        = 5 apples

  (c) The share of each family = 90 ÷ M
                        = $\frac{90}{M}$ apples

10. A class is usually made up of x students. On a particular day, there are $(x − 1)$ students present. Describe what has happened.

Solution
$x − 1$ is 'one less than x'.

This means that one student is absent on that day.

Practice 4.2

Level 1 |GCSE Grade **2**|

1. Find the value of $a + 8$ when
  (a) $a = 3$,
  (b) $a = 7$.

Solution

(a) When $a = 3$,
$$a + 8 = 3 + 8$$
$$= 11$$

(b) When $a = 7$,
$$a + 8 = 7 + 8$$
$$= 15$$

2. Find the value of $10 - b$ when
   (a) $b = 2$,
   (b) $b = 9$.

Solution

(a) When $b = 2$,
$$10 - b = 10 - 2$$
$$= 8$$

(b) When $b = 9$,
$$10 - b = 10 - 9$$
$$= 1$$

3. Find the value of $5c$ when
   (a) $c = 4$,
   (b) $c = 11$.

Solution

(a) When $c = 4$,
$$5c = 5 \times 4$$
$$= 20$$

(b) When $c = 11$,
$$5c = 5 \times 11$$
$$= 55$$

4. Work out the value of $\frac{d}{3}$ when

   (a) $d = 12$,
   (b) $d = 21$.

Solution

(a) When $d = 12$,
$$\frac{d}{3} = \frac{12}{3}$$
$$= 4$$

(b) When $d = 21$,
$$\frac{d}{3} = \frac{21}{3}$$
$$= 7$$

Level 2   GCSE Grade 2⁺

Where necessary, draw and label bar models for each of these questions to represent the relationship between the variables.

5. Mason's age in m years' time will be $(11 + m)$ years.
   (a) Find his age eight years from now.
   (b) Find his age 12 years from now.
   (c) How old is Mason now?

Solution

Mason's age in m years' time = $(11 + m)$ years
(a) When $m = 8$,
   his age $= 11 + 8$
$$= 19 \text{ years}$$

(b) When $m = 12$,
   his age $= 11 + 12$
$$= 23 \text{ years}$$

(c) When $m = 0$,
   his age $= 11 + 0$
$$= 11 \text{ years}$$
Mason is 11 years old now.

6. The length of a rod is L cm. After a length of 10 cm is cut from it, the length of the rod remaining is $(L - 10)$ cm. Find the length of the rod remaining when
   (a) $L = 85$,
   (b) $L = 102$.

Solution

Remaining length of the rod $= (L - 10)$ cm

(a) When $L = 85$,
   the remaining length $= 85 - 10$
$$= 75 \text{ cm}$$

(b) When $L = 102$,
   the remaining length $= 102 - 10$
$$= 92 \text{ cm}$$

7. The number of days in n weeks is $7n$. Find the number of days in
   (a) four weeks,
   (b) nine weeks.

Solution

The number of days in n weeks $= 7n$
(a) When $n = 4$,
   the number of days $= 7 \times 4$
$$= 28$$

(b) When $n = 9$,
   the number of days $= 7 \times 9$
$$= 63$$

8. A ribbon of length 120 cm is cut into p equal parts. The length of each part is $\frac{120}{p}$ cm. Find the length of each part when there are
   (a) five parts,
   (b) eight parts.
   (c) How many parts are there if the length of each part is 10 cm?

Solution

Length of each part when there are p parts $= \frac{120}{p}$ cm

(a) When $p = 5$
   the length of each part $= \frac{120}{5}$
$$= 24 \text{ cm}$$

(b) When $p = 8$,
   the length of each part $= \frac{120}{8}$
$$= 15 \text{ cm}$$

(c) When the length of a part $= 10$ cm,
$$10 = \frac{120}{p}$$
$$10 \times p = 120$$
$$p = 12$$
If each part is 10 cm long, there are 12 parts.

9. Water is being poured into a beaker. After t seconds, the volume of water in the beaker is $(5t + 18)\,cm^3$.
   (a) Find the volume of water when $t = 7$.
   (b) What is the initial volume of water in the beaker?

Solution
The volume of water in the beaker after t seconds
$= (5t + 18)\,cm^3$

(a) When $t = 7$,
the volume of water $= 5 \times 7 + 18$
$\qquad = 53\,cm^3$

(b) When $t = 0$,
the volume of water $= 5 \times 0 + 18$
$\qquad = 18\,cm^3$
Hence, the initial volume of water in the beaker is $18\,cm^3$.

10. Create more than one algebraic expression in x such that the value of each expression is 7 when $x = 3$.

Solution
Some possible expressions are value is 7 when $x = 3$ are
$x + 4$
$10 - x$
$1 + 2x$
$4x - 5$
$16 - 3x$
$6 + \dfrac{x}{3}$
$\dfrac{27}{x} - 2$
$\dfrac{21}{x}$

Challenge 4
There are 500 sheets in a ream of paper. To print a booklet, 30 sheets are needed.
(a) Find the number of sheets remaining if

(i) 16 booklets are printed,
(ii) n booklets are printed, giving your answer in terms of n.
(b) Can 18 booklets be printed from the ream of paper? Explain your answer.

Solution
First, find the number of sheets needed to print the stated number of booklets. Then find the number of remaining sheets in the ream.

(a) (i) Number of sheets needed to print 16 booklets $= 30 \times 16$
$\qquad = 480$
Hence, the number of remaining sheets
$= 500 - 480$
$= 20$

(ii) Number of sheets needed to print n booklets $= 30 \times n$
$\qquad = 30n$
Hence, the number of remaining sheets in the ream $= 500 - 30n$

(b) Number of sheets needed to print 18 booklets
$= 30 \times 18$
$= 540$
$540 > 500$
Since there are only 500 sheets in the ream of paper, it is not sufficient to print 18 booklets

Revision Exercise 4
Where necessary, draw and label bar models to help you represent the relationship between the variables.

1. The capacity of a bowl is 240 ml more than that of a cup. Find the capacity of the bowl when the capacity of the cup is

   (a) 250 ml,
   (b) 280 ml,
   (c) x ml.

Solution
Capacity of the bowl = 240 ml + capacity of the cup

(a) If the capacity of the cup is 250 ml,
the capacity of the bowl $= 240 + 250$
$\qquad = 490\,ml$

(b) If the capacity of the cup is 280 ml,
the capacity of the bowl $= 240 + 280$
$\qquad = 520\,ml$

(c) If the capacity of the cup is x ml,
the capacity of the bowl $= (240 + x)\,ml$

2. In a basketball match, Sophia's score is nine less than Aria's score. Find Sophia's score if Aria's score is
   (a) 13,
   (b) 26,
   (c) a.

Solution
Sophia's score = Aria's score − 9

(a) If Aria's score is 13, Sophia's score $= 13 - 9$
$\qquad\qquad = 4$

(b) If Aria's score is 26, Sophia's score $= 26 - 9$
$\qquad\qquad = 17$

(c) If Aria's score is a, Sophia's score $= a - 9$

3. The monthly salary of a manager is four times the monthly salary of a clerk. Find the monthly salary of the manager if the monthly salary of the clerk is
   (a) £2000,
   (b) £2350,
   (c) £y.

Solution

Manager's monthly salary
= 4 × clerk's monthly salary

(a) If the clerk's monthly salary is £2000, the
manager's monthly salary = 4 × £2000
= £8000

(b) If the clerk's monthly salary is £2350, the
managers monthly salary = 4 × £2350
= £9400

(c) If the clerk's monthly salary is £y, the
manager's monthly salary = 4 × £y
= £4y

4. Sulfur powder is divided equally into five portions
for an experiment. Find the mass of each portion if
the total mass of the sulfur powder is
(a) 120 grams,
(b) 325 grams,
(c) m grams.

Solution

Mass of each portion = total mass ÷ 5

(a) If the total mass is 120 grams,
the mass of each portion = 120 ÷ 5
= 24 grams

(b) If the total mass is 325 grams,
the mass of each portion = 325 ÷ 5
= 65 grams

(c) If the total mass is m grams,
the mass of each portion = m ÷ 5
= $\frac{m}{5}$ grams

5. Find the value of 56 + p when
(a) $p = 12$, (b) $p = 39$.

Solution

(a) When $p = 12$, (b) When $p = 39$,
56 + p = 56 + 12 56 + p = 56 + 39
= 68 = 95

6. Find the value of $q - 15$ when
(a) $q = 17$, (b) $q = 24$.

Solution

(a) When $q = 17$, (b) When $q = 24$,
$q - 15 = 17 - 15$ $q - 15 = 24 - 15$
= 2 = 9

7. Work out the value of 3r when
(a) $r = 7$,
(b) $r = 14$.

Solution

(a) When $r = 7$, (b) When $r = 14$,
3r = 3 × 7 3r = 3 × 14
= 21 = 42

8. Evaluate the value of $\frac{s}{9}$ when
(a) $s = 18$,
(b) $s = 45$.

Solution

(a) When $s = 18$, (b) When $s = 45$,
$\frac{s}{9} = \frac{18}{9}$ $\frac{s}{9} = \frac{45}{9}$
= 2 = 5

9. The temperature of water in a sauce pan is
$(13 + 5t)\,°C$, after being heated on the stove for
t minutes.
(a) Find the temperature when $t = 11$.
(b) What is the initial temperature of the water?

Solution

(a) When $t = 11$,
$13 + 5t = 13 + 5 \times 11$
= 68
After heating for 11 minutes, the temperature
of the water is 68 °C.

(b) When $t = 0$,
$13 + 5t = 13 + 5 \times 0$
= 13
'$t = 0$' means heating for zero minutes, that is,
before heating starts.

Hence, the initial temperature of the water
(before heating) is 13 °C.

10. The amount of money left on a travel card after x
journeys is £$(73 - 5x)$.
(a) Find the amount left after 12 journeys.
(b) Can you use the expression to work out the
amount left after 15 journeys? Explain your
answer.

Solution

(a) The amount of money left after x journeys
= £$(73 - 5x)$
When $x = 12$,
the amount of money left after 12 journeys
= £$(73 - 5 \times 12)$
= £13

(b) When $x = 15$,
$5x = 5 \times 15$
= 75
$73 < 75$
You cannot subtract 75 from 73.
Hence, you cannot use the expression to work
out the amount left after 15 days.

Integrated Examples and Review Exercise 1

Try It!

1. (a) Calculate the product of 23 and 22.
   (b) Work out the answer when 4920 is divided by 8.
   (c) Is the missing number ☐ in
   $4920 \div 8 -$ ☐ $= 23 \times 22$
   a prime number?

Solution

(a) Using the column method,
$23 \times 22 = 506$

```
   23
 × 22
 ────
   46
  460
 ────
  506
    1
```

Alternatively, using the grid method,

×	20	3
20	400	60
2	40	6

$23 \times 22 = 400 + 60 + 40 + 6$
$\qquad\qquad = 506$

(b) $4920 \div 8 = 615$

```
      615
   8)4920
     48
     ──
     12
      8
     ──
     40
     40
     ──
      0
```

(c) $4920 \div 80 -$ ☐ $= 23 \times 22$
   $615 -$ ☐ $= 506$
   ☐ $= 615 - 506$
   ☐ $= 109$

109 has no other factors besides 1 and 109. Hence, the missing number 109 is a prime number.

2. (a) Consider the expression: $228 + 12 \times 31$.
   (i) Estimate the value of the expression by rounding each number to the nearest 10.
   (ii) Use efficient calculation methods to work out the value of the expression.
   (b) Using the result in (a)(ii), calculate $(228 + 12 \times 31) \div 12 \times 3^2$.
   (c) Is the result in (b) a multiple of 7? Explain your answer.

Solution

(a) (i) Rounding each number to the nearest 10,
   $228 + 12 \times 31$
   $\approx 230 + 10 \times 30$
   $= 230 + 300$
   $= 530$
   (ii) 12×31
   $= 12 \times (30 + 1)$
   $= 12 \times 30 + 12 \times 1$
   $= 360 + 12$
   $= 372$
   $228 + 12 \times 31$
   $= 228 + 372$
   $= 228 + 72 + 300$
   $= 300 + 300$
   $= 600$

(b) $(228 + 12 \times 31) \div 12 \times 3^2$
   $= 600 \div 12 \times 3^2$
   $= 600 \div 12 \times 9$
   $= 50 \times 9$
   $= 450$

(c)
```
      64 r 2
   7)450
     42
     ──
     30
     28
     ──
      2
```

$450 \div 7 = 64 \text{ r } 2$
Since the remainder is non-zero, 450 is not divisible by 7.

3. The score for completing a computer game, without hitting any obstacles, is 43 285.
   (a) What is the place value of the digit 2?
   (b) Round the score to the nearest 10 000. Use a number line to explain your reasoning.

(c) Sam loses x points for each obstacle she hits. In the next game, she completes it but hit 2 obstacles.
  (i) Express her score in the next game in terms of x.
  (ii) Find her score in the next game if $x = 300$.

Solution
(a) In the number 43 285, the place value of the digit 2 is hundreds.

(b) Score = 43 285
  = 40 000 (to nearest 10 000)

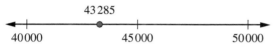

43 285

40 000   45 000   50 000

(c) **(i)** Score in the next game
  = 43 285 − 2x
  (ii) If $x = 300$,
  the score in the next game
  = 43 285 − (2 × 300)
  = 43 285 − 600
  = 42 685

$$\begin{array}{r} 43\,285 \\ -\quad 600 \\ \hline 42\,685 \end{array}$$

Review Exercise 1

1. The price of a car is £23 085.
  (a) Write the price in expanded form.
  (b) What is the value of the digit 3 in £23 085?
  (c) Round the price to the nearest £100. Use a number line to explain your reasoning.

Solution
(a) £23 085
  = £(2 × 10 000 + 3 × 1000 + 8 × 10 + 5 × 1)

(b) In 23 085, the value of the digit 3 is 3000.

(c) Price = £23 085
  = £23 100 (to nearest £100)

2. **(a)** Work out these values.

  (i) 5417 + 2638
  (ii) 9458 − 1247 + 619
  (b) Which answer in **(a)** is smaller?

Solution
(a) **(i)** 5417 + 2638
  = 8055
  (ii) 9458 − 1247 + 619
  = 8211 + 619
  = 8830

(b) 8055 < 8830
  8055 is smaller.

3. Find the missing number in each statement.
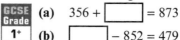
  (a) 356 + ☐ = 873
  (b) ☐ − 852 = 479

Solution
(a) 356 + ☐ = 873
  ☐ = 873 − 356
  = 517
(b) ☐ − 852 = 479
  ☐ = 479 + 852
  = 1331

4. **(a)** **(i)** Use place value counters to work out 25 × 6.
  (ii) Use the grid method to work out 25 × 30.
  (iii) Use your answers to parts **(i)** and **(ii)** to work out 25 × 36.
  (b) Work out 64 × 23.

Solution
(a) **(i)**

	Tens	Ones
	2	5
6	⑩⑩ ⑩⑩ ⑩⑩ ⑩⑩ ⑩⑩ ⑩⑩ ⑩⑩	①①①①① ①①①①① ①①①①① ①①①①① ①①①①① ①①①①①
25 × 6	120	30

25 × 6
= 120 + 30
= 150

(ii)

×	20	5
30	600	150

25 × 30
= 600 + 150
= 750

(iii) 25 × 36 = 25 × (30 + 6)
  = (25 × 30) + (25 × 6)
  = 750 + 150
  = 900

(b)
$$\begin{array}{r} 64 \\ \times\,23 \\ \hline 192 \\ 1280 \\ \hline 1472 \\ \hline \end{array}$$
1

5. A lottery chooses 15 winners to share a prize pot of £7170 between them.

(a) How much money will each winner receive?

(b) How does your answer to part **(a)** change if the prizes are paid in cash, in £10 notes?

Solution

(a) $\frac{7170}{15} = 478$

$$\begin{array}{r} 478 \\ 15\overline{)7170} \\ 60 \\ \hline 117 \\ 105 \\ \hline 120 \\ 120 \\ \hline 0 \end{array}$$

Each winner will receive £478.

(b) $478 = 480$ (to the nearest 10)
The prize amount increases by £2.

6. Find the missing number in each statement.

(a) $\times 11 = 9097$

(b) $952 \div \boxed{} = 17$

Solution

(a) $\boxed{} \times 11 = 9097$

$\boxed{} = 9097 \div 11$

$= 827$

$$\begin{array}{r} 827 \\ 11\overline{)9097} \\ 88 \\ \hline 29 \\ 22 \\ \hline 77 \\ 77 \\ \hline 0 \end{array}$$

(b) $952 \div \boxed{} = 17$

$\boxed{} = 952 \div 17$

$= 56$

$$\begin{array}{r} 56 \\ 17\overline{)952} \\ 85 \\ \hline 102 \\ 102 \\ \hline 0 \end{array}$$

7. (a) Write down the first ten non-zero whole number multiples of 6.

(b) Write down the first ten non-zero whole number multiples of 9.

(c) What is the lowest common whole number multiple of 6 and 9?

(d) Work out the lowest common whole number multiple of 6 and 10.

Solution

(a) The first ten whole number multiples of 6 are 6, 12, 18, 24, 30, 36, 42, 48, 54, 60.

(b) The first ten whole number multiples of 9 are 9, 18, 27, 36, 45, 54, 63, 72, 81, 90.

(c) From **(a)** and **(b)**, the common whole number multiples of 6 and 9 are 18, 36 and 54. The lowest common whole number multiple of 6 and 9 is 18.

(d) The lowest common whole number multiple of 6 and 10 will be the first number in part **(a)** that is divisible by 10. The lowest common whole number multiple of 6 and 10 is 30.

8. Calculate these expressions efficiently by hand, showing each step of your reasoning.

(a) $847 - 169 - 347$

(b) $38 + 47 + 52 + 63$

(c) 65×99

Solution

(a) $847 - 169 - 347$
$= 847 - 347 - 169$
$= 500 - 169$
$= 331$

(b) $38 + 47 + 52 + 63$
$= 38 + 52 + 47 + 63$
$= 90 + 110$
$= 200$

(c) 65×99
$= 65 \times (100 - 1)$
$= 65 \times 100 - 65 \times 1$
$= 6500 - 65$
$= 6500 - 60 - 5$
$= 6440 - 5$
$= 6435$

9. Work out the value of these expressions efficiently by hand.

(a) $56 \times 4 - 76 \div 4$

(b) $(73 + 17) \times 11 - 5^2 \times 4$

(c) $138 - (456 - 69) \div 9$

Solution

(a) $56 \times 4 - 76 \div 4$
$= 224 - 19$
$= 205$

(b) $(73 + 17) \times 11 - 5^2 \times 4$
$= 90 \times 11 - 5^2 \times 4$
$= 90 \times 11 - 25 \times 4$
$= 990 - 100$
$= 890$

(c) $138 - (456 - 69) \div 9$
$= 138 - 387 \div 9$
$= 138 - 43$
$= 95$

10. A spider has eight legs. Find the number of legs that

   (a)   three spiders,
   (b)   nine spiders,
   (c) n spiders have.

Solution

   (a)   Number of legs three spiders have $= 8 \times 3$
$$= 24$$

   (b)   Number of legs nine spiders have $= 8 \times 9$
$$= 72$$

   (c)   Number of legs n spiders have $= 8 \times n$
$$= 8n$$

11. (a)   Find the value of $28 + a$ when $a = 13$.

   (b)   Find the value of $6b - 23$ when $b = 11$.
   (c)   Work out the value of $\frac{150}{c}$ when $c = 30$.
   (d)   Copy and fill in each blank with '<' or '>', assuming the values of a, b and c are the same as in parts **(a)** to **(c)**.
      (i) $28 + a \;\square\; 6b - 23$
      (ii) $6b - 23 \;\square\; \frac{150}{c}$

Solution

   (a)   When $a = 13$,
$$28 + a = 28 + 13$$
$$= 41$$

   (b)   When $b = 11$,
$$6b - 23 = 6 \times 11 - 23$$
$$= 66 - 23$$
$$= 43$$

   (c)   When $c = 30$,
$$\frac{150}{c} = \frac{150}{30}$$
$$= 5$$

   (d)   (i) $28 + a < 6b - 23$
      (ii) $6b - 23 > \frac{150}{c}$

12. (a)   Find the value of each of these square numbers. Explain your decision.

      (i) 4^2 (ii) 5^2 (iii) 6^2
   (b)   Which of these numbers are prime numbers?
      $4^2 + 1$, $5^2 + 1$, $6^2 + 1$
   (c)   Find the highest common whole number factor of 4^2 and 6^2.

Solution

   (a)   (i) $4^2 = 4 \times 4$
$$= 16$$
      (ii) $5^2 = 5 \times 5$
$$= 25$$
      (iii) $6^2 = 6 \times 6$
$$= 36$$

   (b) $4^2 + 1 = 16 + 1$
$$= 17$$
17 has no other whole number factors besides 1 and 17.
$5^2 + 1 = 25 + 1$
$$= 26$$
$26 = 2 \times 13$
26 has whole number factors, 2 and 13, as well as 1 and 26.
$6^2 + 1 = 36 + 1$
$$= 37$$
37 has no other whole number factors besides 1 and 37.
$\therefore$ 17 and 37 are prime numbers.
Hence, $4^2 + 1$ and $6^2 + 1$ are prime numbers.

   (c) $4^2 = 16$
$16 = 1 \times 16$
$$= 2 \times 8$$
$$= 4 \times 4$$
The factors of 4^2 are 1, 2, 4, 8 and 16.
$6^2 = 36$
$36 = 1 \times 36$
$$= 2 \times 18$$
$$= 3 \times 12$$
$$= 4 \times 9$$
$$= 6 \times 6$$
The factors of 6^2 are 1, 2, 3, 4, 6, 9, 12, 18 and 36.
The common factors of 4^2 and 6^2 are 1, 2 and 4.
Hence, the HCF of 4^2 and 6^2 is 4.

13. A bakery makes 1375 cookies. Cookies are packed in boxes. Each box contains eight cookies.

   (a)   How many boxes are packed?
   (b)   What is the number of cookies remaining after packing as many full boxes as possible?
   (c)   The cost of each box of cookies is £3. What is the total cost of all the boxes?

Solution

   (a)   First, find $1375 \div 8$.

```
      171
  8|1375
    8
   ──
    57
    56
    ──
     15
      8
     ──
      7
```

$1375 \div 8 = 171$ r 7
Hence, 171 boxes are packed.

   (b)   The remaining number of cookies $= 7$.

   (c)   Total price of all the boxes
$= 171 \times £3$
$= £513$

```
   171
 ×   3
 ─────
   513
    2
```

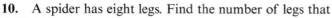

14. The price of a necklace is £x more than the price of a bracelet. The price of the bracelet is £128.

GCSE Grade 2+

(a) Express the price of the necklace in terms of x and represent the relationship using a bar model.

(b) If x = 70, find
   (i) the price of the necklace,
   (ii) the average price of the necklace and the bracelet.

Solution

(a)

£128

Bracelet

£x

Necklace

Price = ?

Price of the necklace
= £128 + £x
= £(128 + x)

(b) **(i)** If x = 70,
the price of the necklace
= £(128 + 70)
= £198
(ii) Average price of the necklace and the bracelet
= (£198 + £128) ÷ 2
= £326 ÷ 2
= £163

15. A dishwasher uses four times as much power as a food blender. The power of the food blender is y watts.

GCSE Grade 3−

(a) Express the power of the dishwasher in terms of y and represent the relationship using a bar model.

(b) If y = 325, find
   (i) the power of the dishwasher,
   (ii) the difference between the power of the dishwasher and the power of the food blender.

Solution

(a)
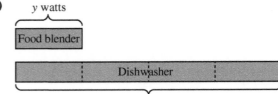
y watts

Food blender

Dishwasher

4y watts

Power of the dishwasher = 4 × y
= 4y watts

(b) **(i)** If y = 325,
the power of the dishwasher
= 4 × 325
= 1300 watts
(ii) Required difference = 1300 − 325
= 975 watts
The power of the food blender is y watts, that is, 325 watts.

16. A cinema gives members a discount of £4 on their own ticket for each non-member they bring to see a film. Tickets usually cost £15 each.

(a) Write an expression for the cost of a member's ticket in terms of n, where n is the number of non-members brought.

(b) Work out how much a ticket costs for a member who brings two non-members.

(c) The terms and conditions state that this deal only applies for up to 3 non-members. Explain why.

Solution

(a) Cost of ticket = £(15 − 4n)

(b) If the member brings 2 non-members, n = 2
Cost of a ticket = £(15 − 4 × 2)
= £7

(c) If the member were to bring 4 non-members, n = 4 and the cost of a ticket = £(15 − 4 × 2) = £(15 − 16) = −1. As the cost of ticket must be a positive number, it should only be possible to bring 3 non-members.

Understanding Fractions

Class Activity 1

Objective: To create representations of fractions.

Work with a partner. Take a number of identical solid shapes such as squares, rectangles or triangles, or different coloured linking cubes, and put them together to form a shape that is your 'whole' on top of a piece of paper. Draw around the outline of your whole. One of you may need to hold the shapes while the other draws around them.

1. How many parts make up your whole?

2. Do you have an odd or even number of parts?

3. Can you fill the outline with half of your solids?

Make another 'whole' from identical shapes on a different sheet of paper. This should have a different number of parts to the first one. You can use the same type of shape as before or try a new set of identical shapes. Take turns to fill the whole with a number of your shapes, each of you saying the fraction that the other has filled in.

4. What fractions did you make?

5. Why do you think all the parts of each 'whole' need to be identical?

6. Make two or more examples where the same fraction is represented with different arrangements of the shapes.

This Class Activity will have multiple solutions depending on the shapes used.

Class Activity 2

Objective: To describe parts of wholes using fractions.

1. What fraction of each shape is shaded?

(a)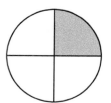

(b)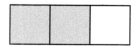

(c)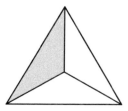

(a) $\frac{1}{4}$ (b) $\frac{2}{3}$ (c) $\frac{1}{3}$

(d)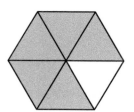

(e)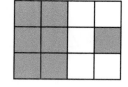

(d) $\frac{5}{6}$ (e) $\frac{7}{12}$

2.

(a) What fraction of this group of children are wearing jeans?

$\frac{5}{6}$

(b) What fraction of this group of children have blonde hair?

$\frac{4}{6}$

3. (a) Copy each diagram. Shade some parts to show the given fraction.

(i) $\frac{2}{7}$

(ii) $\frac{3}{4}$

(iii) $\frac{5}{6}$

(i)

(ii)

(iii)

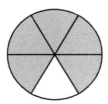

(b) Represent each fraction as a fraction of a group.
Hint: Draw the whole group and circle the section that represents the fraction of the whole group. Draw a different group each time.

Student's answers

4. Ali says all these shapes show $\frac{1}{3}$ shaded. Is he correct? Explain your answer.

(a)

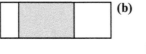

(b)

(c)

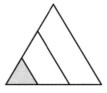

No, Ali is not correct that all these shapes show $\frac{1}{3}$ shaded. He is only correct for **(b)**. Only **(b)** is divided into equal parts to show the fraction.

The shapes in **(a)** and **(c)** are not divided into equal parts. So, what is shaded does not show the fraction $\frac{1}{3}$.

If Ali is incorrect about any of the shapes, redraw them to show $\frac{1}{3}$ shaded.

Each of the following shapes shows $\frac{1}{3}$ shaded.

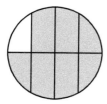

(a)

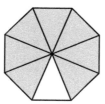

(c)

5. In which diagram is the shaded portion $\frac{7}{8}$ of the whole diagram? Explain your answer.

(a) 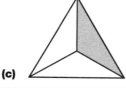 **(b)**

In diagram **(b)**, the shaded portion is $\frac{7}{8}$ of the whole diagram. This diagram is divided into 8 equal parts. The diagram in **(a)** is not divided

into equal parts.

6. If you considered your class to be a whole, write down some fractions of that whole. For example, what fraction of your class wear glasses?

Student's answer

Class Activity 3
Objective: To explore fractions in daily life.
1. What fraction of this 50p coin is shaded?

$\frac{6}{7}$ of the 50p coin is shaded.

2. Write down the fraction of shaded panes in this window frame.

Fraction of shaded panes $= \frac{2}{6}$

3. **(a)** The whole is all of these counters together. How many counters are shown?

8 counters

(b) Write down the fraction of purple counters.

Fraction of purple counters = $\dfrac{5}{8}$

(c) Write down the fraction of green counters.

Fraction of green counters = $\dfrac{3}{8}$

4. Use some counters or shapes to show $\dfrac{2}{5}$ and $\dfrac{6}{9}$.

In the diagram below, fraction of shaded rectangles = $\dfrac{2}{5}$.

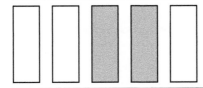

In the diagram below, fraction of shaded counters = $\dfrac{6}{9}$.

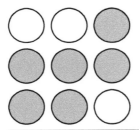

Class Activity 4

Objective: To write improper fractions and mixed numbers.

1. **(a)** Write down the improper fraction and the whole number represented by the shaded portion in each diagram. Part **(i)** has been done for you.

(i)

whole　　　whole　　　whole　　　whole

$$\dfrac{\boxed{12}}{\boxed{3}} = \boxed{4}$$

(answer given as sample) $\dfrac{12}{3} = 4$

(ii)

 　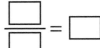
whole　　　　whole　　　　whole

$$\dfrac{\boxed{}}{\boxed{}} = \boxed{}$$

$\dfrac{15}{5} = 3$

(b) Write down the improper fraction and the whole number represented by the eggs. One whole box of eggs contains six eggs.

$$\frac{\square}{\square} = \square$$

whole   whole

$$\frac{12}{6} = 2$$

---

2. (a) Write down the improper fraction and the mixed number represented by the shaded portion in each diagram. Part **(i)** has been done for you.

(i)

whole   whole   whole

$$\frac{14}{4} = 3 \; \frac{2}{4}$$

(answer given as sample) $\dfrac{14}{4} = 3\dfrac{2}{4}$

(ii)

whole   whole

$$\frac{\square}{\square} = \square \; \frac{\square}{\square}$$

$$\frac{13}{5} = 2\frac{3}{5}$$

(b) Write down the improper fraction and the mixed number represented by the eggs. One whole box of eggs contains six eggs.

whole

$$\frac{\square}{\square} = \square \; \frac{\square}{\square}$$

$$\frac{11}{6} = 1\frac{5}{6}$$

---

3. Make up two improper fractions of your own and represent them in two or more different ways.

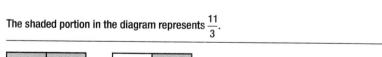

whole   whole   whole

The shaded portion in the diagram represents $\dfrac{11}{3}$.

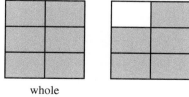

whole

The shaded portion in the diagram represents $\dfrac{11}{6}$.

---

4. Make up two mixed numbers of your own and represent them in two or more different ways.

whole

The shaded portion in the diagram represents $1\frac{3}{4}$.

whole

The diagram represents $1\frac{2}{5}$.

Class Activity 5

Objective: To identify equivalent fractions.

1. Fold a rectangular piece of paper into two halves. Shade half of the piece of paper.

   One equal part out of two equal parts,

   i.e. $\frac{1}{2}$, is shaded.

2. Fold the same paper in half again. Two equal parts out of four equal parts,

   i.e. $\dfrac{\boxed{2}}{\boxed{4}}$, are shaded.

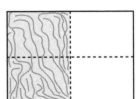

3. Fold the same paper in half again. **Four** equal parts out of eight equal parts,

   i.e. $\dfrac{\boxed{4}}{\boxed{8}}$, are shaded.

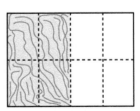

4. Fold the same paper in half again. Eight equal parts out of **sixteen** equal parts,

   i.e. $\dfrac{\boxed{8}}{\boxed{16}}$, are shaded.

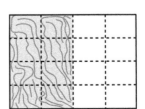

5. (a) Take a new piece of paper. Divide it into three equal parts and shade two of them. Write down how much is shaded as a fraction of the whole page.

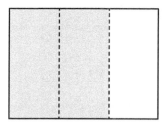

2 equal parts out of 3 equal parts are now shaded. This is $\frac{2}{3}$.

(b) Now fold the paper in half again and write down the fraction that is shaded now.

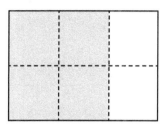

Four equal parts out of six equal parts are shaded. This is $\frac{4}{6}$.

(c) Now fold the paper in half again and write down the fraction that is shaded now.

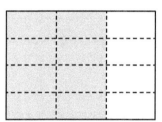

Eight equal parts out of twelve equals parts are shaded. This is $\frac{8}{12}$.

Class Activity 6

Objective: To compare fractions.

1. The diagram is a fraction wall. Each row is a bar model that divides a whole into equal parts.

$\frac{1}{2}$					$\frac{1}{2}$				
$\frac{1}{3}$			$\frac{1}{3}$			$\frac{1}{3}$			
$\frac{1}{4}$		$\frac{1}{4}$		$\frac{1}{4}$			$\frac{1}{4}$		
$\frac{1}{5}$		$\frac{1}{5}$		$\frac{1}{5}$		$\frac{1}{5}$		$\frac{1}{5}$	
$\frac{1}{6}$		$\frac{1}{6}$	$\frac{1}{6}$		$\frac{1}{6}$		$\frac{1}{6}$		$\frac{1}{6}$
$\frac{1}{7}$	$\frac{1}{7}$		$\frac{1}{7}$	$\frac{1}{7}$		$\frac{1}{7}$		$\frac{1}{7}$	$\frac{1}{7}$
$\frac{1}{8}$	$\frac{1}{8}$	$\frac{1}{8}$	$\frac{1}{8}$	$\frac{1}{8}$	$\frac{1}{8}$	$\frac{1}{8}$		$\frac{1}{8}$	
$\frac{1}{9}$	$\frac{1}{9}$	$\frac{1}{9}$	$\frac{1}{9}$	$\frac{1}{9}$	$\frac{1}{9}$	$\frac{1}{9}$	$\frac{1}{9}$	$\frac{1}{9}$	
$\frac{1}{10}$	$\frac{1}{10}$	$\frac{1}{10}$	$\frac{1}{10}$	$\frac{1}{10}$	$\frac{1}{10}$	$\frac{1}{10}$	$\frac{1}{10}$	$\frac{1}{10}$	$\frac{1}{10}$

0   1

(a) Use the fraction wall to arrange the fractions $\frac{1}{2},\frac{1}{3},\frac{1}{4},\frac{1}{5},\frac{1}{6},\frac{1}{7},\frac{1}{8},\frac{1}{9},\frac{1}{10}$ from the smallest to the greatest. Explain your answer.

The fractions arranged from the smallest to the greatest are

$$\frac{1}{10},\frac{1}{9},\frac{1}{8},\frac{1}{7},\frac{1}{6},\frac{1}{5},\frac{1}{4},\frac{1}{3},\frac{1}{2}.$$

(b) From the fraction wall, you can see $\frac{1}{2}=\frac{2}{4}$. That is, $\frac{1}{2}$ and $\frac{2}{4}$ are equivalent fractions. Use the wall to write down four other pairs of equivalent fractions.

Some possible pairs of equivalent fractions from the fraction wall:

$\frac{1}{2}$ and $\frac{2}{4}$, $\frac{1}{2}$ and $\frac{3}{6}$, $\frac{1}{2}$ and $\frac{4}{8}$, $\frac{1}{2}$ and $\frac{5}{10}$, $\frac{1}{3}$ and $\frac{2}{6}$, $\frac{1}{3}$ and $\frac{3}{9}$, $\frac{1}{4}=\frac{2}{8}$, $\frac{1}{5}=\frac{2}{10}$

$\frac{2}{3}=\frac{4}{6}$, $\frac{2}{3}=\frac{6}{9}$, $\frac{2}{4}=\frac{3}{6}$, $\frac{2}{4}=\frac{4}{8}$, $\frac{2}{4}=\frac{5}{10}$, $\frac{3}{4}=\frac{6}{8}$, $\frac{2}{5}=\frac{4}{10}$, $\frac{3}{5}=\frac{6}{10}$, $\frac{4}{5}=\frac{8}{10}$

2. Use the fraction wall to decide which fraction is greater in each pair. Explain your answer.

(a) $\frac{2}{3},\frac{2}{7}$

$\frac{2}{3}>\frac{2}{7}$ $\qquad$ $\frac{2}{3}$ is greater.

When a whole bar (one row in the fraction wall) is divided into equal parts, one out of 3 equal parts is greater than one out of 7 equal parts,

$\frac{1}{3}>\frac{1}{7}$.

Hence, 2 out of 3 equal parts is greater than 2 out of 7 equal parts, $\frac{2}{3}>\frac{2}{7}$.

(b) $\frac{4}{5},\frac{4}{9}$

$\frac{4}{5}>\frac{4}{9}$ $\qquad$ $\frac{4}{5}$ is greater.

Same reasoning as for **(a)**.

3. Which fraction is greater, $\frac{11}{5}$ or $\frac{27}{5}$? Explain your answer.

Both fractions have the same denominator, 5. For their numerators, 27 > 11.

Hence, $\frac{27}{5}>\frac{11}{5}$

$\frac{27}{5}$ is greater.

4. Choose values that make these true:

(a) $\frac{2}{5}<\frac{2}{\Box}$ $\qquad\qquad$ **(b)** $\frac{2}{5}<\frac{\Box}{5}$

Student's answer

5. Choose values that make these true:

(a) $\dfrac{4}{7} < \dfrac{4}{\square}$

(b) $\dfrac{3}{7} < \dfrac{\square}{7}$

Student's answer

_____

Try It!

Section 5.1

1. Draw this number line and mark the fraction $\dfrac{2}{3}$ on your number line.

Solution

The fraction $\dfrac{2}{3}$ is marked on the number line.

2. The photo shows a collection of balloons. What fraction of the balloons are blue?

Solution

Number of balloons in the whole collection = 11
Number of blue balloons = 2

Fraction of blue balloons = $\dfrac{2}{11}$

3. (a) Draw an arrangement of four green tiles, six purple tiles and three orange tiles.

(b) What fraction of the tiles are purple?

Solution

(a) The diagram below shows a possible arrangement of the tiles.

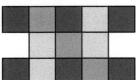

(b) Total number of tiles = 4 + 6 + 3
    = 13
    Number of purple tiles = 6

    Fraction of purple tiles = $\dfrac{6}{13}$

4. (a) Draw a rectangular bar and use it to show $\dfrac{5}{9}$.

(b) What fraction added to $\dfrac{5}{9}$ makes 1?

Solution

(a) The bar is 1 whole. It is divided into 9 equal parts of which 5 equal parts are shaded.

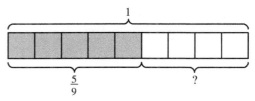

The shaded portion is $\dfrac{5}{9}$.

(b) The shaded portion and the unshaded portion make up the whole, 1.
Number of unshaded parts = 9 − 5
                        = 4
Therefore the unshaded portion is $\dfrac{4}{9}$ of the whole bar.

$\dfrac{5}{9} + \dfrac{4}{9} = \dfrac{9}{9}$

$= 1$

Hence, the fraction that when added to $\dfrac{5}{9}$ makes 1 is $\dfrac{4}{9}$.

5. (a) Draw a rectangular bar and use it to show $\dfrac{3}{8}$.

(b) Work out $1 - \dfrac{3}{8}$. Explain your answer.

Solution

(a) The bar is 1 whole. It is divided into 8 equal parts of which 3 are shaded.

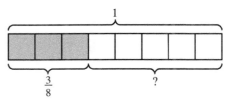

The shaded portion is $\dfrac{3}{8}$.

(b) $1 - \dfrac{3}{8}$ = the unshaded portion. You can see that there are 5 equal parts in the unshaded portion, so this is $\dfrac{5}{8}$ of the whole bar.

$= \dfrac{8}{8} - \dfrac{3}{8} = \dfrac{5}{8}$

6. The acid in a beaker is divided into 12 equal cups. Seven cups are used for experiments. What fraction of the original amount of acid is left? Use a bar model to explain your answer.

Solution

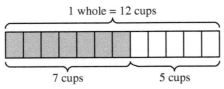

1 whole = 12 cups

7 cups   5 cups

Number of cups left = 12 − 7
$$= 5$$

Fraction of the acid left $= \dfrac{5}{12}$

7. **(a)** Express 49 minutes as a fraction of an hour.
(b) Express 5 hours as a fraction of a day.

Solution
(a) Fraction of 49 minutes in an hour

$= \dfrac{49 \text{ minutes}}{1 \text{ hour}}$

$= \dfrac{49 \text{ minutes}}{60 \text{ minutes}}$ There are 60 minutes in an hour.

$= \dfrac{49}{60}$

(b) Fraction of 5 hours in a day

$= \dfrac{5 \text{ hours}}{1 \text{ day}}$

$= \dfrac{5 \text{ hours}}{24 \text{ hours}}$ 1 day has 24 hours.

$= \dfrac{5}{24}$

Section 5.2

8. Express each improper fraction as a whole number or a mixed number. Use diagrams to show your reasoning.

(a) $\dfrac{8}{4}$ **(b)** $\dfrac{4}{3}$

Solution

(a) $\dfrac{8}{4}$ is 8 fourths.

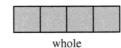

whole   whole

There are exactly 2 wholes.

∴ $\dfrac{8}{4} = 2$.

(b) $\dfrac{4}{3}$ is 4 thirds.

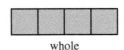

whole

$\dfrac{4}{3} = \dfrac{3}{3} + \dfrac{1}{3}$ (3 thirds + 1 third)

$= 1 + \dfrac{1}{3}$

$= 1\dfrac{1}{3}$

9. Convert each mixed number to an improper fraction, using diagrams to show your reasoning.

(a) $1\dfrac{5}{6}$ **(b)** $4\dfrac{7}{8}$

Solution

(a)

$1\dfrac{5}{6}$

1 whole = 6 sixths

$1\dfrac{5}{6}$ = 1 whole + 5 sixths

$= 6$ sixths + 5 sixths

$= 11$ sixths

$= \dfrac{11}{6}$

(b)

$4\dfrac{7}{8}$

1 whole = 8 eighths

$4\dfrac{7}{8}$ = 4 wholes + 7 eighths

$= 4 \times 8$ eighths + 7 eighths

$= 32$ eighths + 7 eighths

$= 39$ eighths

$= \dfrac{39}{8}$

10. Represent the numbers $\dfrac{14}{3}$ and $2\dfrac{1}{2}$ on a number line.

Solution

$\dfrac{14}{3} = \dfrac{3}{3} + \dfrac{3}{3} + \dfrac{3}{3} + \dfrac{3}{3} + \dfrac{2}{3}$

$= 1 + 1 + 1 + 1 + \dfrac{2}{3}$

$= 4 + \dfrac{2}{3}$

$= 4\dfrac{2}{3}$

Thus, $\dfrac{14}{3}$ lies between 4 and 5.

$2\dfrac{1}{2}$ lies between 2 and 3.

The number line below shows the given numbers.

11. A rod of length 5 m is divided into 3 pieces. How long is each piece?

Solution

Length of each piece

$$= 5 \div 3$$
$$= \frac{5}{3}$$
$$= \frac{3}{3} + \frac{2}{3}$$
$$= 1 + \frac{2}{3}$$
$$= 1\frac{2}{3}\,\text{m}$$

Section 5.3

12. Find five equivalent fractions for each of these fractions.

(a) $\frac{1}{4}$ **(b)** $\frac{2}{3}$

Solution

(a) $\frac{1\times2}{4\times2} = \frac{2}{8}$

$\frac{1\times3}{4\times3} = \frac{3}{12}$

$\frac{1\times4}{4\times4} = \frac{4}{16}$

$\frac{1\times5}{4\times5} = \frac{5}{20}$

$\frac{1\times6}{4\times6} = \frac{6}{24}$

Five equivalent fractions for $\frac{1}{4}$ are

$\frac{2}{8}, \frac{3}{12}, \frac{4}{16}, \frac{5}{20}$ and $\frac{6}{24}$.

(b) $\frac{2\times2}{3\times2} = \frac{4}{6}$

$\frac{2\times3}{3\times3} = \frac{6}{9}$

$\frac{2\times4}{3\times4} = \frac{8}{12}$

$\frac{2\times5}{3\times5} = \frac{10}{15}$

$\frac{2\times6}{3\times6} = \frac{12}{18}$

Five equivalent fractions for $\frac{2}{3}$ are

$\frac{4}{6}, \frac{6}{9}, \frac{8}{12}, \frac{10}{15}$ and $\frac{12}{18}$.

13. Find the missing parts to make the fractions in each pair equivalent.

(a) $\frac{2}{9} = \frac{\square}{36}$ **(b)** $\frac{4}{13} = \frac{20}{\square}$

(c) $\frac{\square}{5} = \frac{18}{45}$ **(d)** $\frac{6}{\square} = \frac{54}{99}$

Solution

(a) $\frac{2}{9} = \frac{2\times4}{9\times4}$ $36 \div 9 = 4$

$= \frac{8}{36}$

The missing part is 8.

(b) $\frac{4}{13} = \frac{4\times5}{13\times5}$ $20 \div 4 = 5$

$= \frac{20}{65}$

The missing part is 65.

(c) $\frac{18}{45} = \frac{18\div9}{45\div9}$ $45 \div 5 = 9$

$= \frac{2}{5}$

The missing part is 2.

(d) $\frac{54}{99} = \frac{54\div9}{99\div9}$ $54 \div 6 = 9$

$= \frac{6}{11}$

The missing part is 11.

14. Reduce these fractions to the lowest terms by completing the missing parts.

(a) $\frac{24}{48} = \frac{\square}{2}$ **(b)** $\frac{18}{72} = \frac{1}{\square}$

Solution

(a) $48 \div 2 = 24$

$\frac{24}{48} = \frac{24\div24}{48\div24}$

$= \frac{1}{2}$

The missing part is 1.

(b) $18 \div 18 = 1$

$\frac{18}{72} = \frac{18\div18}{72\div18}$

$= \frac{1}{4}$

The missing part is 4.

15. Reduce these fractions to the lowest terms.

(a) $\frac{24}{28}$ **(b)** $\frac{63}{72}$

Solution

(a) $\frac{24}{28} = \frac{24\div4}{28\div4}$

$= \frac{6}{7}$

(b) $\frac{63}{72} = \frac{63\div9}{72\div9}$

$= \frac{7}{8}$

16. Which of these pairs are equivalent fractions?

(a) $\frac{3}{4}, \frac{15}{20}$

(b) $\frac{4}{5}, \frac{28}{40}$

(c) $\frac{7}{15}, \frac{21}{45}$

Solution

(a) $\frac{3}{4}$ is already in its lowest terms.

$$\frac{15}{20} = \frac{15 \div 5}{20 \div 5}$$
$$= \frac{3}{4}$$

Both fractions reduce to $\frac{3}{4}$ in the lowest terms.

Hence, $\frac{3}{4}$ and $\frac{15}{20}$ are equivalent fractions.

(b) $\frac{4}{5}$ is already in its lowest terms.

$$\frac{28}{40} = \frac{28 \div 4}{40 \div 4}$$
$$= \frac{7}{10}$$

The fractions do not reduce to the same fraction in the lowest terms.

∴ $\frac{4}{5}$ and $\frac{28}{40}$ are not equivalent fractions.

(c) $\frac{7}{15}$ is already in its lowest terms.

$$\frac{21}{45} = \frac{21 \div 3}{45 \div 3}$$
$$= \frac{7}{15}$$

Both fractions reduce to $\frac{7}{15}$ in the lowest terms.

Hence, $\frac{7}{15}$ and $\frac{21}{45}$ are equivalent fractions.

Section 5.4

17. Which fraction is smaller, $\frac{8}{9}$ or $\frac{5}{9}$? Use a bar model to explain your answer.

Solution

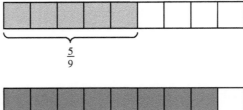

Both fractions have the same denominator, 9. Comparing their numerators, 5 < 8

Hence, $\frac{5}{9} < \frac{8}{9}$

$\frac{5}{9}$ is smaller.

18. Which fraction is greater, $\frac{2}{7}$ or $\frac{2}{13}$? Use a bar model to explain your answer.

Solution

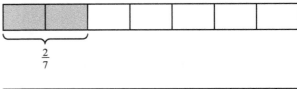

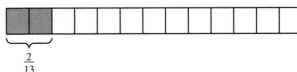

Both fractions have the same numerator, 2. Comparing their denominators,
7 < 13

∴ $\frac{2}{7} > \frac{2}{13}$

$\frac{2}{7}$ is greater.

19. Which number is smaller, $\frac{37}{6}$ or $4\frac{5}{6}$?

Solution

Convert $4\frac{5}{6}$ to an improper fraction.

$4\frac{5}{6}$ = 4 wholes + 5 sixths
$= 4 \times 6$ sixths + 5 sixths
$= 24$ sixths + 5 sixths
$= 29$ sixths
$= \frac{29}{6}$

The fractions, $\frac{37}{6}$ and $\frac{29}{6}$, have the same denominator, 6. For their numerators,
$29 < 37$

$\therefore \frac{29}{6} < \frac{37}{6}$

$\frac{29}{6} = 4\frac{5}{6}$ is smaller.

Alternatively, convert $\frac{37}{6}$ to a mixed number.

$\frac{37}{6} = 6\frac{1}{6}$

Comparing the two mixed numbers, $6\frac{1}{6}$ and $4\frac{5}{6}$, the whole number parts $4 < 6$.

Hence, $4\frac{5}{6} < 6\frac{1}{6}$

$\therefore 4\frac{5}{6}$ is smaller.

Section 5.5

20. Find $\frac{3}{4}$ of 24 kg. Justify your answer in two different ways.

Solution

Method 1

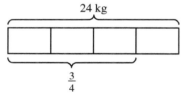

24 kg

$\frac{3}{4}$

From the bar model, $\frac{1}{4}$ of 24 kg $= 24 \div 4$
$= 6$ kg

$\frac{3}{4}$ of 24 kg $= 3 \times 6$
$= 18$ kg

Method 2

$\frac{3}{4}$ of 24 kg $= \frac{3}{\cancel{4}_1} \times \cancel{24}^6$
$= 3 \times 6$
$= 18$ kg

21. A novel has 200 pages. You have read $\frac{65}{100}$ of it. How many pages do you have left to read?

Solution

200 pages

read	not read

$\frac{65}{100}$

Method 1
Number of pages read
$= \frac{65}{100}$ of 200
$= \frac{65}{\cancel{100}_1} \times \cancel{200}^2$
$= 65 \times 2$
$= 130$

$\therefore$ number of pages that have not been read
$= 200 - 130$
$= 70$

Method 2
Fraction of pages not read
$= 1 - \frac{65}{100}$
$= \frac{100}{100} - \frac{65}{100}$
$= \frac{35}{100}$

Number of pages not read
$= \frac{35}{100}$ of 200
$= \frac{35}{\cancel{100}_1} \times \cancel{200}^2$
$= 35 \times 2$
$= 70$

22. Find the number of minutes in two-thirds of an hour.

Solution
Two-thirds of an hour $= \frac{2}{3}$ of an hour
$= \frac{2}{3}$ of 60 minutes
$= \frac{2}{\cancel{3}_1} \times \cancel{60}^{20}$ minutes
$= 2 \times 20$ minutes
$= 40$ minutes

Practice 5.1

Level 1 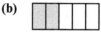 **GCSE Grade 2⁻**

1. What fraction of each whole is shaded?

(a)

(b)

(c)

Solution

(a) $\frac{1}{2}$

(b) $\frac{2}{5}$

(c) $\frac{7}{15}$

2. Copy each diagram. Shade some parts to show the given fraction.

(a) $\frac{1}{4}$

(b) $\frac{6}{12}$

Solution

(a)

(b)

3. If these blue circles represent a quarter, copy and add to the drawing to create the whole.

Solution

4. (a) Write down the fraction of red beads out of all the beads shown.

(b) Write down the fraction of cats out of all the animals shown.

Solution

(a) Total number of beads = 7
Number of red beads = 3
∴ fraction of red beads = $\frac{3}{7}$

(b) Total number of animals = 6

Number of cats = 2

Fraction of cats = $\frac{2}{6} = \frac{1}{3}$

5. In which diagram is the shaded portion $\frac{1}{5}$ of the whole diagram? Explain your answer.

(a)

(b)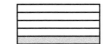

Solution

The shaded portion in diagram **(b)** is $\frac{1}{5}$ of the whole diagram. Diagram **(b)** is divided into 5 equal parts of which one is shaded. But diagram **(a)** is not divided into equal parts. So, what is shaded is not $\frac{1}{5}$ of the whole diagram.

6. (a) Copy the number line and mark $\frac{3}{6}$, $\frac{4}{6}$ and $\frac{5}{6}$ on it.

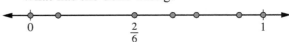

(b) Saira has shown $\frac{2}{6}$ on the number line below. What has she done wrong?

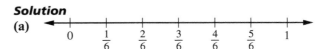

Solution

(a)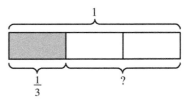

(b) The number line is not divided into equal intervals/parts. So, the total length of two parts on her number line does not represent $\frac{2}{6}$.

Level 2   GCSE Grade **2**

7. Find the fraction which makes 1 when added to the given fraction.

(a) $\frac{1}{3}$

(b) $\frac{2}{5}$

Solution

(a)

The bar is 1 whole. The shaded portion is $\frac{1}{3}$.
The shaded and unshaded portions make up the whole.

Number of unshaded parts = 3 − 1
= 2

∴ the unshaded portion = $\frac{2}{3}$

$\frac{1}{3} + \frac{2}{3} = \frac{3}{3}$ (whole)

Hence, the fraction that when added to $\frac{1}{3}$ makes 1 is $\frac{2}{3}$.

(b)

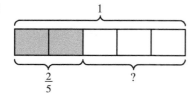

$$\frac{2}{5} \qquad ?$$

When a whole is made up of 5 equal parts,

then $\frac{2}{5} + \frac{3}{5} = \frac{5}{5}$

$= 1$

Hence, the fraction that when added to $\frac{2}{5}$

makes 1 is $\frac{3}{5}$.

8. (a) Express 43 seconds as a fraction of a minute.
(b) Express 19 minutes as a fraction of an hour.
(c) Express 11 hours as a fraction of a day.

Solution
(a) 43 seconds as a fraction of a minute $= \frac{43}{60}$

(b) 19 minutes as a fraction of an hour $= \frac{19}{60}$

(c) 11 hours as a fraction of a day $= \frac{11}{24}$

9. A fence has eight equal sections. Seven sections are painted. Express the number of unpainted sections as a fraction of the whole fence.

Solution
Number of unpainted sections $= 8 - 7$
$= 1$
Hence, the fraction of unpainted sections in the whole fence $= \frac{1}{8}$

10. (a) Draw two or more wholes and represent the fraction $\frac{9}{16}$ of each whole.

(b) Draw one of your wholes again and represent the fraction $\frac{3}{4}$ of the whole.

Solution
(a) To draw and shade a diagram to represent the fraction $\frac{9}{16}$, you can

　1. draw a rectangular bar or any shape like a rectangle or square,
　2. divide the shape into 16 equal parts,
　3. shade any 9 of the parts. The shaded portion is $\frac{9}{16}$.

　Alternatively, you can
　1. draw 16 similar shapes like counters, stars or triangles,

2. shade any 9 of the shapes.
The fraction of the shaded shapes is $\frac{9}{16}$.

Two possible diagrams are shown below. The shaded portion in each diagram represents $\frac{9}{16}$.

(i)

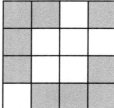

(ii)

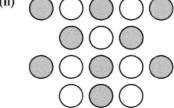

(b) Possible solution using the whole in **(i)**:

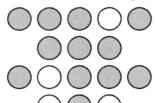

Possible solution using the whole in **(ii)**:

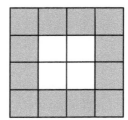

Practice 5.2

Level 1 　GCSE Grade **2 / 2⁺**

1. Sort these numbers into groups. Explain your choices.

$$\frac{7}{3}, \quad \frac{3}{4}, \quad \frac{4}{4}, \quad 3\frac{1}{5}, \quad \frac{2}{9}, \quad 5\frac{2}{9}, \quad \frac{9}{7}, \quad \frac{4}{6}$$

Solution
$\frac{3}{4}, \frac{2}{9}$ and $\frac{4}{6}$ are proper fractions.

$\frac{7}{3}, \frac{4}{4}$ and $\frac{9}{7}$ are improper fractions.

$3\frac{1}{5}$ and $5\frac{2}{9}$ are mixed numbers.

2. **(a)** Write down the improper fraction and the mixed number or whole number that is represented by the shaded parts in each diagram.

(i)

whole   whole

(ii)

whole   whole   whole

(b) Write down the improper fraction and the mixed number that is represented by the cookies in the diagram. One whole tray of cookies contains six cookies.

whole

Solution

(a) **(i)** $\dfrac{23}{8} = 2\dfrac{7}{8}$

(ii) $\dfrac{32}{9} = 3\dfrac{5}{9}$

(b) $\dfrac{10}{6} = 1\dfrac{4}{6}$

3. Write each improper fraction as a mixed number or a whole number.

(a) $\dfrac{13}{5}$ **(b)** $\dfrac{13}{8}$

(c) $\dfrac{16}{8}$ **(d)** $\dfrac{16}{7}$

Hint: Draw diagrams to explain your reasoning.

Solution

(a) $\dfrac{13}{5}$ is 13 fifths.

Draw shapes with 5 equal parts as a whole to show 13 fifths.

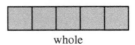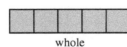

whole   whole

From the diagram,

$\dfrac{13}{5} = 2$ wholes + 3 fifths

$\quad = 2 + \dfrac{3}{5}$

$\quad = 2\dfrac{3}{5}$

Alternatively, it can be done using repeated addition.

$\dfrac{13}{5} = \dfrac{5}{5} + \dfrac{5}{5} + \dfrac{3}{5}$

$\quad = 1 + 1 + \dfrac{3}{5}$

$\quad = 2\dfrac{3}{5}$

(b) $\dfrac{13}{8}$ is 13 eighths.

$\dfrac{13}{8} = \dfrac{8}{8} + \dfrac{5}{8}$

$\quad = 1 + \dfrac{5}{8}$

$\quad = 1\dfrac{5}{8}$

(c) $\dfrac{16}{8}$ is 16 eighths.

$\dfrac{16}{8} = \dfrac{8}{8} + \dfrac{8}{8}$

$\quad = 1 + 1$

$\quad = 2$

(d) $\dfrac{16}{7}$ is 16 sevenths.

$\dfrac{16}{7} = \dfrac{7}{7} + \dfrac{7}{7} + \dfrac{2}{7}$

$\quad = 1 + 1 + \dfrac{2}{7}$

$\quad = 2\dfrac{2}{7}$

4. Convert each mixed number to an improper fraction.

(a) $1\dfrac{3}{7}$ **(b)** $2\dfrac{1}{5}$

(c) $3\dfrac{7}{8}$ **(d)** $4\dfrac{7}{10}$

Hint: Draw diagrams to explain your reasoning.

Solution

(a) *Method 1*

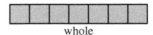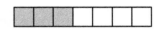

whole

The shaded portion in the diagram represents $1\dfrac{3}{7}$. There are altogether 10 sevenths.

$\therefore 1\dfrac{3}{7} = \dfrac{10}{7}$

Method 2

1 whole = 7 sevenths

$1\frac{3}{7}$ = 1 whole + 3 sevenths

= 7 sevenths + 3 sevenths

= 10 sevenths

$= \frac{10}{7}$

(b) $2\frac{1}{5}$

1 whole = 5 fifths

$2\frac{1}{5}$ = 2 wholes + 1 fifth

= 2 × 5 fifths + 1 fifth

= 10 fifths + 1 fifth

= 11 fifths

$= \frac{11}{5}$

(c) $3\frac{7}{8}$

1 whole = 8 eighths

= 3 wholes + 7 eighths

= 3 × 8 eighths + 7 eighths

= 24 eighths + 7 eighths

= 31 eighths

$= \frac{31}{8}$

(d) $4\frac{7}{10}$

1 whole = 10 tenths

$4\frac{7}{10}$ = 4 wholes + 7 tenths

= 4 × 10 tenths + 7 tenths

= 40 tenths + 7 tenths

= 47 tenths

$= \frac{47}{10}$

5. Find the missing values.

(a) $2 = \frac{\square}{5}$ **(b)** $3 = \frac{\square}{7}$ **(c)** $8 = \frac{\square}{1}$

Solution

(a) The denominator is 5, so 1 whole = 5 fifths

Hence, 2 wholes = 2 × 5 fifths

= 10 fifths

∴ $2 = \frac{10}{5}$

The missing part is 10.

(b) The denominator is 7 so 1 whole = 7 sevenths

3 wholes = 3 × 7 sevenths

= 21 sevenths

∴ $3 = \frac{21}{7}$

The missing part is 21.

(c) The denominator is 1, so 1 whole $= \frac{1}{1}$

8 wholes $= 8 \times \frac{1}{1}$

$= \frac{8}{1}$

The missing part is 8.

6. Represent each pair of numbers on a number line.

(a) $\frac{5}{4}, 3\frac{4}{5}$ **(b)** $\frac{15}{6}, 4\frac{2}{3}$

Solution

(a) $\frac{5}{4} = 1\frac{1}{4}$

Thus, $\frac{5}{4}$ lies between 1 and 2.

$3\frac{4}{5}$ lies between 3 and 4.

The number line below shows the given numbers.

(b) $\frac{15}{6} = \frac{6}{6} + \frac{6}{6} + \frac{3}{6}$

$= 1 + 1 + \frac{3}{6}$

$= 2\frac{3}{6}$

Thus, $\frac{15}{6}$ lies between 2 and 3.

$4\frac{2}{3}$ lies between 4 and 5.

The number line below shows the given numbers.

7. 17 pizzas are shared equally among six groups of students. What fraction of the pizzas does each group get?

Solution

Fraction of the pizzas each group gets

= 17 ÷ 6

$= \frac{17}{6}$

$= \frac{6}{6} + \frac{6}{6} + \frac{5}{6}$

$= 1 + 1 + \frac{5}{6}$

$= 2\frac{5}{6}$

8. Susie wants to give all the people at her birthday party a slice of cake. She has 29 people at the party. If she divides each cake into eight slices, how many whole cakes will she need?

Solution

As each slice of cake is cut into eight, Susie will need 29 eighths to have enough for her whole class.

$$\frac{29}{8} = \frac{8}{8} + \frac{8}{8} + \frac{8}{8} + \frac{5}{8}$$

$$= 1 + 1 + 1 + \frac{5}{8}$$

$$= 3\frac{5}{8}$$

Susie needs $3\frac{5}{8}$ cakes to have enough slices for all her guests.

Since $3\frac{5}{8} > 3$, 4 cakes should be bought.

9. Write two improper fractions between 3 and 4 with different denominators. Draw diagrams or use number lines to represent your fractions.

Solution

Think of two mixed numbers between 3 and 4 with different denominators. Convert the mixed numbers to improper fractions.

For example, $3\frac{1}{2}$ and $3\frac{3}{4}$.

$3\frac{1}{2} = \frac{7}{2}$ and $3\frac{3}{4} = \frac{15}{4}$.

The shaded portion in the above diagram represents $\frac{7}{2}$.

The shaded portion in the above diagram represents $\frac{15}{4}$.

Practice 5.3

Level 1   GCSE Grade 2⁻ / 2

1. Find an equivalent fraction for each of these fractions.

(a) $\frac{1}{5}$ (b) $\frac{1}{6}$ (c) $\frac{4}{10}$

Solution

(a) $\frac{1 \times 6}{5 \times 6} = \frac{6}{30}$

An equivalent fraction for $\frac{1}{5}$ is $\frac{6}{30}$.

(b) $\frac{1 \times 8}{6 \times 8} = \frac{8}{48}$

An equivalent fraction for $\frac{1}{6}$ is $\frac{8}{48}$.

(c) $\frac{4 \div 2}{10 \div 2} = \frac{2}{5}$

An equivalent fraction for $\frac{4}{10}$ is $\frac{2}{5}$.

Note: These are only example answers.

2. Find five equivalent fractions for each of these fractions.

(a) $\frac{2}{5}$ (b) $\frac{4}{7}$ (c) $\frac{12}{20}$

Solution

(a) $\frac{2 \times 2}{5 \times 2} = \frac{4}{10}$

$\frac{2 \times 3}{5 \times 3} = \frac{6}{15}$

$\frac{2 \times 4}{5 \times 4} = \frac{8}{20}$

$\frac{2 \times 5}{5 \times 5} = \frac{10}{25}$

$\frac{2 \times 6}{5 \times 6} = \frac{12}{30}$

Five equivalent fractions for $\frac{2}{5}$ are $\frac{4}{10}, \frac{6}{15}, \frac{8}{20}, \frac{10}{25}$ and $\frac{12}{30}$.

(b) $\frac{4 \times 2}{7 \times 2} = \frac{8}{14}$

$\frac{4 \times 3}{7 \times 3} = \frac{12}{21}$

$\frac{4 \times 4}{7 \times 4} = \frac{16}{28}$

$\frac{4 \times 5}{7 \times 5} = \frac{20}{35}$

$\frac{4 \times 6}{7 \times 6} = \frac{24}{42}$

Five equivalent fractions for $\frac{4}{7}$ are $\frac{8}{14}, \frac{12}{21}, \frac{16}{28}, \frac{20}{35}$ and $\frac{24}{42}$.

(c) $\frac{12 \div 2}{20 \div 2} = \frac{6}{10}$

$\frac{12 \div 4}{20 \div 4} = \frac{3}{5}$

$\frac{12 \times 2}{20 \times 2} = \frac{24}{40}$

$\frac{12 \times 3}{20 \times 3} = \frac{36}{60}$

$\frac{12 \times 4}{20 \times 4} = \frac{48}{80}$

Five equivalent fractions for $\frac{12}{20}$ are $\frac{6}{10}, \frac{3}{5}, \frac{4}{40}, \frac{36}{60}$ and $\frac{48}{80}$.

3. Reduce each fraction to its simplest form.

(a) $\dfrac{30}{100}$ 　　　　　(b) $\dfrac{5}{50}$

(c) $\dfrac{16}{64}$ 　　　　　(d) $\dfrac{33}{121}$

(e) $\dfrac{72}{96}$ 　　　　　(f) $\dfrac{48}{120}$

(g) $\dfrac{34}{102}$ 　　　　　(h) $\dfrac{104}{130}$

Solution

(a) $\dfrac{3}{100} = \dfrac{30 \div 10}{100 \div 10}$

$= \dfrac{3}{10}$

(b) $\dfrac{5}{50} = \dfrac{5 \div 5}{50 \div 5}$

$= \dfrac{1}{10}$

(c) $\dfrac{16}{64} = \dfrac{16 \div 8}{64 \div 8}$

$= \dfrac{2}{8}$

$= \dfrac{2 \div 2}{8 \div 2}$

$= \dfrac{1}{4}$

(d) $\dfrac{33}{121} = \dfrac{33 \div 11}{121 \div 11}$

$= \dfrac{3}{11}$

(e) $\dfrac{72}{96} = \dfrac{72 \div 12}{96 \div 12}$

$= \dfrac{6}{8}$

$= \dfrac{6 \div 2}{8 \div 2}$

$= \dfrac{3}{4}$

(f) $\dfrac{48}{120} = \dfrac{48 \div 12}{120 \div 12}$

$= \dfrac{4}{10}$

$= \dfrac{4 \div 2}{10 \div 2}$

$= \dfrac{2}{5}$

(g) $\dfrac{34}{102} = \dfrac{34 \div 2}{102 \div 2}$

$= \dfrac{17}{51}$

$= \dfrac{17 \div 17}{51 \div 17}$

$= \dfrac{1}{3}$

(h) $\dfrac{104}{130} = \dfrac{104 \div 2}{130 \div 2}$

$= \dfrac{52}{65}$

$= \dfrac{52 \div 13}{65 \div 13}$

$= \dfrac{4}{5}$

4. Which might be the odd one out of $\dfrac{8}{12}$, $\dfrac{18}{27}$ and $\dfrac{28}{35}$?

Solution

$\dfrac{8}{12} = \dfrac{8 \div 4}{12 \div 4}$

$= \dfrac{2}{3}$

$\dfrac{18}{27} = \dfrac{18 \div 9}{27 \div 9}$

$= \dfrac{2}{3}$

$\dfrac{28}{35} = \dfrac{28 \div 7}{35 \div 7}$

$= \dfrac{4}{5}$

Therefore $\dfrac{28}{35}$ is the odd one out because it is not an equivalent fraction to $\dfrac{2}{3}$.

Level 2　　　GCSE Grade **2 / 2⁺**

5. Find the missing values to make the fractions in each pair equivalent.

(a) $\dfrac{7}{10} = \dfrac{\square}{100}$ 　　　(b) $\dfrac{3}{4} = \dfrac{\square}{36}$

(c) $\dfrac{5}{12} = \dfrac{20}{\square}$ 　　　(d) $\dfrac{\square}{5} = \dfrac{36}{60}$

(e) $\dfrac{7}{9} = \dfrac{42}{\square}$ 　　　(f) $\dfrac{8}{\square} = \dfrac{64}{88}$

Solution

(a) $100 \div 10 = 10$

$\dfrac{7}{10} = \dfrac{7 \times 10}{10 \times 10}$

$= \dfrac{70}{100}$

The missing part is 70.

(b) $36 \div 4 = 9$

$\dfrac{3}{4} = \dfrac{3 \times 9}{4 \times 9}$

$= \dfrac{27}{36}$

The missing part is 27.

(c) $20 \div 5 = 4$

$$\frac{5}{12} = \frac{5 \times 4}{12 \times 4}$$
$$= \frac{20}{48}$$

The missing part is 48.

(d) $60 \div 5 = 12$

$$\frac{36}{60} = \frac{36 \div 12}{60 \div 12}$$
$$= \frac{3}{5}$$

The missing part is 3.

(e) $42 \div 7 = 6$

$$\frac{7}{9} = \frac{7 \times 6}{9 \times 6}$$
$$= \frac{42}{54}$$

The missing part is 54.

(f) $64 \div 8 = 8$

$$\frac{64}{88} = \frac{64 \div 8}{88 \div 8}$$
$$= \frac{8}{11}$$

The missing part is 11.

6. Which of these pairs are equivalent fractions?

(a) $\frac{2}{3}, \frac{14}{28}$ **(b)** $\frac{5}{6} = \frac{30}{36}$

(c) $\frac{7}{12}, \frac{77}{132}$ **(d)** $\frac{11}{44}, \frac{22}{84}$

(e) $\frac{7}{9}, \frac{63}{81}$ **(f)** $\frac{56}{84}, \frac{8}{12}$

Solution

(a) $\frac{2}{3}$ is already in its lowest terms.

$$\frac{14}{28} = \frac{14 \div 14}{28 \div 14}$$
$$= \frac{1}{2}$$

The two fractions do not reduce to the same fraction in the lowest terms.

$\therefore \frac{2}{3}$ and $\frac{14}{28}$ are not equivalent fractions.

(b) $\frac{5}{6}$ is already in its lowest terms.

$$\frac{30}{36} = \frac{30 \div 6}{36 \div 6}$$
$$= \frac{5}{6}$$

Both fractions reduce to $\frac{5}{6}$ in the lowest terms.

Hence, $\frac{5}{6}$ and $\frac{30}{36}$ are equivalent fractions.

(c) $\frac{7}{12}$ is already in its lowest terms.

$$\frac{77}{132} = \frac{77 \div 11}{132 \div 11}$$
$$= \frac{7}{12}$$

Both fractions reduce to $\frac{7}{12}$ in the lowest terms.

Hence, $\frac{7}{12}$ and $\frac{77}{132}$ are equivalent fractions.

(d) $\frac{11}{44} = \frac{11 \div 11}{44 \div 11}$

$$= \frac{1}{4}$$

$$\frac{22}{84} = \frac{22 \div 2}{84 \div 2}$$
$$= \frac{11}{42}$$

The fractions do not reduce to the same fraction in the lowest terms.

$\therefore \frac{11}{44}$ and $\frac{22}{84}$ are not equivalent fractions.

(e) $\frac{7}{9}$ is already in its lowest terms.

$$\frac{63}{81} = \frac{63 \div 9}{81 \div 9}$$
$$= \frac{7}{9}$$

Both fractions reduce to $\frac{7}{9}$ in the lowest terms.

Hence, $\frac{7}{9}$ and $\frac{63}{81}$ are equivalent fractions.

(f) $\frac{56}{84} = \frac{56 \div 7}{84 \div 7}$

$$= \frac{8}{12}$$
$$= \frac{8 \div 4}{12 \div 4}$$
$$= \frac{2}{3}$$

$$\frac{8}{12} = \frac{8 \div 4}{12 \div 4}$$
$$= \frac{2}{3}$$

Both fractions reduce to the same fraction $\frac{2}{3}$ in the lowest terms.

$\therefore \frac{56}{84}$ and $\frac{8}{12}$ are equivalent fractions.

7. Siti has $\frac{6}{8}$ kg of white rice and Jane has $\frac{9}{12}$ kg of brown rice. Do they have the same amount of rice? Explain your answer.

Solution

$$\frac{6}{8} = \frac{6 \div 2}{8 \div 2}$$

$$= \frac{3}{4}$$

$$\frac{9}{12} = \frac{9 \div 3}{12 \div 3}$$

$$= \frac{3}{4}$$

Both fractions reduce to the same fraction $\frac{3}{4}$ in the lowest terms.

Hence, $\frac{6}{8}$ and $\frac{9}{12}$ are equivalent fractions.

$$\frac{6}{8} = \frac{9}{12}$$

∴ Siti and Jane have the same amount of rice.

8. (a) $\frac{\square}{5}$ and $\frac{8}{20}$ are equivalent fractions. Find the missing value $\square$.

(b) $\frac{12}{\bigcirc}$ and $\frac{8}{20}$ are equivalent fractions. Find the missing value $\bigcirc$.

Solution

(a) $\frac{8}{20}$

$$= \frac{8 \div 4}{20 \div 4}$$

$$= \frac{2}{5}$$

The missing value is 2.

(b) $\frac{8}{20}$

$$= \frac{8 \times 12}{20 \times 12}$$

$$= \frac{96}{240}$$

$$= \frac{96 \div 8}{240 \div 8}$$

$$= \frac{12}{30}$$

The missing value is 30.

Practice 5.4

Level 1 GCSE Grade **2⁺**

1. Write down the fractions represented by the shaded portions of the shapes. Connect the two fractions using an inequality sign '<' or '>'.

(a)

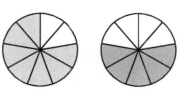

(b)

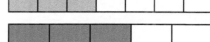

Solution

(a) The fraction that represents the shaded portion of the shape in

(i) $\frac{7}{9}$ (ii) $\frac{5}{9}$

$$\frac{7}{9} > \frac{5}{9}$$

(b) The fraction that represents the shaded portion of the shape in

(i) $\frac{3}{7}$ (ii) $\frac{3}{5}$

$$\frac{3}{7} < \frac{3}{5}$$

2. Copy and fill in the blank with an inequality sign '<' or '>'.

(a) $\frac{1}{5}$ ——— $\frac{1}{8}$ **(b)** $\frac{2}{3}$ ——— $\frac{2}{5}$

(c) $\frac{3}{7}$ ——— $\frac{3}{4}$ **(d)** $\frac{19}{100}$ ——— $\frac{19}{1000}$

Solution

(a) $\frac{1}{5} > \frac{1}{8}$ **(b)** $\frac{2}{3} > \frac{2}{5}$

(c) $\frac{3}{7} < \frac{3}{4}$ **(d)** $\frac{19}{100} > \frac{19}{1000}$

3. Which fraction in each pair is smaller? Use bar models to explain your answers.

(a) $\frac{3}{6}, \frac{5}{6}$ **(b)** $\frac{7}{10}, \frac{2}{10}$

(c) $\frac{2}{11}, \frac{5}{11}$ **(d)** $\frac{13}{15}, \frac{9}{15}$

Solution

(a) $\frac{3}{6}$

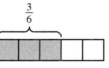

$\frac{5}{6}$

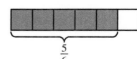

$$\frac{3}{6} < \frac{5}{6}$$

i.e. $\frac{3}{6}$ is smaller.

(b)

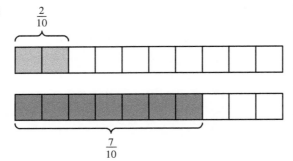

$$\frac{2}{10} < \frac{7}{10}$$

i.e. $\frac{2}{10}$ is smaller.

(c)

$$\frac{2}{11} < \frac{5}{11}$$

i.e. $\frac{2}{11}$ is smaller.

(d)

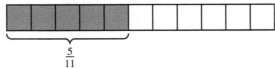

$$\frac{9}{15} < \frac{13}{15}$$

i.e. $\frac{9}{15}$ is smaller.

Level 2   GCSE Grade **3⁻**

4. Which number in each pair is greater? Use bar models to explain your answers.

(a) $1\frac{2}{9}, \frac{5}{9}$

(b) $\frac{16}{5}, 1\frac{4}{5}$

Solution

(a)

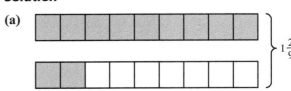

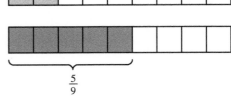

$1\frac{2}{9}$ is one whole and two ninths; it is greater than 1.

$\frac{5}{9}$ is five ninths which is smaller than 1.

$\therefore 1\frac{2}{9} > \frac{5}{9}$

$1\frac{2}{9}$ is greater.

Alternatively, convert $1\frac{2}{9}$ to an improper fraction to compare with $\frac{5}{9}$.

$1\frac{2}{9} = 1$ whole $+ \frac{2}{9}$

$\qquad = \frac{9}{9} + \frac{2}{9}$

$\qquad = \frac{11}{9}$

The fractions, $\frac{11}{9}$ and $\frac{5}{9}$, have the same denominator, 9. Comparing their numerators, $11 > 5$.

$\therefore \frac{11}{9} > \frac{5}{9}$

i.e. $1\frac{2}{9}$ is greater.

(b)

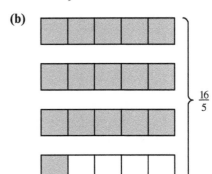

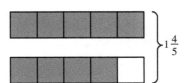

Convert $1\frac{4}{5}$ to an improper fraction.

$1\frac{4}{5} = 1 \text{ whole} + \frac{4}{5}$

$= \frac{5}{5} + \frac{4}{5}$

$= \frac{9}{5}$

The fractions, $\frac{16}{5}$ and $\frac{9}{5}$, have the same denominator, 5. For their numerators, 16 > 9.

$\therefore \frac{16}{5} > \frac{9}{5}$

$\frac{16}{5}$ is greater.

5. Arrange the fractions $\frac{5}{7}, \frac{5}{4}$ and $\frac{5}{9}$ from the smallest to the greatest.

Solution

The three fractions have the same numerator, 5.
For their denominators,
9 > 7 > 4.

$\therefore \frac{5}{9} < \frac{5}{7} < \frac{5}{4}$

The fractions arranged from the smallest to the greatest are $\frac{5}{9}, \frac{5}{7}$ and $\frac{5}{4}$.

6. Arrange the numbers $\frac{5}{7}, 1\frac{3}{7}$ and $\frac{3}{7}$ from the greatest to the smallest.

Solution

$1\frac{3}{7} = 1 \text{ whole} + \frac{3}{7}$

$= \frac{7}{7} + \frac{3}{7}$

$= \frac{10}{7}$

The fractions, $\frac{5}{7}, \frac{10}{7}$ and $\frac{3}{7}$, have the same

denominator, 7.
For their numerators, 10 > 5 > 3.

$\therefore \frac{10}{7} > \frac{5}{7} > \frac{3}{7}$

i.e. $1\frac{3}{7} > \frac{5}{7} > \frac{3}{7}$

Arranged from the greatest to the smallest, the numbers are
$1\frac{3}{7}, \frac{5}{7}$ and $\frac{3}{7}$.

7. Arrange the fractions $\frac{5}{7}, \frac{5}{8}$ and $\frac{13}{7}$ from the smallest to the greatest.

Solution

The fractions, $\frac{5}{7}$ and $\frac{5}{8}$, have the same numerator, 5.

For their denominators, 8 > 7.

$\therefore \frac{5}{8} < \frac{5}{7}$ (1)

The fractions, $\frac{5}{7}$ and $\frac{13}{7}$, have the same

denominator, 7. For their numerators, 5 < 13.

$\therefore \frac{5}{7} < \frac{13}{7}$ (2)

From (1) and (2)

$\therefore \frac{5}{8} < \frac{5}{7} < \frac{13}{7}$

Arranged from the smallest to the greatest, the fractions are $\frac{5}{8}, \frac{5}{7}$ and $\frac{13}{7}$.

8. A pole is $2\frac{3}{8}$ m long. A mast is $\frac{21}{8}$ m long. Which one is longer? Explain your answer.

Solution

Convert $2\frac{3}{8}$ to an improper fraction.

$2\frac{3}{8} = 2 \text{ wholes} + \frac{3}{8}$

$= \frac{8}{8} + \frac{8}{8} + \frac{3}{8}$

$= \frac{19}{8}$

The fractions, $\frac{19}{8}$ and $\frac{21}{8}$, have the same

denominator, 8. For their numerators, 21 > 19.

$\frac{21}{8} > \frac{19}{8}$

$\therefore \frac{21}{8}$ m is longer than $\frac{19}{8}$ m $\left(2\frac{3}{8}\text{m}\right)$.

The mast is longer than the pole.

9. Write a fraction that lies between $\frac{3}{4}$ and $\frac{13}{4}$. Explain your answer.

Solution

There are many possible fractions that lie between $\frac{3}{4}$ and $\frac{13}{4}$.

Case 1: Consider those fractions that have the same

denominator, 4, as $\frac{3}{4}$ and $\frac{13}{4}$, and lie between $\frac{3}{4}$ and

$\frac{13}{4}$. Two examples are $\frac{5}{4}$ and $\frac{11}{4}$.

Case 2: Consider the fractions that lie between the

equivalent fractions of $\frac{3}{4}$ and $\frac{13}{4}$.

$\frac{3 \times 2}{4 \times 2} = \frac{6}{8}, \frac{13 \times 2}{4 \times 2} = \frac{26}{8}$

$\frac{6}{8} = \frac{3}{4}, \frac{26}{8} = \frac{13}{4}$

Hence, consider fractions with denominator, 8, that

lie between $\frac{6}{8}$ and $\frac{26}{8}$.

Some examples are $\frac{7}{8}$, $\frac{10}{8}$ and $\frac{25}{8}$.

Similarly, you can consider other equivalent fractions of $\frac{3}{4}$ and $\frac{13}{4}$.

Practice 5.5

Level 1   GCSE Grade 2^+

1. There are 9 fish in a pond. Find

    (a) $\frac{1}{3}$ of the 9 fish,

    (b) $\frac{2}{3}$ of the 9 fish.

    Solution

    Method 1

    (a) $\frac{1}{3}$ of the 9 fish

    $= 9 \div 3$
    $= 3$ fish

    (b) $\frac{2}{3}$ of the 9 fish

    $= 2 \times 3$
    $= 6$ fish

    Method 2

    (a) $\frac{1}{3}$ of the 9 fish

    $= \frac{1}{\cancel{3}_1} \times \cancel{9}^3$

    $= 1 \times 3$
    $= 3$ fish

    (b) $\frac{2}{3}$ of the 9 fish

    $= \frac{2}{\cancel{3}_1} \times \cancel{9}^3$

    $= 2 \times 3$
    $= 6$ fish

2. There are 15 beads on a table. Find

    (a) $\frac{1}{5}$ of the 15 beads,

    (b) $\frac{4}{5}$ of the 15 beads.

    Solution

    (a) $\frac{1}{5}$ of the 15 beads

    $= 15 \div 5$
    $= 3$ beads

    (b) $\frac{4}{5}$ of the 15 beads

    $= 4 \times 3$
    $= 12$ beads

3. Calculate these values.

    (a) $\frac{2}{7}$ of $28\,\text{kg}$ (b) $\frac{4}{9}$ of £108

    (c) $\frac{3}{10}$ of $480\,\text{ml}$ (d) $\frac{80}{100}$ of $400\,\text{m}$

    Solution

    (a) $\frac{2}{7}$ of $28\,\text{kg}$

    $= \frac{2}{\cancel{7}_1} \times \cancel{28}^4$

    $= 2 \times 4$
    $= 8\,\text{kg}$

    (b) $\frac{4}{9}$ of £108

    $= \frac{4}{9} \times 108$

    $= 4 \times 12$
    $= £48$

    (c) $\frac{3}{10}$ of $480\,\text{ml}$

    $= \frac{3}{10} \times 480$

    $= 3 \times 48$
    $= 144\,\text{ml}$

    (d) $\frac{88}{100}$ of $400\,\text{m}$

    $= \frac{80}{100} \times 400$

    $= 80 \times 4$
    $= 320\,\text{m}$

Level 2   GCSE Grade 3^-

4. The price of an adult ticket for a show is £18. The price of a child ticket is $\frac{1}{2}$ of the price of an adult ticket. Find the price of a child ticket.

    Solution

    Price of a child ticket

    $= \frac{1}{2}$ of £18

    $= \frac{1}{2} \times 18$

    $= £9$

5. There are 40 marks available in a test. David gets $\frac{5}{8}$ of the full marks. How many marks does David get?

    Solution

    David's marks

    $= \frac{5}{8}$ of 40

    $= \frac{5}{8} \times 40$

    $= 5 \times 5$
    $= 25$

6. (a) Find the number of minutes in three-quarters of an hour.

(b) Find the number of hours in $\frac{1}{6}$ of a day.

Solution

(a) Three-quarters of an hour

$= \frac{3}{4}$ of an hour

$= \frac{3}{4}$ of 60 minutes

$= \frac{3}{4} \times 60$ minutes

$= 3 \times 15$

$= 45$ minutes

(b) 1 day = 24 hours

$\frac{1}{6}$ of a day

$= \frac{1}{6}$ of 24 hours

$= \frac{1}{6} \times 24$ hours

$= 4$ hours

7. There are 50 households in a small town. $\frac{3}{10}$ of the households have pets.

(a) How many households have pets?

(b) How many households do not have pets?

Solution

(a) Number of households that have pets

$= \frac{3}{10}$ of 50

$= \frac{3}{10} \times 50$

$= 3 \times 5$

$= 15$

(b) Number of households that do not have pets

$= 50 - 15$

$= 35$

8. A pack has 36 jelly beans and $\frac{2}{9}$ of the jelly beans are red. Find the number of jelly beans that are not red.

Solution

Fraction of the jelly beans that are not red

$= 1 - \frac{2}{9}$

$= \frac{9}{9} - \frac{2}{9}$

$= \frac{7}{9}$

∴ number of jelly beans that are not red

$= \frac{7}{9}$ of 36

$= \frac{7}{9} \times 36$

$= 7 \times 4$

$= 28$

9. A box has 54 apples. You can take $\frac{5}{9}$ or $\frac{11}{18}$ of the total number of apples. Which fraction would you choose to get more apples? Explain your answer.

Solution

Determine which fraction, $\frac{5}{9}$ or $\frac{11}{18}$, is greater.

$\frac{5 \times 2}{9 \times 2} = \frac{10}{18}$

$\frac{5}{9}$ and $\frac{10}{18}$ are equivalent fractions, i.e. $\frac{10}{18} = \frac{5}{9}$

The fractions, $\frac{10}{18}$ and $\frac{11}{18}$, have the same denominator, 18. For their numerators, 11 > 10.

∴ $\frac{11}{18} > \frac{10}{18}$

i.e. $\frac{11}{18} > \frac{5}{9}$

Choosing a greater fraction of the total number of apples will get a greater number of apples.

I would choose the fraction $\frac{11}{18}$ so as to get more apples.

Alternatively, you can find the number of apples with each fraction.

$\frac{5}{9}$ of the total number of apples

$= \frac{5}{9} \times 54$

$= 5 \times 6$

$= 30$ apples

$\frac{11}{18}$ of the total number of apples

$= \frac{11}{18} \times 54$

$= 11 \times 3$

$= 33$ apples

33 apples > 30 apples

Hence, choose the fraction $\frac{11}{18}$ to get more apples.

Challenge 5

 Mr Miller has a monthly income of £3600. He spends $\frac{1}{4}$ of it on a home loan and $\frac{3}{24}$ of it on food. What fraction of the income is remaining?

Solution

$\frac{1}{4} = \frac{1 \times 6}{4 \times 6}$

$= \frac{6}{24}$

i.e. Mr Miller spends $\frac{6}{24}$ of his income on the home loan and $\frac{3}{24}$ of it on food.

The bar model below represents the situation.

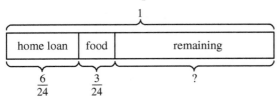

The whole bar is divided into 24 equal parts of which 6 equal parts represent the amount spent on the home loan, 3 equal parts represents the amount spent on food and the rest of the equal parts shows the fraction remaining.

Fraction of the income spent $= \dfrac{6}{24} + \dfrac{3}{24}$

$\qquad\qquad\qquad\qquad = \dfrac{9}{24}.$

$\therefore$ fraction of the income remaining
$=$ 1 − fraction of the income spent

$= 1 - \dfrac{9}{24}$

$= \dfrac{24}{24} - \dfrac{9}{24}$

$= \dfrac{15}{24}$

Revision Exercise 5

1. What fraction is the shaded portion in each diagram?

(a)

(b)

(c)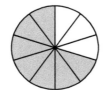

(d)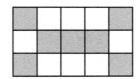

Solution

(a) $\dfrac{3}{4}$ (b) $\dfrac{1}{6}$

(c) $\dfrac{7}{10}$ (d) $\dfrac{7}{15}$

2. What fraction of the eggs are white?

Chapter 5 Understanding Fractions

Solution

$\dfrac{3}{9}$

3. Write the shaded portion as an improper fraction and a mixed number.

whole   whole

Solution

$\dfrac{5}{2} = 2\dfrac{1}{2}$

4. Four cans in a box form a whole. Write the portion of 13 cans as a mixed number and as an improper fraction.

whole   whole   whole

Solution

$\dfrac{13}{4} = 3\dfrac{1}{4}$

5. Write each improper fraction as a mixed number or a whole number.

(a) $\dfrac{11}{3}$ (b) $\dfrac{15}{4}$

(c) $\dfrac{15}{5}$ (d) $\dfrac{30}{7}$

Solution

(a) Using repeated addition

$\dfrac{11}{3} = \dfrac{3}{3} + \dfrac{3}{3} + \dfrac{3}{3} + \dfrac{2}{3}$

$\qquad = 1 + 1 + 1 + \dfrac{2}{3}$

$\qquad = 3\dfrac{2}{3}$

(b) $\dfrac{15}{4} = \dfrac{4}{4} + \dfrac{4}{4} + \dfrac{4}{4} + \dfrac{3}{4}$

$\qquad = 1 + 1 + 1 + \dfrac{3}{4}$

$\qquad = 3\dfrac{3}{4}$

(c) $\dfrac{15}{5} = \dfrac{5}{5} + \dfrac{5}{5} + \dfrac{5}{5}$

$\qquad = 1 + 1 + 1$

$\qquad = 3$

(d) $\dfrac{30}{7} = \dfrac{7}{7} + \dfrac{7}{7} + \dfrac{7}{7} + \dfrac{7}{7} + \dfrac{2}{7}$

$\qquad = 1 + 1 + 1 + 1 + \dfrac{2}{7}$

$\qquad = 4\dfrac{2}{7}$

6. Convert each mixed number to an improper

fraction.

(a) $1\frac{2}{3}$ (b) $2\frac{3}{5}$

(c) $3\frac{5}{6}$ (d) $4\frac{1}{8}$

Solution

(a) 1 whole = 3 thirds

$1\frac{2}{3} = 1$ whole $+ \frac{2}{3}$

$= \frac{3}{3} + \frac{2}{3}$

$= \frac{5}{3}$

(b) $2\frac{3}{5}$

1 whole = 5 fifths

$2\frac{3}{5} = 2$ wholes $+ \frac{3}{5}$

$= \frac{5}{5} + \frac{5}{5} + \frac{3}{5}$

$= \frac{13}{5}$

(c) $3\frac{5}{6}$

1 whole = 6 sixths

$3\frac{5}{6} = 3$ wholes $+ \frac{5}{6}$

$= \frac{6}{6} + \frac{6}{6} + \frac{6}{6} + \frac{5}{6}$

$= \frac{23}{6}$

(d) $4\frac{1}{8}$

1 whole = 8 eighths

$4\frac{1}{8} = 4$ wholes $+ \frac{1}{8}$

$= 4 \times 8$ eighths $+ \frac{1}{8}$

$= 32$ eighths $+ \frac{1}{8}$

$= \frac{33}{8}$

7. Find the missing numbers if the given fractions are

equivalent.

(a) $\frac{2}{5}, \frac{\square}{20}$ (b) $\frac{10}{\square}, \frac{28}{42}$

Solution

(a) $20 \div 5 = 4$

$\frac{2}{5} = \frac{2 \times 4}{5 \times 4}$

$= \frac{8}{20}$

The missing number is 8.

(b) Reduce the fraction $\frac{28}{42}$ to its lowest terms.

$\frac{28}{42} = \frac{28 \div 7}{42 \div 7}$

$= \frac{4}{6}$

$= \frac{4 \div 2}{6 \div 2}$

$= \frac{2}{3}$

$10 \div 2 = 5$

$\frac{2}{3} = \frac{2 \times 5}{3 \times 5}$

$= \frac{10}{15}$

Since $\frac{28}{42} = \frac{2}{3}$,

$\therefore \frac{28}{42} = \frac{10}{15}$.

The missing number is 15.

8. Which one is smaller in each pair? Explain your

answer.

(a) $\frac{1}{10}, \frac{1}{20}$ (b) $\frac{19}{100}, \frac{59}{100}$

Solution

(a) The fractions, $\frac{1}{10}$ and $\frac{1}{20}$, have the same numerator, 1.

For their denominators, $20 > 10$.

$\therefore \quad \frac{1}{20} < \frac{1}{10}$

i.e. $\frac{1}{20}$ is smaller.

(b) The fractions, $\frac{19}{100}$ and $\frac{59}{100}$, have the same denominator, 100.

For their numerators, $19 < 59$.

$\therefore \quad \frac{19}{100} < \frac{59}{100}$

i.e. $\frac{19}{100}$ is smaller.

9. Reduce each fraction to its simplest form.

(a) $\frac{16}{20}$ (b) $\frac{8}{48}$ (c) $\frac{81}{90}$ (d) $\frac{14}{56}$

Solution

(a) $\frac{16}{20} = \frac{16 \div 4}{20 \div 4}$

$= \frac{4}{5}$

(b) $\frac{8}{48} = \frac{8 \div 8}{48 \div 8}$

$= \frac{1}{6}$

(c) $\frac{81}{90} = \frac{81 \div 9}{90 \div 9}$

$= \frac{9}{10}$

(d) $\dfrac{14}{56} = \dfrac{14 \div 7}{56 \div 7}$

$\qquad = \dfrac{2}{8}$

$\qquad = \dfrac{2 \div 2}{8 \div 2}$

$\qquad = \dfrac{1}{4}$

10. Find these quantities.

(a) $\dfrac{3}{8}$ of £32   **(b)** $\dfrac{5}{6}$ of 54 cm

(c) $\dfrac{4}{9}$ of 18 grams   **(d)** $\dfrac{7}{6}$ of 120 minutes

Solution

(a) $\dfrac{3}{8}$ of £32

$\qquad = \dfrac{3}{8} \times 32$

$\qquad = 3 \times 4$

$\qquad = £12$

(b) $\dfrac{5}{6}$ of 54 cm

$\qquad = \dfrac{5}{6} \times 54$

$\qquad = 5 \times 9$

$\qquad = 45\,\text{cm}$

(c) $\dfrac{4}{9}$ of 18 grams

$\qquad = \dfrac{4}{9} \times 18$

$\qquad = 4 \times 2$

$\qquad = 8\,\text{grams}$

(d) $\dfrac{7}{6}$ of 120 minutes

$\qquad = \dfrac{7}{6} \times 120$

$\qquad = 7 \times 20$

$\qquad = 140\,\text{minutes}$

11. There are 132 ml of a mixture. One-third of it is vinegar and the rest is water. Calculate

(a) the volume of vinegar,

(b) the volume of water in the mixture.

Solution

(a) Volume of vinegar

$\qquad = \dfrac{1}{3}$ of 132 ml

$\qquad = \dfrac{1}{3} \times 132$

$\qquad = 132 \div 3$

$\qquad = 44\,\text{ml}$

(b) Volume of water

$\qquad = 132 - 44$

$\qquad = 88\,\text{ml}$

12. Sophia takes $\dfrac{3}{4}$ of an hour to do an assignment. Dan takes $\dfrac{3}{5}$ of an hour to do the same task.

(a) Who is faster? Explain your answer.

(b) How many minutes does the faster person take?

Solution

(a) Amount of time Sophia takes

$\qquad = \dfrac{3}{4}$ of an hour

$\qquad = \dfrac{3}{4}$ of 60 minutes

$\qquad = \dfrac{3}{4} \times 60$ minutes

$\qquad = 45$ minutes

Amount of time Dan takes

$\qquad = \dfrac{3}{5}$ of an hour

$\qquad = \dfrac{3}{5} \times 60$ minutes

$\qquad = 36$ minutes

$36 < 45$

Since Dan takes less time than Sophia, Dan is faster.

Alternatively, you can determine which fraction, $\dfrac{3}{4}$ or $\dfrac{3}{5}$, is smaller to find out who takes a smaller fraction of an hour (i.e. less time).

(b) From **(a)**, the faster person, Dan, takes 36 minutes.

6 Tenths, Hundredths and Thousandths

Class Activity 1

Objective: To explore the rules for multiplying a decimal by 10, 100 and 1000.

The number $3.75 = 3 + \dfrac{7}{10} + \dfrac{5}{100}$.

1. Work out these products.
   (a) 3×10

   $3 \times 10 = 30$
   _____

   (b) 3×100

   $3 \times 100 = 300$
   _____

   (c) 3×1000

   $3 \times 1000 = 3000$
   _____

2. (a) Copy and complete this place value table.

Number	Hundreds	Tens	Ones	Tenths
$\dfrac{7}{10}$				7
$\dfrac{7}{10} \times 10$			7	0
$\dfrac{7}{10} \times 100$		7	0	0
$\dfrac{7}{10} \times 1000$	7	0	0	0

   (b) Copy and fill in the blanks.

   (i) $\dfrac{7}{10} \times 10 = 7$ tenths $\times 10$
   $\qquad = $ _____ tenths
   $\qquad = $ _____ (a whole number)

   $\dfrac{7}{10} \times 10 = 7$ tenths $\times 10$
   $\qquad = 70$ tenths
   $\qquad = 7$
   _____

   (ii) $\dfrac{7}{10} \times 100 = 7$ tenths $\times 100$
   $\qquad = $ _____ tenths
   $\qquad = $ _____ (a whole number)

   $\dfrac{7}{10} \times 100 = 7$ tenths $\times 100$
   $\qquad = 700$ tenths
   $\qquad = 70$
   _____

(iii) $\frac{7}{10} \times 1000 = 7$ tenths $\times 1000$

$= \underline{\hspace{2cm}}$ tenths

$= \underline{\hspace{2cm}}$ (a whole number)

$\frac{7}{10} \times 1000 = 7$ tenths $\times 1000$

$= 7000$ tenths

$= 700$

---

3. (a) Copy and complete this place value table.

Number	Tens	Ones	Tenths	Hundredths
$\frac{5}{100}$			0	5
$\frac{5}{100} \times 10$			5	
$\frac{5}{100} \times 100$		5		
$\frac{5}{100} \times 1000$	5	0		

(b) Copy and fill in the blanks.

(i) $\frac{5}{100} \times 10 = 5$ hundredths $\times 10$

$= \underline{\hspace{2cm}}$ hundredths

$= \underline{\hspace{2cm}}$ tenths

$\frac{5}{100} \times 10 = 5$ hundredths $\times 10$

$= 50$ hundredths

$= 5$ tenths

(ii) $\frac{5}{100} \times 100 = 5$ hundredths $\times 100$

$= \underline{\hspace{2cm}}$ hundredths

$= \underline{\hspace{2cm}}$ (a whole number)

$\frac{5}{100} \times 100 = 5$ hundredths $\times 100$

$= 500$ hundredths

$= 5$

(iii) $\frac{5}{100} \times 1000 = 5$ hundredths $\times 1000$

$= \underline{\hspace{2cm}}$ hundredths

$= \underline{\hspace{2cm}}$ (a whole number)

$\frac{5}{100} \times 1000 = 5$ hundredths $\times 1000$

$= 5000$ hundredths

$= 50$

---

4. Using the answers in Questions **1** to **3**, copy and complete this place value table.

Number	Thousands	Hundreds	Tens	Ones	Tenths	Hundredths
3.75				3	7	5
3.75 × 10			3	7	5	
3.75 × 100		3	7	5		
3.75 × 1000	3	7	5	0		

5. When a decimal number is multiplied by 10, 100 and 1000, how does the position of each of its digits change in the place value table?

When a decimal number is multiplied by
- **10, each digit moves one place to the left,**
- **100, each digit moves two places to the left,**
- **1000, each digit moves three places to the left.**

Class Activity 2

Objective: To find the rules for dividing a decimal by 10, 100 and 1000.

The number 476 in expanded form is $4 \times 100 + 7 \times 10 + 6 \times 1$.

1. **(a)** Copy and complete this place value table.

Number	Hundreds	Tens	Ones	Tenths
400	4	0	0	
$400 \div 10$		4	0	
$400 \div 100$			4	
$400 \div 1000$				4

(b) Copy and fill in the blanks.

(i) $400 \div 10 = \dfrac{400}{10}$

$\qquad = $ _____

$400 \div 10 = \dfrac{400}{10}$
$\qquad = 40$

(ii) $400 \div 100 = \dfrac{400}{100}$

$\qquad = $ _____

$400 \div 100 = \dfrac{400}{100}$
$\qquad = 4$

(iii) $400 \div 1000 = \dfrac{400}{1000}$

$\qquad = \dfrac{4}{10}$

$\qquad = $ _____ tenths

$400 \div 1000 = \dfrac{400}{1000}$
$\qquad = \dfrac{4}{10}$
$\qquad = 4 \text{ tenths}$

2. **(a)** Copy and complete this place value table.

Number	Tens	Ones	Tenths	Hundredths
70	7	0		
$70 \div 10$		7		
$70 \div 100$			7	
$70 \div 1000$			0	7

(b) Working in a similar way to Question **1**, copy and fill in the blanks.

(i) $70 \div 10 =$ _____

$$70 \div 10 = \frac{70}{10}$$
$$= 7$$

(ii) $70 \div 100 =$ _____ tenths

$$70 \div 100 = \frac{70}{100}$$
$$= \frac{7}{10}$$
$$= 7 \text{ tenths}$$

(iii) $70 \div 1000 =$ _____ hundredths

$$70 \div 1000$$
$$= \frac{70}{1000}$$
$$= \frac{7}{100}$$
$$= 7 \text{ hundredths}$$

3. **(a)** Copy and complete this place value table.

Number	Ones	Tenths	Hundredths	Thousandths
6	6			
6 ÷ 10		6		
6 ÷ 100		0	6	
6 ÷ 1000		0	0	6

(b) Working in a similar way to Question **1**, copy and fill in the blanks.
(i) $6 \div 10 =$ _____ tenths

$$6 \div 10 = \frac{6}{10}$$
$$= 6 \text{ tenths}$$

(ii) $6 \div 100 =$ _____ hundredths

$$6 \div 100 = \frac{6}{100}$$
$$= 6 \text{ hundredths}$$

(iii) $6 \div 1000 =$ _____ thousandths

$$6 \div 1000 = \frac{6}{1000}$$
$$= 6 \text{ thousandths}$$

4. Using the results in Questions **1** to **3**, copy and complete the place value table.

Number	Hundreds	Tens	Ones	Tenths	Hundredths	Thousandths
476	4	7	6			
476 ÷ 10		4	7	6		
476 ÷ 100			4	7	6	
476 ÷ 1000			0	4	7	6

5. When a decimal number is divided by 10, 100 and 1000, how does the position of each of its digits change in the place value table?

When a decimal number is divided by
- 10, each digit moves one place to the right,
- 100, each digit moves two places to the right,
- 1000, each digit moves three places to the right.

Try It!

Section 6.1

1. (a) Write the number 5.093 in expanded form and in words.
(b) Show that $5.093 = 5\frac{93}{1000}$.

Solution

(a) $5.093 = 5 \times 1 + 9 \times \frac{1}{100} + 3 \times \frac{1}{1000}$

The number is five, nine hundredths and three thousandths.

(b) $5.093 = 5 + \frac{9}{100} + \frac{3}{1000}$

$= 5 + \frac{9 \times 10}{100 \times 10} + \frac{3}{1000}$

$= 5 + \frac{90}{1000} + \frac{3}{100}$

$= 5\frac{93}{1000}$

2. Write down the value represented by the digit 4 in each of these numbers.
(a) 50.413 **(b)** 2.948

Solution

(a) In the number 50.413, the digit 4 is in the tenths place.
∴ the digit 4 represents $\frac{4}{10}$.

(b) In the number 2.948, the digit 4 is in the hundredths place.
∴ the digit 4 represents $\frac{4}{100}$.

3. The prices of two packs of steak are £8.67 and £8.64. Which pack costs less? Explain your reasoning.

Solution

Method 1:
The price of the first pack = £8.67
                                       = £8 and 67 pence
The price of the second pack = £8.64
                                       = £8 and 64 pence
64 pence is less than 67 pence.

Hence, the pack with price £8.64 costs less.

Method 2: Plot the two numbers on a number line.

On the number line, 8.64 is on the left of 8.67.
∴ 8.64 is smaller.
Hence, the £8.64 pack of steak costs less.

Method 3: Write the numbers in expanded form.

$8.67 = 8 + \frac{6}{10} + \frac{7}{100}$

$8.64 = 8 + \frac{6}{10} + \frac{4}{100}$

The two numbers both contain the same number of ones and the same number of tenths.

However $\frac{4}{100}$ is smaller than $\frac{7}{100}$,

so, overall, 8.64 is smaller.

Hence, the £8.64 pack of steak costs less.

4. The mass of melon C is 3.147 kg. The mass of melon D is 3.145 kg. Which melon is heavier? Explain your reasoning.

Solution

Compare the numbers in a place value table.

Ones	Tenths	Hundredths	Thousandths
3	1	4	7
3	1	4	5

The two numbers have the same number of ones, tenths and hundredths.

However, 7 thousandths > 5 thousandths, so 3.147 is greater. Melon C is heavier.

5. James took 2.73 seconds to work out a sum and Gloria took 2.736 seconds to work out the same sum. Who was slower?

Solution

$2.73 = 2 + \frac{7}{10} + \frac{3}{100} + \frac{0}{1000}$

$2.736 = 2 + \frac{7}{10} + \frac{3}{100} + \frac{6}{1000}$

Ones	Tenths	Hundredths	Thousandths
2	7	3	0
2	7	3	6

Both the expanded form of the two numbers and the place value table show that the numbers have the same number of ones, tenths and hundredths.

Since 6 thousandths is greater than 0 thousandths, 2.736 is greater. The person who is slower to work out the sum is the person who took the longest. Since 2.736 seconds is greater than 2.73 seconds, Gloria was the slowest.

Section 6.2

6. Convert each decimal to a fraction in its simplest form.
(a) 0.4   (b) 0.028

Solution

(a) $0.4 = \dfrac{4}{10}$

$ = \dfrac{4 \div 2}{10 \div 2}$

$ = \dfrac{2}{5}$

(b) $0.028 = \dfrac{2}{100} + \dfrac{8}{1000}$

$ = \dfrac{20}{1000} + \dfrac{8}{1000}$

$ = \dfrac{28}{1000}$

$ = \dfrac{28 \div 4}{1000 \div 4}$

$ = \dfrac{7}{250}$

7. Convert each decimal to a mixed number in its simplest form.
(a) 71.25   (b) 7.125

Solution

(a) $71.25 = 71 + \dfrac{25}{100}$

$ = 71 + \dfrac{25 \div 25}{100 \div 25}$

$ = 71 + \dfrac{1}{4}$

$ = 71\dfrac{1}{4}$

(b) $7.125 = 7 + \dfrac{125}{1000}$

$ = 7 + \dfrac{125 \div 125}{1000 \div 125}$

$ = 7 + \dfrac{1}{8}$

$ = 7\dfrac{1}{8}$

8. Write each fraction as a decimal.
(a) $\dfrac{3}{5}$ (b) $\dfrac{11}{50}$

Solution

(a) $\dfrac{3}{5} = \dfrac{3 \times 2}{5 \times 2}$

$\phantom{\dfrac{3}{5}} = \dfrac{6}{10}$

$\phantom{\dfrac{3}{5}} = 0.6$

(b) $\dfrac{11}{50} = \dfrac{11 \times 2}{50 \times 2}$

$\phantom{\dfrac{11}{50}} = \dfrac{22}{100}$

$\phantom{\dfrac{11}{50}} = 0.22$

9. Write each mixed number as a decimal.
(a) $2\dfrac{4}{25}$ (b) $16\dfrac{9}{200}$

Solution

(a) $2\dfrac{4}{25} = 2 + \dfrac{4 \times 4}{25 \times 4}$

$\phantom{2\dfrac{4}{25}} = 2 + \dfrac{16}{100}$

$\phantom{2\dfrac{4}{25}} = 2.16$

(b) $16\dfrac{9}{200}$

$ = 16 + \dfrac{9 \times 5}{200 \times 5}$

$ = 16 + \dfrac{45}{1000}$

$ = 16.045$

Section 6.3

10. Work out these multiplications using place value tables.
(a) 39.6×10
(b) 3.965×100
(c) 3.965×1000

Solution

Number	Hundreds	Tens	Ones	Tenths
39.6		3	9	6
39.6 × 10	3	9	6	

(a) $39.6 \times 10 = 396$

Number	Thousands	Hundreds	Tens	Ones	Tenths	Hundredths	Thousandths
3.965				3	9	6	5
3.965 × 100		3	9	6	5		
3.965 × 1000	3	9	6	5			

(b) $3.965 \times 100 = 396.5$

(c) $3.965 \times 1000 = 3965$

11. The price of a pen is £1.40. How much is the total price of
(a) 10 pens,   (b) 1000 pens?

Solution

(a) Total price of 10 pens
$= £1.40 \times 10$
$= £14.0$
$= £14$

(b) Total price of 1000 pens
$= £1.40 \times 1000$
$= £1400$

12. Frances and Isobel are asked to calculate 5.8×1000. Frances says the answer is 5800. Isobel says the answer is 58 000. Who is correct? Explain your answer.

Solution

Number	Thousands	Hundreds	Tens	Ones	Tenths
5.8				5	8
5.8 × 1000	5	8	0	0	

As 5.8 is multiplied by 1000, each digit moves three places to the left in the place value table. This leaves the 'Ones' and 'Tens' columns without a digit, so you need to use 0 as a place holder.

Therefore, $5.8 \times 1000 = 5800$. Frances is correct.

13. Work out these divisions using place value holders.
    (a) $5.21 \div 10$
    (b) $52.1 \div 100$
    (c) $8521 \div 1000$

Solution

Number	Ones	Tenths	Hundredths	Thousandths	Ten thousandths
5.21	5	2	1		
5.21 ÷ 10	0	5	2	1	
5.21 ÷ 100	0	0	5	2	1

(a) $5.21 \div 10 = 0.521$

(b) $52.1 \div 100 = 0.521$

(c)

Number	Thousands	Hundreds	Tens	Ones	Tenths	Hundredths	Thousandths
8521	8	5	2	1			
8521 ÷ 1000				8	5	2	1

$8521 \div 1000 = 8.521$

14. Alice and Gillian are asked to calculate $54 \div 1000$. Alice says the answer is 0.54. Gillian says the answer is 0.054. Who is correct? Explain your answer

Solution

Number	Tens	Ones	Tenths	Hundredths	Thousandths
54	5	4			
54 ÷ 1000			0	5	4

As 54 is divided by 1000, each digit moves three places to the right in the place value table. This leaves the 'Tenths' column without a digit, so you need to use 0 as a place holder.

Therefore, $54 \div 1000 = 0.054$. Gillian is correct.

15. A manufacturer pours 350 litres of juice equally into containers. Find the volume of juice in each container if there are
    (a) 100 containers,
    (b) 1000 containers.

Solution

(a) Volume of juice in each container
    $= 350 \div 100$
    $= 3.5$ litres

(b) Volume of juice in each container
    $= 350 \div 1000$
    $= 0.35$ litres

16. (a) Express 375 ml in litres.
    (b) Express 4.2 kg in grams.
    Hint: You could use place value tables to help explain your reasoning.

Solution

(a) 375 ml
    $= 375 \div 1000$ litres
    $= 0.375$ litres

(b) $4.2 \, \text{kg} = 4.2 \times 1000 \, \text{g}$
    $= 4200 \, \text{g}$

17. (a) The width of a king-size bed is 150 cm. Express the width in
    (i) mm,   (ii) metres.
    (b) The time taken to solve a problem is 0.4 hours. Express the time taken in minutes.
    (c) The price for 1 kg of prawns is £23. Find the price of 1 gram of prawns in pence.

Solution

(a) (i) Width of the bed
        $= 150 \, \text{cm}$
        $= 150 \times 10 \, \text{mm}$
        $= 1500 \, \text{mm}$
    (ii) Width of the bed
        $= 150 \, \text{cm}$
        $= 150 \div 100 \, \text{m}$
        $= 1.50 \, \text{m}$

(b) Time taken $= 0.4$ hours
    $= 0.4 \times 60$ minutes
    $= 0.4 \times 10 \times 6$ minutes
    $= 4 \times 6$ minutes
    $= 24$ minutes

(c) Price of 1 kilogram of prawns
    $= £23 \div 1000$
    $= £0.023$
    $= £0.023 \times 100\text{p}$
    $= 2.3\text{p}$

Section 6.4

18. A flower shop has 61 red roses and 39 yellow roses. Find the percentage of red roses.

Solution

Total number of roses
$= 61 + 39$
$= 100$

Fraction of red roses
$= \dfrac{61}{100}$

$\therefore$ percentage of red roses
$= 61\%$

19. Express these fractions as percentages.
    (a) $\frac{1}{10}$ (b) $\frac{2}{5}$ (c) $\frac{9}{25}$

Solution

(a)   *Method 1*   *Method 2*

$$\frac{1}{10} = \frac{1 \times 10}{10 \times 10} \qquad \frac{1}{10} = \frac{1}{10} \times 100\%$$
$$= \frac{10}{100} \qquad\qquad = \frac{1}{\cancel{10}_1} \times \cancel{100}^{10}\%$$
$$= 10\% \qquad\qquad = 10\%$$

(b)   *Method 1*   *Method 2*

$$\frac{2}{5} = \frac{2 \times 20}{5 \times 20} \qquad \frac{2}{5} = \frac{2}{5} \times 100\%$$
$$= \frac{40}{100} \qquad\qquad = \frac{2}{\cancel{5}_1} \times \cancel{100}^{20}\%$$
$$= 40\% \qquad\qquad = 40\%$$

(c)   *Method 1*   *Method 2*

$$\frac{9}{25} = \frac{9 \times 4}{25 \times 4} \qquad \frac{9}{25} = \frac{9}{25} \times 100\%$$
$$= \frac{36}{100} \qquad\qquad = \frac{9}{\cancel{25}_1} \times \cancel{100}^{4}\%$$
$$= 36\% \qquad\qquad = 36\%$$

20. Express these percentages as fractions in their simplest form.
    (a) 30%   (b) 35%   (c) 68%

Solution

(a) $30\% = \frac{30}{100}$ (b) $35\% = \frac{35}{100}$
$$= \frac{30 \div 10}{100 \div 10} \qquad\qquad = \frac{35 \div 5}{100 \div 5}$$
$$= \frac{3}{10} \qquad\qquad\qquad = \frac{7}{20}$$

(c) $68\% = \frac{68}{100}$
$$= \frac{68 \div 4}{100 \div 4}$$
$$= \frac{17}{25}$$

21. Express these decimals as percentages.
    (a) 0.67   (b) 0.04   (c) 0.4

Solution

(a)   *Method 1*   *Method 2*

$$0.67 = \frac{67}{100} \qquad 0.67 = 0.67 \times 100\%$$
$$\qquad\qquad\qquad\quad = 67\%$$
$$= 67\%$$

(b)   *Method 1*   *Method 2*

$$0.04 = \frac{4}{100} \qquad 0.04 = 0.04 \times 100\%$$
$$\qquad\qquad\qquad\quad = 4\%$$
$$= 4\%$$

(c)   *Method 1*   *Method 2*

$$0.4 = \frac{4}{10} \qquad 0.4 = 0.4 \times 100\%$$
$$\qquad\qquad\qquad\quad = 40\%$$
$$= \frac{40}{100}$$
$$= 40\%$$

22. Express these percentages as decimals.
    (a) 47%   (b) 60%   (c) 6%

Solution

(a) $47\% = \frac{47}{100}$ (b) $60\% = \frac{60}{100}$
$$= 0.47 \qquad\qquad\qquad = 0.60$$
$$\qquad\qquad\qquad\qquad\qquad = 0.6$$

(c) $6\% = \frac{6}{100}$
$$= 0.06$$

23. A basket has 14 good apples and 6 rotten apples.
    (a) How many apples are there altogether?
    (b) Find the percentage of good apples in the basket.

    Hint: Draw a bar model to help you.

Solution

(a) Altogether, there are 14 + 6 = 20 apples.

(b) Percentage of good apples in the basket
$$= \frac{14}{20} \times 100\%$$
$$= \frac{14}{\cancel{20}_1} \times \cancel{100}^{5}\%$$
$$= 14 \times 5$$
$$= 70\%$$

Section 6.5

24. Find 30% of 80 kg.

Solution

30% of 80 kg
$$= 30\% \times 80$$
$$= \frac{30}{100} \times 80$$
$$= \frac{30 \times 80}{100}$$
$$= \frac{2400}{100}$$
$$= 24 \text{ kg}$$

25. The usual price of a sofa is £3500. The sale price of the sofa is 65% of its usual price. Calculate the sale price of the sofa.

    Hint: Read one sentence of the question at a time. Draw a bar model. Add the information to your bar model.

Solution

A bar model can be drawn to represent the information.

£3500

Sale price	Discount

65%

Sale price of the sofa

$= 65\%$ of £3500

$= 65\% \times £3500$

$= \dfrac{65}{100} \times £3500$

$= £\dfrac{65}{\cancel{100}_1} \times \cancel{3500}^{35}$

$= £65 \times 35$

$= £2275$

Practice 6.1

Level 1 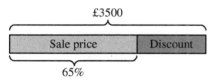 **GCSE Grade 1⁺ / 2**

1. Write each decimal number in expanded form. Then write the expanded form in words.

(a) 12.3   (b) 9.34

(c) 9.034   (d) 0.934

Solution

(a) $12.3 = 1 \times 10 + 2 \times 1 + 3 \times \dfrac{1}{10}$

The number is twelve and three tenths.

(b) $9.34 = 9 \times 1 + 3 \times \dfrac{1}{10} + 4 \times \dfrac{1}{100}$

The number is nine, three tenths and four hundredths.

(c) $9.034 = 9 \times 1 + 3 \times \dfrac{1}{100} + 4 \times \dfrac{1}{1000}$

The number is nine, three hundredths and four thousandths.

(d) $0.934 = 9 \times \dfrac{1}{10} + 3 \times \dfrac{1}{100} + 4 \times \dfrac{1}{1000}$

The number is nine tenths, three hundredths and four thousandths.

2. Write each expression as a decimal.

(a) $1 + \dfrac{4}{10} + \dfrac{7}{100}$ (b) $\dfrac{1}{10} + \dfrac{4}{100} + \dfrac{7}{1000}$

(c) $30 + \dfrac{5}{10} + \dfrac{8}{1000}$ (d) $3 + \dfrac{8}{100} + \dfrac{1}{1000} + \dfrac{5}{10}$

Solution

(a) $1 + \dfrac{4}{10} + \dfrac{7}{100} = 1.47$

(b) $\dfrac{1}{10} + \dfrac{4}{100} + \dfrac{7}{1000} = 0.147$

(c) $30 + \dfrac{5}{10} + \dfrac{8}{1000}$

$= 30 + \dfrac{5}{10} + \dfrac{0}{100} + \dfrac{8}{1000}$

$= 30.508$

(d) $3 + \dfrac{8}{100} + \dfrac{1}{1000} + \dfrac{5}{10} = 3.581$

3. Write down the value represented by the digit 5 in each number.

(a) 2.567   (b) 0.258

(c) 5.67   (d) 9.105

Solution

(a) In the number 2.567, the digit 5 is in the tenths place.

∴ the digit 5 represents $\dfrac{5}{10}$.

(b) In the number 0.258, the digit 5 represents $\dfrac{5}{100}$.

(c) In the number 5.67, the digit 5 represents 5 ones.

(d) In the number 9.105, the digit 5 represents $\dfrac{5}{1000}$.

4. Copy and fill in the blanks with '<' or '>'.

(a) 3.24 _____ 5.17   (b) 2.48 _____ 3.46

(c) 1.924 _____ 1.93   (d) 15.037 _____ 15.032

Explain your reasoning using a number line or a place value table.

Solution

(a) 3.24 < 5.17

(b) 2.48 < 3.6

(c) 1.924 < 1.93

(d) 15.037 > 15.032

5. Which is the smaller number in each pair? Explain your reasoning.

(a) 0.273, 0.28   (b) 3.507, 3.50

(c) 16.98, 16.91   (d) 1.698, 1.699

Solution

Students can use the number line, a place value table or the expanded forms of the two numbers to compare the digits.

(a) The two numbers, 0.273 and 0.28, have the same number of ones and tenths. Since 7 hundredths is smaller than 8 hundredths, 0.273 is smaller.

(b) The two numbers, 3.507 and 3.50, have the same number of ones, tenths and hundredths. 3.50 has no thousandths while 3.507 has 7 thousandths. Since $\dfrac{0}{1000}$ is smaller than $\dfrac{7}{1000}$, 3.50 is smaller.

(c) The two numbers, 16.98 and 16.91, have the same number of tens, ones and tenths. Since 1 hundredth is smaller than 8 hundredths, 16.91 is smaller.

(d) The two numbers, 1.698 and 1.699, have the same number of ones, tenths and hundredths. Since 8 thousandths is smaller than 9 thousandths,

1.698 is smaller.

Level 2

GCSE Grade 2

6.

Shop A
£1.99 a kg

Shop B
£1.95 a kg

In which shop are tomatoes cheaper?

Solution
$1.95 < 1.99$
Hence, tomatoes are cheaper in shop B.

7. In a 100 m race, Alice's time was 11.32 seconds and Sophia's time was 11.38 seconds. Who was faster?

Solution
$11.32 < 11.38$
Hence, Alice was faster.

8. The mass of diamond A is 0.237 grams. The mass of diamond B is 0.23 grams.
  (a) Write down the number of decimal places in
    (i) 0.237, **(ii)** 0.23.
  (b) Which diamond is heavier?

Solution
  (a) **(i)** 0.237 has three decimal places.
    (ii) 0.23 has two decimal places.

  (b) Since $0.237 > 0.230$,
    i.e. $0.237 > 0.23$,
    diamond A is heavier.

9. The number 7.8 ☐ 1 is greater than 7.865. What are the possible values of the missing digit ☐?

Solution
If $7.8 \boxed{} 1 > 7.865$, the possible values of the missing digit ☐ are 7, 8 and 9.

10. Write down a decimal number which is between $\frac{3}{10}$ and 0.5.

Solution
$\frac{3}{10} = 0.3$
Some decimal numbers which are between $\frac{3}{10}$ (or 0.3) and 0.5 are
0.31, 0.374, 0.4, 0.409, 0.49, 0.499.

Practice 6.2

Level 1

GCSE Grade 1⁺/2⁺

1. Express each decimal as a fraction in its simplest form.
  (a) 0.3 **(b)** 0.8
  (c) 0.12 **(d)** 0.08

Solution
  (a) $0.3 = \frac{3}{10}$

  (b) $0.8 = \frac{8}{10}$
    $= \frac{8 \div 2}{10 \div 2}$
    $= \frac{4}{5}$

  (c) $0.12 = \frac{12}{100}$
    $= \frac{12 \div 4}{100 \div 4}$
    $= \frac{3}{25}$

  (d) $0.08 = \frac{8}{100}$
    $= \frac{8 \div 4}{100 \div 4}$
    $= \frac{2}{25}$

2. Express each decimal as a mixed number in its simplest form.
  (a) 3.5 **(b)** 3.6
  (c) 4.32 **(d)** 5.06

Solution
  (a) $3.5 = 3\frac{5}{10}$
    $= 3\frac{5 \div 5}{10 \div 5}$
    $= 3\frac{1}{2}$

  (b) $3.6 = 3\frac{6}{10}$
    $= 3\frac{6 \div 2}{10 \div 2}$
    $= 3\frac{3}{5}$

  (c) $4.32 = 4\frac{32}{100}$
    $= 4\frac{32 \div 4}{100 \div 4}$
    $= 4\frac{8}{25}$

  (d) $5.06 = 5\frac{6}{100}$
    $= 5\frac{6 \div 2}{100 \div 2}$
    $= 5\frac{3}{50}$

3. Write each fraction as a decimal.
  (a) $\frac{1}{2}$ **(b)** $\frac{3}{5}$
  (c) $\frac{9}{20}$ **(d)** $\frac{2}{25}$

Solution
  (a) $\frac{1}{2} = \frac{1 \times 5}{2 \times 5}$
    $= \frac{5}{10}$
    $= 0.5$

  (b) $\frac{3}{5} = \frac{3 \times 2}{5 \times 2}$
    $= \frac{6}{10}$
    $= 0.6$

  (c) $\frac{9}{20} = \frac{9 \times 5}{20 \times 5}$
    $= \frac{45}{100}$
    $= 0.45$

  (d) $\frac{2}{25} = \frac{2 \times 4}{25 \times 4}$
    $= \frac{8}{100}$
    $= 0.08$

4. Write each mixed number as a decimal.

(a) $1\frac{1}{4}$ (b) $2\frac{4}{5}$

(c) $3\frac{1}{20}$ (d) $4\frac{7}{25}$

Solution

(a) $1\frac{1}{4} = 1 + \frac{1 \times 25}{4 \times 25}$ (b) $2\frac{4}{5} = 2 + \frac{4 \times 2}{5 \times 2}$

$\quad = 1 + \frac{25}{100}$ $\quad = 2 + \frac{8}{10}$

$\quad = 1.25$ $\quad = 2.8$

(c) $3\frac{1}{20} = 3 + \frac{1 \times 5}{20 \times 5}$ (d) $4\frac{7}{25} = 4 + \frac{7 \times 4}{25 \times 4}$

$\quad = 3 + \frac{5}{100}$ $\quad = 4 + \frac{28}{100}$

$\quad = 3.05$ $\quad = 4.28$

Level 2   **GCSE Grade 2⁺**

5. The number line shows the scale in tenths between 0 and 1.

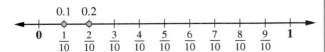

(a) Copy and complete the number line by marking 0.3, 0.4, 0.5, …, 0.9 on it.

(b) What is the relationship between the scale in tenths and the scale in decimals 0.1, 0.2, 0.3, …, 0.9?

(c) Use the number line to copy and complete these number sentences.

0.3 ___ 0.4

___ > 0.6

___ < ___

Solution

(a)

0.1 0.2 0.3 0.4 0.5 0.6 0.7 0.8 0.9

0   $\frac{1}{10}$ $\frac{2}{10}$ $\frac{3}{10}$ $\frac{4}{10}$ $\frac{5}{10}$ $\frac{6}{10}$ $\frac{7}{10}$ $\frac{8}{10}$ $\frac{9}{10}$ 1

(b) They are the same.

(c) $0.3 < 0.4$

e.g. $0.8 > 0.6$

e.g. $0.1 <$ e.g. 0.2

6. Express each decimal as a fraction in its simplest form.

(a) 0.004   (b) 0.125

Solution

(a) $0.004 = \frac{4}{1000}$ (b) $0.125 = \frac{125}{1000}$

$\quad = \frac{4 \div 4}{1000 \div 4}$ $\quad = \frac{125 \div 125}{1000 \div 125}$

$\quad = \frac{1}{250}$ $\quad = \frac{1}{8}$

7. Express each decimal as a mixed number in its simplest form.

(a) 2.016   (b) 2.106

Solution

(a) $2.016 = 2\frac{16}{1000}$ (b) $2.106 = 2\frac{106}{1000}$

$\quad = 2\frac{16 \div 8}{1000 \div 8}$ $\quad = 2\frac{106 \div 2}{1000 \div 2}$

$\quad = 2\frac{2}{125}$ $\quad = 2\frac{53}{500}$

8. Write each fraction as a decimal.

(a) $\frac{5}{8}$ (b) $\frac{6}{250}$

Solution

(a) $\frac{5}{8} = \frac{5 \times 125}{8 \times 125}$ (b) $\frac{6}{250} = \frac{6 \times 4}{250 \times 4}$

$\quad = \frac{625}{1000}$ $\quad = \frac{24}{1000}$

$\quad = 0.625$ $\quad = 0.024$

9. Write each mixed number as a decimal.

(a) $5\frac{33}{200}$ (b) $6\frac{9}{500}$

Solution

(a) $5\frac{33}{200} = 5 + \frac{33 \times 5}{200 \times 5}$ (b) $6\frac{9}{500} = 6 + \frac{9 \times 2}{500 \times 2}$

$\quad = 5 + \frac{165}{1000}$ $\quad = 6 + \frac{18}{1000}$

$\quad = 5.165$ $\quad = 6.018$

10. The mass of a fish is $1\frac{13}{25}$ kg. The mass of a crab is 1.62 kg. Which one is heavier?

Solution

First, express the fraction $1\frac{13}{25}$ as a decimal.

$1\frac{13}{25} = 1 + \frac{13 \times 4}{25 \times 4}$

$\quad = 1 + \frac{52}{100}$

$\quad = 1.52$

Since $1.62 > 1.52$, the mass of the crab is greater than the mass of fish.

∴ the crab is heavier.

Practice 6.3

Level 1   **GCSE Grade 2 / 2⁺**

Use place value tables in **Questions 1** to **3** to help you.

1. Work out these products.

(a) 24.8×10 (b) 2.48×10

(c) 0.236×100 (d) 23.006×100

(e) 93.8×1000 (f) 9.38×1000

Solution

(a)

Number	Hundreds	Tens	Ones	Tenths
24.8		2	4	8
24.8 × 10	2	4	8	

$24.8 \times 10 = 248$

(b)

Number	Tens	Ones	Tenths	Hundredths
24.8		2	4	8
24.8 × 10	2	4	8	

$2.48 \times 10 = 24.8$

(c)

Number	Tens	Ones	Tenths	Hundredths	Thousandths
0.236		0	2	3	6
0.236 × 100	2	3	6		

$0.236 \times 100 = 23.6$

(d)

Number	Thousands	Hundreds	Tens	Ones	Tenths	Hundredths	Thousandths
23.006			2	3	0	0	6
23.006 × 100	2	3	0	0	6		

$23.006 \times 100 = 2300.6$

(e)

Number	Ten thousands	Thousands	Hundreds	Tens	Ones	Tenths
93.8				9	3	8
93.8 × 1000	9	3	8	0	0	

$93.8 \times 1000 = 93800$

(f)

Number	Thousands	Hundreds	Tens	Ones	Tenths	Hundredths
93.8				9	3	8
93.8 × 1000	9	3	8	0		

$9.38 \times 1000 = 9380$

2. Find the values of these quotients.

(a) $41.9 \div 10$ **(b)** $40.19 \div 10$

(c) $908.1 \div 100$ **(d)** $9081 \div 100$

(e) $53\,904 \div 1000$ **(f)** $5394 \div 1000$

Solution

(a)

Number	Tens	Ones	Tenths	Hundredths
41.9	4	1	9	
41.9 × 10		4	1	9

$41.9 \div 10 = 4.19$

(b)

Number	Tens	Ones	Tenths	Hundredths	Thousandths
40.19	4	0	1	9	
40.19 ÷ 100		4	0	1	9

$40.19 \div 10 = 4.019$

(c)

Number	Hundreds	Tens	Ones	Tenths	Hundredths	Thousandths
908.1	9	0	8	1		
908.1 ÷ 100			9	0	8	1

$908.1 \div 100 = 9.081$

(d)

Number	Thousands	Hundreds	Tens	Ones	Tenths	Hundredths
9081	9	0	8	1		
9081 ÷ 100			9	0	8	1

$9081 \div 100 = 90.81$

(e)

Number	Ten thousands	Thousands	Hundreds	Tens	Ones	Tenths	Hundredths	Thousandths
53904	5	3	9	0	4			
53904 ÷ 1000				5	3	9	0	4

$53\,904 \div 1000 = 53.904$

(f)

Number	Thousands	Hundreds	Tens	Ones	Tenths	Hundredths	Thousandths
5394	5	3	9	4			
5394 ÷ 1000				5	3	9	4

$5394 \div 1000 = 5.394$

3. Which is bigger: 0.374×10 or 0.0375×100?
Explain your answer.

Solution
$0.374 \times 10 = 3.74$
$0.0375 \times 100 = 3.75$
$3.74 < 3.75$
Therefore, 0.0375×100 is bigger.

4. Express the given measurements in the specified units.

(a) 267 cm in metres

(b) 3.6 litres in ml

(c) 1590 grams in kg

(d) £3 in pence

(e) 0.25 hours in minutes

(f) 4.8 km in metres

Hint: When you express 267 cm in metres, do you expect the number of metres to be bigger or smaller than the number of cm, which is 267?

Solution

(a) 267 cm
$= 267 \div 100\,\text{m}$
$= 2.67\,\text{m}$

(b) 3.6 litres
$= 3.6 \times 1000\,\text{ml}$
$= 3600\,\text{ml}$

(c) 1590 grams
$= 1590 \div 1000\,\text{kg}$
$= 1.590\,\text{kg}$
$= 1.59\,\text{kg}$

(d) £3 = $3 \times 100\text{p}$
$= 300\text{p}$

(e) 0.25 hours
$= 0.25 \times 60$ minutes
$= 15$ minutes

(f) 4.8 km = $4.8 \times 1000\,\text{m}$
$= 4800\,\text{m}$

5. The price of a book is £4.95. Find the total price of
    (a) 10 books,   **(b)** 100 books.

Solution
(a) Total price of 10 books
    = £4.92 × 10
    = £49.5
    = £49.50

(b) Total price of 100 books
    = £4.95 × 100
    = £495

6. Which is the odd one out of 2.3 × 100, 0.23 × 1000 and 20.3 × 10? Explain your answer.

Solution
    2.3 × 100 = 230
  0.23 × 1000 = 230
  20.3 × 10 = 203
Therefore, 20.3 × 10 is the odd one odd.

7. Ross says 'to multiply a decimal number by 10, you just add a 0'. Do you agree with Ross? Explain your answer.

Solution
Ross is not correct. If a decimal number is multiplied by 10, each digit moves one place to the left in the place value table. For example, 0.53 × 10 = 5.3.

8. The mass of a heap of sand is 237 kg.
  (a) Find the mass of
    (i) $\frac{1}{100}$ of the heap,   **(ii)** $\frac{1}{1000}$ of the heap.

  (b) What is the number of decimal places in answer **(a)(ii)**?

Solution
(a) **(i)** Mass of $\frac{1}{100}$ of the heap

$$= \frac{1}{100} \text{ of } 237\,\text{kg}$$

$$= \frac{1}{100} \times 237$$

$$= \frac{237}{100}$$

$$= 237 \div 100$$

$$= 2.37\,\text{kg}$$

    (ii) Mass of $\frac{1}{1000}$ of the heap

$$= \frac{1}{100} \times 237\,\text{kg}$$

$$= \frac{237}{1000}$$

$$= 237 \div 1000$$

$$= 0.237\,\text{kg}$$

(b) 0.237 kg has 3 decimal places.

9. A car completes a journey of 36 km in 0.4 hours.
  (a) Express the length of the journey in metres.
  (b) Express the time of travel in minutes.
  (c) How many metres does the car travel in one minute?

Solution
(a) 36 km = 36 × 1000 m
           = 36 000 m
The journey is 36 000 m.

(b) 0.4 hours
    = 0.4 × 60 minutes
    = 24 minutes
The time of travel is 24 minutes.

(c) From **(a)** and **(b)**, the car travels 36 000 metres in 24 minutes.
∴ in one minute, the car travels 36 000 ÷ 24
= 1500 metres.

Practice 6.4

1. **(a)** Write down the percentage of shaded squares in the Diagram 1.
  (b) Do the shaded squares in Diagram 2 represent the same percentage? How do you know?

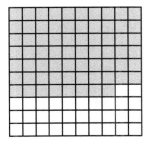

Diagram 1

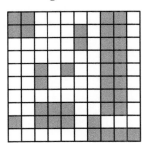

Diagram 2

Solution
(a) In Diagram 1, 68 small squares out of the total 100 squares are shaded. The fraction of shaded squares = $\frac{68}{100}$.
Hence, the percentage of shaded squares in Diagram 1 = 68%.

(b) In Diagram 2, 37 small squares out of the total 100 squares are shaded. The fraction of shaded squares $= \dfrac{37}{100}$.

The percentage of shaded squares in Diagram 2 is 37%. Therefore, the shaded squares in Diagram 2 do not represent the same percentage.

2. At a school party, there are 64 students and 36 parents. Find the percentage of students at the party.

Solution

Total number of students and parents = 64 + 36
$$= 100$$

Fraction of students in the party $= \dfrac{64}{100}$

∴ percentage of students in the party = 64%.

3. Express these fractions as percentages.

(a) $\dfrac{3}{10}$ **(b)** $\dfrac{1}{4}$

(c) $\dfrac{3}{5}$ **(d)** $\dfrac{17}{25}$

Solution

(a) *Method 1*

$$\dfrac{3}{10} = \dfrac{3 \times 10}{10 \times 10}$$

$$= \dfrac{30}{100}$$

$$= 30\%$$

Method 2

$$\dfrac{3}{10} = \dfrac{3}{10} \times 100\%$$

$$= \dfrac{3}{\cancel{10}_1} \times \cancel{100}^{10}\%$$

$$= 3 \times 10\%$$

$$= 30\%$$

Note: Students can use either method to express a fraction as a percentage.

(b) $\dfrac{1}{4} = \dfrac{1}{4} \times 100\%$

$$= \dfrac{1}{\cancel{4}_1} \times \cancel{100}^{25}\%$$

$$= 25\%$$

(c) $\dfrac{3}{5} = \dfrac{3}{5} \times 100\%$

$$= \dfrac{3}{\cancel{5}_1} \times \cancel{100}^{20}\%$$

$$= 3 \times 20\%$$

$$= 60\%$$

(d) $\dfrac{17}{25} = \dfrac{17}{25} \times 100\%$

$$= \dfrac{17}{\cancel{25}_1} \times \cancel{100}^{4}\%$$

$$= 17 \times 4\%$$

$$= 68\%$$

4. Write each percentage as a fraction in its simplest form.

(a) 80%   **(b)** 48%

(c) 8%   **(d)** 45%

Solution

(a) $80\% = \dfrac{80}{100}$ **(b)** $48\% = \dfrac{48}{100}$

$$= \dfrac{80 \div 20}{100 \div 20} \qquad\qquad = \dfrac{48 \div 4}{100 \div 4}$$

$$= \dfrac{4}{5} \qquad\qquad\qquad = \dfrac{12}{25}$$

(c) $8\% = \dfrac{8}{100}$ **(d)** $45\% = \dfrac{45}{100}$

$$= \dfrac{8 \div 4}{100 \div 4} \qquad\qquad = \dfrac{45 \div 5}{100 \div 5}$$

$$= \dfrac{2}{25} \qquad\qquad\qquad = \dfrac{9}{20}$$

5. Express these decimals as percentages.

(a) 0.09   **(b)** 0.9

(c) 0.21   **(d)** 0.56

Solution

(a) *Method 1*

$$0.09 = \dfrac{9}{100}$$

$$= 9\%$$

Method 2

$$0.09 = 0.09 \times 100\%$$

$$= 9\%$$

Note: Students can use either method to express a decimal as a percentage.

(b) $0.9 = 0.9 \times 100\%$

$$= 90\%$$

(c) $0.21 = 0.21 \times 100\%$

$$= 21\%$$

(d) $0.56 = 0.56 \times 100\%$

$$= 56\%$$

6. Express these percentages as decimals.

(a) 40%   **(b)** 4%

(c) 38%   **(d)** 59%

Solution

(a) $40\% = \dfrac{40}{100}$ **(b)** $4\% = \dfrac{4}{100}$

$$= 0.40 \qquad\qquad\qquad = 0.04$$

$$= 0.4$$

(c) $38\% = \dfrac{38}{100}$ **(d)** $59\% = \dfrac{59}{100}$

$$= 0.38 \qquad\qquad\qquad = 0.59$$

7. Group together the fractions, decimals and percentages that represent an equal proportion, assuming they are all of the same quantity.

0.88	4%	$\frac{2}{5}$	$\frac{22}{25}$
$\frac{6}{20}$	40%	0.04	88%
0.4	$\frac{8}{200}$	30%	0.3

Solution

Represent all the given values as decimals in order to group them together.

0.88
$\frac{22}{25} = 0.88$
$88\% = 0.88$

0.04
$4\% = 0.04$
$\frac{8}{200} = 0.04$

0.4
$\frac{2}{5} = 0.4$
$40\% = 0.4$

0.3
$30\% = 0.3$
$\frac{6}{20} = 0.3$

Level 2   GCSE Grade **2⁺/3⁻**

8. A shelf has 29 mathematics books and 21 science books. Find
  (a) the fraction of mathematics books on the shelf,
  (b) the percentage of mathematics books on the shelf.

Solution
(a) Total number of books
  $= 29 + 21$
  $= 50$
  $\therefore$ fraction of mathematics books $= \frac{29}{50}$
(b) Percentage of mathematics books
  $= \frac{29}{50} \times 100\%$
  $= 58\%$

9. A class has 25 students. There are 14 boys in the class. Find
  (a) the percentage of boys in the class,
  (b) the percentage of girls in the class.

Solution
(a) Percentage of boys in the class
  $= \frac{14}{25} \times 100\%$
  $= 56\%$

(b) Number of girls in the class
  $= 25 - 14 = 11$
  $\therefore$ percentage of girls $= \frac{11}{25} \times 100\%$
  $= 44\%$

Practice 6.5

Level 1   GCSE Grade **2⁺**

1. Find these values.
  (a) 10% of 80 kg   **(b)** 30% of 120 cm
  (c) 40% of 30 days   **(d)** 80% of £65
  Hint: Draw bar models to help you.

Solution
(a) 10% of 80 kg
  $= 10\% \times 80$
  $= \frac{10}{100} \times 80$
  $= \frac{1}{10} \times 80$
  $= 8 \text{ kg}$

(b) 30% of 120 cm
  $= 30\% \times 120$
  $= \frac{30}{100} \times 120$
  $= 3 \times 12$
  $= 36 \text{ cm}$

(c) 40% of 30 days
  $= 40\% \times 30$
  $= \frac{40}{100} \times 30$
  $= 4 \times 3$
  $= 12 \text{ days}$

(d) 80% of £65
  $= 80\% \times 65$
  $= \frac{80}{100} \times 65$
  $= \frac{8 \times 65}{10}$
  $= \frac{520}{10}$
  $= £52$

2. Work out these values.
  (a) 5% of 400 km
  (b) 15% of 540 ml
  (c) 25% of 96 kg
  (d) 65% of 320 m²
  Hint: Draw bar models to help you.

Solution
(a) 5% of 400 km
  $= 5\% \times 400$
  $= \frac{5}{100} \times 400$
  $= 5 \times 4$
  $= 20 \text{ km}$

(b) 15% of 540 ml
  $= 15\% \times 540$
  $= \frac{15}{100} \times 540$
  $= \frac{15 \times 54}{10}$
  $= \frac{810}{10}$
  $= 81 \text{ ml}$

(c) 25% of 96 kg
  $= 25\% \times 96$
  $= \frac{25}{100} \times 96$
  $= \frac{1}{4} \times 96$
  $= 24 \text{ kg}$

(d) 65% of 320 m²
  $= 65\% \times 320$
  $= \frac{65}{100} \times 320$
  $= \frac{13}{20} \times 320$
  $= 13 \times 16$
  $= 208 \text{ m}^2$

3. Is 35% of £20 more than, less than or the same as 20% of £35? Justify your answer.

Solution

35% of £20 = 35% × 20

$= \frac{35}{100} \times 20$

$= £7$

20% of £35 = 20% × 35

$= \frac{20}{100} \times 35$

$= \frac{1}{5} \times 35$

$= £7$

They are the same.

Level 2 **GCSE Grade 3⁻**

4. The usual price of a TV is £1400. It is in a sale with 20% off. Find its sale price.

Hint: You may draw a bar model to help you.

Solution

A bar model can be drawn to represent the information.

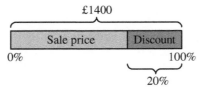

If the usual price £1400 is considered a whole (100%) and the discount is 20%, then the sale price is 100% − 20% = 80% of the usual price.

Sale price of the TV

= 80% of £1400

$= £\frac{80}{100} \times 1400$

= £80 × 14

= £1120

Alternatively, find the discount.

Discount = 20% × £1400

= £280

∴ sale price of TV

= usual price − discount

= £1400 − £280

= £1120

5. A car's full tank of petrol holds 60 litres. It is now only 35% full. How many litres of petrol are there in the tank?

Hint: You may draw a bar model to help you.

Solution

Amount of petrol in the tank

= 35% of 60 litres

$= \frac{35}{100} \times 60$

$= \frac{7}{20} \times 60$

= 7 × 3

= 21 litres

6. A block of copper and zinc alloy is 50 kg. 60% of the block is copper. Find the mass of

(a) copper in the block,

(b) zinc in the block.

Hint: You may draw a bar model to help you.

Solution

(a) Mass of copper in the block

= 60% of 50 kg

$= \frac{60}{100} \times 50$

$= \frac{60}{2}$

= 30 kg

(b) Mass of zinc

= 50 − 30

= 20 kg

7. The full price of a table in shop A is £120. It is sold at 35% discount. The full price of the same table in shop B is £140. It is sold at 45% discount. In which shop is the discounted table cheaper? Explain your answer.

Solution

If the usual price of the table in shop A is £120 and the discount is 35%, then the sale price is 100% − 35% = 65% of the usual price.

Sale price of table in shop A

= 65% of £120

$= £\frac{65}{100} \times 120$

= £78

If the usual price of the table in shop B is £140 and the discount is 45%, then the sale price is 100% − 45% = 55% of the usual price.

Sale price of table in shop B

= 55% of £140

$= £\frac{55}{100} \times 140$

= £77

Therefore, the discounted table is cheaper in shop B.

8. A car park has 360 cars. 15% of the cars are white. 30% of the cars are grey. Find the number of cars which are

(a) white,

(b) neither white nor grey.

Solution

(a) Number of white cars

= 15% of 360

$= \frac{15}{100} \times 360$

= 54

(b) Number of grey cars
$= 30\%$ of 360
$= \frac{30}{100} \times 360$
$= 108$

∴ number of cars which are neither white nor grey
$= 360 - 54 - 108$
$= 198$

9. Three students, Robert, William and Samira, are asked to draw a bar model to represent the following problem.

The usual price of a designer handbag is £972. In the sale, the price is reduced by 30%.

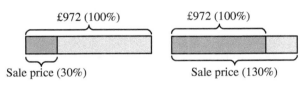

Robert's bar model | William's bar model

£972 (100%) | £972 (100%)

Sale price (30%) | Sale price (130%)

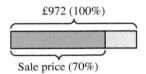

Samira's bar model

£972 (100%)

Sale price (70%)

Which bar model do you think is correct and why?

Solution
The usual price of the designer handbag is £972, therefore this is equivalent to 100% (the whole bar).

It is reduced by 30%, therefore the sale price is $100\% - 30\% = 70\%$ of the usual price.

Therefore, Samira's bar model is correct.

Challenge 6

 In a flowerbed, 0.3 of the flowers are red and $\frac{7}{25}$ are yellow. The rest are pink. Find the percentage of pink flowers in the flowerbed.

Solution
Assume that there are 100 flowers in the flowerbed.
∴ number of red flowers $= 0.3$ of 100
$= 0.3 \times 100$
$= 30$

Number of yellow flowers $= \frac{7}{25}$ of 100
$= \frac{7}{25} \times 100$
$= 7 \times 4$
$= 28$

∴ the number of pink flowers $= 100 - 30 - 28$
$= 42$

Fraction of pink flowers in the flowerbed $= \frac{42}{100}$

Hence, the percentage of pink flowers in the flowerbed
$= \frac{42}{100} \times 100\%$
$= 42\%$

Revision Exercise 6

1. Stick insect A is 29.57 cm long. Stick insect B is 29.6 cm long.
   (a) Express 29.57 in expanded form.
   (b) Write down the place value of the digit 6 in 29.6.
   (c) Which stick insect is longer? Explain your answer.

Solution
(a) $29.57 = 2 \times 10 + 9 \times 1 + 5 \times \frac{1}{10} + 7 \times \frac{1}{100}$

(b) In 29.6, the place value of the digit 6 is tenths.

(c) The two numbers, 29.57 and 29.6, have the same number of tens and ones. But 6 tenths in 29.6 is greater than 5 tenths in 29.57. So, 29.6 > 29.57. Hence, the length of stick insect B is greater than the length of stick insect A.
∴ stick insect B is longer.

2. Express these numbers as fractions or mixed numbers in their simplest form.
   (a) 0.84   **(b)** 1.25   **(c)** 3.08

Solution
(a) $0.84 = \frac{84}{100}$
$= \frac{84 \div 4}{100 \div 4}$
$= \frac{21}{25}$

(b) $1.25 = 1\frac{25}{100}$
$= 1\frac{25 \div 25}{100 \div 25}$
$= 1\frac{1}{4}$

(c) $3.08 = 3\frac{8}{100}$
$= 3\frac{8 \div 4}{100 \div 4}$
$= 3\frac{2}{25}$

3. Express these numbers as decimals.
   (a) $\frac{8}{25}$ **(b)** $3\frac{1}{2}$ **(c)** $4\frac{3}{50}$

Solution
(a) $\frac{8}{25} = \frac{8 \times 4}{25 \times 4}$
$= \frac{32}{100}$
$= 0.32$

(b) $3\frac{1}{2} = 3\frac{1 \times 5}{2 \times 5}$
$= 3\frac{5}{10}$
$= 3.5$

(c) $4\frac{3}{50} = 4\frac{3 \times 2}{50 \times 2}$

$\qquad = 4\frac{6}{100}$

$\qquad = 4.06$

4. Copy and complete the table, converting each number into a decimal, fraction and percentage. Write the fractions in their simplest form. Note that these are all decimals, fractions and percentages of the same quantity.

Decimal	Fraction	Percentage
0.05		
0.24		
	$\frac{39}{50}$	
	$\frac{17}{20}$	
		35%
		80%

Solution

Decimal	Fraction	Percentage
0.05	$\frac{1}{20}$	5%
0.24	$\frac{6}{25}$	24%
0.78	$\frac{39}{50}$	78%
0.85	$\frac{17}{20}$	85%
0.35	$\frac{7}{20}$	35%
0.8	$\frac{4}{5}$	80%

5. Work out these values.
(a) 38.16×10 **(b)** 5.893×1000
(c) $9.68 \div 10$ **(d)** $67.4 \div 100$
(e) 5.301×100 **(f)** $9065 \div 1000$

Solution
(a) $38.16 \times 10 = 381.6$
(b) $5.893 \times 1000 = 5893$
(c) $9.68 \div 10 = 0.968$
(d) $67.4 \div 100 = 0.674$
(e) $5.301 \times 100 = 530.1$
(f) $9065 \div 1000 = 9.065$

6. **(a)** Express 9.36 m in cm.
(b) Express 0.6 hours in minutes.
(c) Express 6503 grams in kg.
(d) Express 287 ml in litres.

Solution
(a) $9.36\,\text{m} = 9.36 \times 100\,\text{cm}$
$\qquad = 936\,\text{cm}$

(b) 0.6 hours $= 0.6 \times 60$ minutes
$\qquad = 0.6 \times 10 \times 6$
$\qquad = 6 \times 6$
$\qquad = 36$ minutes

(c) 6503 grams
$\qquad = 6503 \div 1000\,\text{kg}$
$\qquad = 6.503\,\text{kg}$

(d) $287\,\text{ml} = 287 \div 1000$ litres
$\qquad = 0.287$ litres

7. A cake has a mass of 400 grams. 30% of the cake is flour. Find the mass of
(a) flour in the cake,
(b) the other ingredients in the cake.

Solution
(a) Mass of the flour in the cake
$\qquad = 30\%$ of 400 grams
$\qquad = \frac{30}{100} \times 400$
$\qquad = 30 \times 4$
$\qquad = 120$ grams.

(b) Mass of other ingredients in the cake
$\qquad = 400 - 120$
$\qquad = 280$ grams

8. John obtains 2000 calories of energy from food in a day. 25% of the energy is from his breakfast. How many calories of energy are provided by
(a) his breakfast,
(b) his other food?

Solution
(a) Calories of energy provided by his breakfast
$\qquad = 25\%$ of 2000
$\qquad = \frac{25}{100} \times 2000$
$\qquad = 25 \times 20$
$\qquad = 500$

(b) Calories of energy provided by his other food
$\qquad = 2000 - 500$
$\qquad = 1500$

9. **(a)** Ava earns £2500 a month. She saves £375 and spends the rest. What percentage of her income does she save?
(b) Ben earns £3000 a month. He saves 12% of his income. Does he save more money than Ava in a month? Explain your answer.

Solution

(a) Fraction of her income saved $= \dfrac{375}{2500}$

$\therefore$ percentage of her income saved

$= \dfrac{375}{2500} \times 100\%$

$= \dfrac{375}{25}$

$= \dfrac{375 \div 25}{25 \div 25}$

$= 15\%$

(b) Income that Ben saves

$= 12\%$ of £3000

$= 12\% \times £3000$

$= £\dfrac{12}{100} \times 3000$

$= £360$

Therefore, Ben does not save more money than Ava in a month.

10. Cindy wins a prize. She is offered 30% of £1600 (Option A) or $\dfrac{2}{5}$ of £1300 (Option B). Which option should she take to get the most money? Explain your answer.

Solution

Option A:

30% of £1600

$= £\dfrac{30}{100} \times 1600$

$= £480$

Option B:

$\dfrac{2}{5}$ of £1300

$= \dfrac{2}{5} \times £1300$

$= £520$

Therefore, Cindy should take Option B to get more money.

Introduction to Ratio

Class Activity 1

Objective: To represent information using ratios.

1.

Diagram 1   Diagram 2

(a) What is the ratio of the number of cats to the number of dogs in
    (i) Diagram 1,   **(ii)** Diagram 2?

The ratio of the number of cats to the number of dogs is 2 : 1.   The ratio of the number of cats to the number of dogs is 1 : 2.

(b) Are the ratios in **(a)(i)** and **(a)(ii)** the same? Explain your answer.

The ratios in **(a)(i)** and **(a)(ii)** are not the same.
In **(a)(i)**, 2 : 1 refers to 2 cats and 1 dog, but in **(a)(ii)**, 1 : 2 refers to 1 cat and 2 dogs.

2.

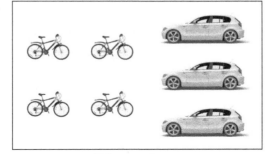 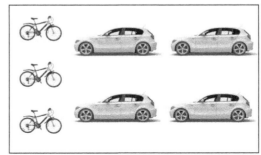

Diagram 3   Diagram 4

(a) Write down the ratio of the number of bicycles to the number of cars in
    (i) Diagram 3,   **(ii)** Diagram 4.

The ratio of the number of bicycles to the number of is 4 : 3.   The ratio of the number of bicycles to the number of cars is 3 : 4.

(b) Are the ratios in **(a)(i)** and **(a)(ii)** the same? Explain your answer.

The ratios are not the same.

The first number in each ratio in **(a)** represents the number of bicycles and the second number is the number of cars.

The ratio 4 : 3 in **(a)(i)** refers to 4 bicycles and 3 cars, but the ratio 3 : 4 in **(a)(ii)** refers to 3 bicycles and 4 cars.

3. Make up your own pair of examples to show that $2:3 \neq 3:2$.

Student's examples

Class Activity 2

Objective: To understand the relationship between ratios and fractions.

The fraction of boys in Year 7 is $\frac{5}{11}$.

1. Draw a bar model to represent the information.

    > The fraction of boys in Year 7 is $\frac{5}{11}$ so the ratio of the number of boys to the number of boys and girls in Year 7 is 5 : 11.
    >
    > 11 equal parts represent the total number of boys and girls in Year 7 and 5 parts represent the number of boys.
    >
    > Hence, 11 − 5 = 6 parts represent the number of girls.
    >
    > The bar model below represents the information.

2. What is the ratio of the number of boys to the number of girls in Year 7?

    Note: The fraction $\frac{5}{11}$ means that the ratio of the number of boys to the number of boys and girls in Year 7 is 5 : 11.

    > Ratio of the number of boys to the number of girls in Year 7 = 5 : 6.

3. What is the fraction of girls in Year 7?
    Hint: Use your bar model to explain your reasoning.

    > Fraction of girls in Year 7 = $\frac{6}{11}$

4. Explain what the ratio 6 : 11 represents.
    Write your answer as a complete sentence beginning '6 : 11 is the ratio of'.

    > 6 : 11 is the ratio of the number of girls to the number of boys and girls in Year 7.

5. There are 99 boys and girls in Year 7. Use your bar model to work out the number of boys and the number of girls in Year 7.

    > If there are 99 boys and girls in Year 7,
    >
    > 11 parts represent 99 boys and girls.
    >
    > 1 part represents 99 ÷ 11 = 9 boys and girls.

    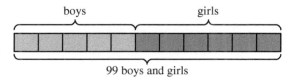

    99 boys and girls

    > 5 parts represent 9 × 5 = 45 boys.
    >
    > 6 parts represent 9 × 6 = 54 girls.
    >
    > Hence, the number of boys = 45 and the number of girls = 54.

Class Activity 3

Objective: To understand equivalent ratios.

Some students prepare sandwiches for a picnic. They use six slices of brown bread and eight slices of white bread. Copy and fill in the blanks for Questions **1** to **4**.

1. Number of brown bread slices : number of white bread slices = __:__.

   6 : 8

   _____

2. Two slices of bread of the same kind are used to form a sandwich.

   Number of brown bread sandwiches : number of white bread sandwiches = __:__.

   3 : 4

   _____

3. Each rectangular sandwich is cut into two large triangular sandwiches.

   Number of large brown bread triangular sandwiches : number of large white bread triangular sandwiches = __:__.

   6 : 8

   _____

4. Each triangular sandwich is cut into two small triangular sandwiches.

   Number of small triangular brown bread triangular sandwiches : number of small white bread triangular sandwiches = __:__.

   12 : 16

   _____

5. What's the same and what's different about the ratios in Questions **1** to **4**?

   The ratios in Questions **1** to **4** are equivalent. Each ratio can be divided by a number to produce the ratio 3 : 4.

   _____

Try It!

Section 7.1

1. Ryan borrows four science books and one history book from the library.
   (a) Draw a bar model to represent this information.
   (b) Write the ratio of the number of science books to the number of history books.
   (c) Write the ratio of the number of history books to the number of science books.

   Solution
   (a) The bar model is shown below.

   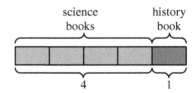

   (b) Ratio of the number of science books to the number of history books = 4 : 1.

   (c) Ratio of the number of history books to the number of science books = 1 : 4.

2. There are four butterflies, seven bees and six birds in a garden.
   (a) Draw a bar model to represent this information.
   (b) Write the ratio of the number of bees to the number of birds.
   (c) Write the ratio of the number of birds to the number of butterflies.
   (d) Write the ratio of the number of butterflies to the total number of butterflies, bees and birds in the garden.

   Solution
   (a) The bar model is shown below.

   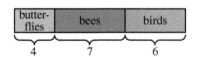

   (b) Ratio of the number of bees to the number of birds = 7 : 6.

   (c) Ratio of the number of birds to the number of butterflies = 6 : 4.

   (d) Total number of butterflies, bees and birds
   = 4 + 7 + 6
   = 17
   Ratio of the number of butterflies to the total number of butterflies, bees and birds in the garden = 4 : 17.

3. There are five adults and seven children in a doctor's waiting room.
  (a) Draw a bar model to represent this information.
  (b) Alix says the ratio of the number of children to the number of adults is 7 : 5. Is Alix correct? Explain your answer.
  (c) Becky says the ratio of the number of adults to the total number of people in the waiting room is 12 : 5. Is Becky correct? Explain your answer.

Solution
(a) The bar model is shown below.

(b) Ratio of the number of children to the number of adults = 7 : 5.
Therefore, Alix is correct.

(c) Total number of people in the clinic = 5 + 7
                                                        = 12

Ratio of the number of adults to the total number of people in the clinic = 5 : 12.

Therefore, Becky is incorrect. Becky has the ratio in the wrong order.

4. The length of a red ribbon is 4 m. The length of a blue ribbon is 3 m.
  (a) Write down the ratio of the length of the red ribbon to the length of the blue ribbon.
  (b) Explain what the ratio 3 : 7 means in this context.
  Hint: Draw a bar model to represent this information.

Solution
The bar model representing the information is shown below.

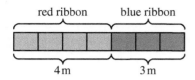

(a) Ratio of the length of the red ribbon to the length of the blue ribbon
= 4 m : 3 m
= 4 : 3

(b) In this context, the ratio 3 : 7 is the ratio of the length of the red ribbon to the total length of the red and blue ribbons.

Section 7.2

5. The ratio of the mass of copper to the mass of zinc in an alloy is 9 : 2.
  (a) Express the mass of copper as a fraction of the mass of zinc.
  (b) Use a bar model to find the mass of copper as a fraction of the total mass of the alloy.

Solution
(a) The mass of copper as a fraction of the mass of zinc = $\frac{9}{2}$.

(b) A bar model representing this information is shown below.

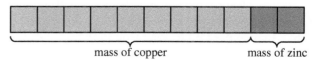

The total number of parts in the model
= 9 + 2
= 11
The mass of copper as a fraction of the total mass of the alloy = $\frac{9}{11}$.

6. The fraction of lemon juice in a drink is $\frac{3}{14}$.
  (a) Write the ratio of the volume of the lemon juice to the volume of the drink.
  (b) Use a bar model to find the ratio of the volume of lemon juice to the volume of other liquids in the drink.

Solution
(a) The ratio of the volume of the lemon juice to the volume of the drink = 3 : 14.

(b) A bar model representing this information is shown below.

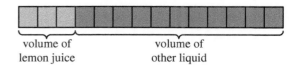

The ratio of the volume of lemon juice to the volume of other liquid in the drink = 3 : 11.

7. Ben has a bottle of milk and a carton of juice. The ratio of the volume of milk to the volume of juice is 5 : 3.
  (a) Express the volume of juice as a fraction of the volume of milk.
  (b) If the volume of juice is 270 ml, find the volume of milk.
  Hint: Draw a bar model to help you.

Solution
(a) A bar model representing this information is shown below.

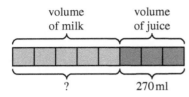

volume of milk | volume of juice

? | 270 ml

The volume of juice as a fraction of the volume of milk $= \frac{3}{5}$.

(b) If the volume of juice is 270 ml,
3 parts represent 270 ml
1 part represents $270 \div 3 = 90$ ml

5 parts represent $90 \times 5 = 450$ ml
Hence, the volume of milk is 450 ml.

8. In a compound formed from iron and sulfur, the fraction of iron in the total mass of the compound is $\frac{7}{11}$.
   (a) Find the ratio of the mass of iron to the mass of sulfur in the compound.
   (b) If there are 64 grams of sulfur, calculate the mass of iron in the same sample.

Solution

(a) You are given that $\frac{\text{mass of iron}}{\text{total mass}} = \frac{7}{11}$.

Assume there are 11 equal parts in the total mass of the compound.
Mass of iron = 7 parts
∴ mass of sulfur = 11 − 7
           = 4 parts
This bar model below represents the information.

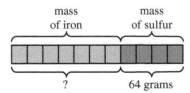

mass of iron | mass of sulfur

? | 64 grams

Hence, the ratio of the mass of iron to the mass of sulfur = 7 : 4.

(b) If the mass of sulfur is 64 grams,
4 parts represent 64.
1 part represents $64 \div 4 = 16$ g
7 parts represent $16 \times 7 = 112$ g
The mass of iron is 112 g.

Section 7.3

9. Write down two equivalent ratios for each ratio. Use bar models to explain your reasoning.
   (a) 1 : 4   **(b)** 60 : 30

Solution

Note: There are many possible equivalent ratios which students can write for each of these given ratios.

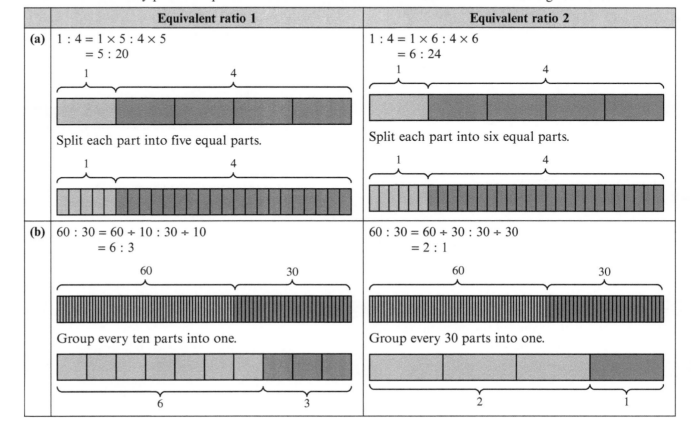

Equivalent ratio 1	Equivalent ratio 2
(a) $1 : 4 = 1 \times 5 : 4 \times 5$ $= 5 : 20$ 1 4 Split each part into five equal parts. 1 4	$1 : 4 = 1 \times 6 : 4 \times 6$ $= 6 : 24$ 1 4 Split each part into six equal parts. 1 4
(b) $60 : 30 = 60 \div 10 : 30 \div 10$ $= 6 : 3$ 60 30 Group every ten parts into one. 6 3	$60 : 30 = 60 \div 30 : 30 \div 30$ $= 2 : 1$ 60 30 Group every 30 parts into one. 2 1

10. Reduce each ratio to its simplest form.
(a)   9 : 36   (b)   12 : 26
(c)   32 : 16   (d)   39 : 24

Solution
(a)   9 : 36 = 9 ÷ 9 : 36 ÷ 9
          = 1 : 4

(b)   12 : 26 = 12 ÷ 2 : 26 ÷ 2
            = 6 : 13

(c)   32 : 16 = 32 ÷ 2 : 16 ÷ 2
            = 16 : 8
            = 16 ÷ 8 : 8 ÷ 8
            = 2 : 1
      Note: Students who have not used the HCF to
             divide the ratio will have to simplify the
             ratio in stages.
             32 : 16 = 32 ÷ 16 : 16 ÷ 16
                   = 2 : 1

(d)   39 : 24
      = 39 ÷ 3 : 24 ÷ 3
      = 13 : 8

11. In a recipe, the ratio of the mass of chicken to the
mass of tomato is 60 : 36.
(a)   Write the ratio in its simplest form.
(b)   If the mass of chicken is 150 g, what is the
      total mass of chicken and tomato?

Solution
(a)   The ratio = 60 : 36
                = 60 ÷ 6 : 36 ÷ 6
                = 10 : 6
                = 10 ÷ 2 : 6 ÷ 2
                = 5 : 3

(b)   The bar model represents the information.

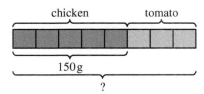

      If the mass of the chicken is 150 g,
      5 parts represent 150 g
      1 part represents 150 g ÷ 5 = 30 g
      8 parts represent 30 g × 8 = 240 g
      Hence, the total price of the bag and the
      tomato is 240 g.

Practice 7.1

Level 1

1. Write the ratio of the number of red roses to the
number of yellow roses in the bunch. Draw a bar
model to represent the information.

Solution

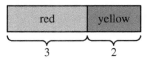

3 : 2

2. What is the ratio of the number of dogs to the
number of sheep? Draw a bar model to represent
this information.

Solution

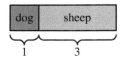

1 : 3

3. Find the ratio of the price of a calculator to the
price of a watch from the bar model.

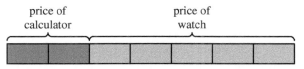

Solution
2 : 5

4. State the ratio of the length of a table to the width
of a table from the bar model.

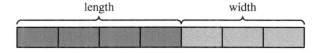

Solution
4 : 3

5. The image shows some old telephone boxes and post boxes. Write the ratio of the number of telephone boxes to the number of post boxes.

Solution

3 : 2

6. Write down the ratio of
    (a) the number of blue squares to the number of red squares,
    (b) the number of orange squares to the number of white squares,
    (c) the number of red squares to the number of orange squares,
    (d) the number of white squares to the number of red squares.

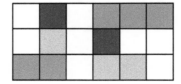

Solution

(a) 2 : 5   (b) 3 : 8
(c) 5 : 3   (d) 8 : 5

7. The image shows ten macarons. Find the ratio of
    (a) the number of purple macarons to the number of green macarons,
    (b) the number of green macarons to the number of red macarons,
    (c) the number of orange macarons to the total number of macarons.

Solution

(a) 2 : 3   (b) 3 : 2   (c) 3 : 10

8. The price of a book is £7. The price of a magazine is £3.
    (a) Jack says the ratio of the price of the book to the price of the magazine is 7 : 3. Is Jack correct? Explain your reasoning.
    (b) Dani says the ratio of the price of the magazine to the total price of the book and the magazine is 3 : 21. Is Dani correct? Explain your reasoning.

Solution

(a) The ratio of the price of the book to
     the price of the magazine = £7 : £3
                               = 7 : 3
     Therefore, Jack is correct.

(b) Total price of the book and the magazine
     = £7 + £3
     = £10
     ∴ the ratio of the price of the magazine to the total price
     = £3 : £10
     = 3 : 10
     Therefore, Dani is incorrect. The correct ratio is 3 : 10.

9. The ratio of the number of male contestants to the number of female contestants in a game show is 4 : 7.
    (a) What is the meaning of the ratio 7 : 4 in this context?
    (b) What is the meaning of the ratio 11 : 4 in this context?

Solution

(a) The ratio 7: 4 is the ratio of the number of female contestants to the number of male contestants.

(b) The ratio 11 : 4 is the ratio of the total number of contestants to the number of male contestants.

10. Make up your own question, using a real-life context where the quantities are in the ratio of 2 : 3.

Solution

Student's own answer

Practice 7.2

1. First draw a bar model to represent the information. Then express the first part of each ratio as a fraction of the two parts together (i.e. the whole), writing your answer as a full sentence.
    (a) In a rectangle, the ratio of the width to the length = 1 : 3.

(b) In a zoo, the ratio of the number of lions to the number of zebras = 2 : 5.

(c) In a sauce, the ratio of the volume of water to the volume of vinegar = 7 : 4.

(d) At a concert, the ratio of the number of adult tickets sold to the number of child tickets sold = 11 : 6.

Solution

(a) The bar model representing this information is as shown.

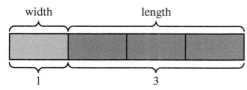

The width as a fraction of the length is $\frac{1}{3}$.

(b) The bar model to representing this information is as shown.

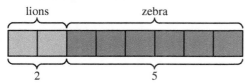

The number of lions as a fraction of the number of zebras is $\frac{2}{5}$.

(c) The bar model to representing this information is as shown.

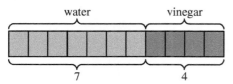

The volume of water as a fraction of the volume of vinegar is $\frac{7}{4}$.

(d) The bar model representing this information is as shown.

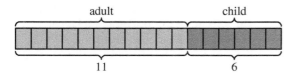

The price of an adult ticket as a fraction of the price of a child ticket is $\frac{11}{6}$.

2. First draw a bar model to represent the information in each context. Then express each fraction as a ratio of the given part to the whole, writing your answer as a full sentence.

(a) The fraction of boys in a group of newborn babies = $\frac{1}{2}$.

(b) The fraction of red roses in a bunch of roses = $\frac{3}{10}$.

(c) The area of a living room as a fraction of the area of a bedroom = $\frac{12}{5}$.

(d) The mass of a dog as a fraction of the mass of a cat = $\frac{15}{8}$.

Solution

(a) The bar model representing this information is as shown.

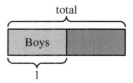

The ratio of boys to the total number of newborn babies is 1 : 2.

(b) The bar model representing this information is as shown.

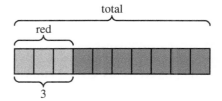

The ratio of the number of red roses to the total number of roses in a bunch is 3 : 10.

(c) The bar model representing this information is as shown.

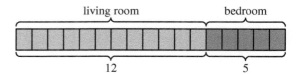

The ratio of the area of a living room to the area of a bedroom is 12 : 5.

(d) The bar model representing this information is as shown.

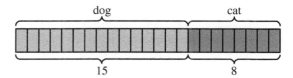

The ratio of the mass of a dog to the mass of a cat is 15 : 8.

3. (a) In the bar model, a represents the price of a spoon and b represents the price of a fork. Find the ratio $a : b$.

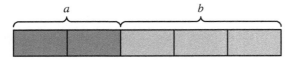

(b) In the bar model, p represents the maximum temperature on a day and q represents the minimum temperature on the same day.

   (i) Find the ratio $p : q$.

   (ii) Adam says the bar model shows that the maximum temperature was 5 °C and the minimum temperature was 4 °C. Is Adam correct? Explain your answer.

Solution

(a) $a : b = 2 : 3$

(b) **(i)** $p : q = 5 : 4$

   (ii) Adam is not correct. As p and q are in a ratio, they would both need to be multiplied by a specified number to find the exact temperatures for the day. If this number was 1, Adam would be correct.

Level 2   GCSE Grade **3⁻**

4. The fraction of adults in a cinema is $\frac{7}{9}$. What is the ratio of the number of adults to the number of children in the cinema?

Solution
Fraction of adults in the cinema $= \frac{7}{9}$.

Hence, the ratio of the number of adults to the number of people in the cinema is $7 : 9$.
Assume that 9 parts represent the total number of people in the cinema and
the number of adults $= 7$ parts
$\therefore$ the number of children $= 9 - 7$
$\qquad\qquad\qquad\qquad = 2$ parts
Hence, the ratio of the number of adults to the number of children in the cinema $= 7 : 2$
Alternatively, a bar model can be used.

You are given that $\dfrac{\text{number of adults}}{\text{total number of people}} = \dfrac{7}{9}$.

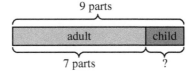

From the diagram, number of children $= 9 - 7$
$\qquad\qquad\qquad\qquad\qquad\quad = 2$ parts
$\therefore$ the ratio of the number of adults to the number of children $= 7 : 2$.

5. The ratio of the length to the width of the Union Jack is $2 : 1$. If the length of the flag is 108 cm, find the width of the flag.

Solution
The bar model below represents the information.

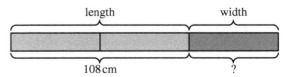

If the length of the flag is 108 cm,
2 parts represent 108 cm
1 part represents $108 \div 2 = 54$ cm
Hence, the width of the flag is 54 cm.

6. The ratio of the area of the garden to the area of the house of a home is $3 : 7$. The area of the house is 350 m². What is the area of the garden?

Solution
The bar model below represents the information.

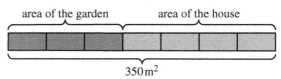

If the area of the house is 350 m²,
7 parts represent 350 m²
1 part represents $350 \div 7 = 50$ m²
3 parts represent $50 \times 3 = 150$ m²
Hence, the area of the garden is 150 m².

7. The ratio of the price of a shirt to the price of a jacket is $3 : 8$.

(a) Draw a bar model to represent this information.
(b) Express the price of the jacket as a fraction of the price of the shirt.
(c) If the price of the shirt is £21, find the price of the jacket.

Solution
(a) The bar model below represents the information.

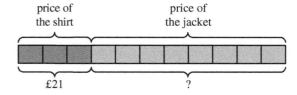

(b) The price of the jacket as a fraction of the price of the shirt $= \dfrac{8}{3}$

(c) If the price of the shirt is £21,
3 parts represent £21
1 part represents £21 ÷ 3 = £7
8 parts represent £7 × 8 = £56
Hence, the price of the jacket is £56.

8. In a class, the ratio of the number of boys to the total number of boys and girls is 5 : 12.
(a) Find the ratio of the number of girls to the number of boys.
(b) If there are 14 girls in the class, find the number of boys.

Solution
(a) You are given that $\dfrac{\text{number of boys}}{\text{total number of boys and girls}} = \dfrac{5}{12}$.

The bar model below represents the information.

boys   girls

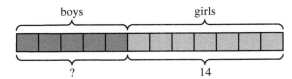

?   14

In the model, the number of girls = 12 − 5
= 7 parts
Hence, the ratio of the number of girls to the number of boys = 7 : 5

(b) If there are 14 girls in the class,
7 parts represent 14 students
1 part represents 14 ÷ 7 = 2 students
5 parts represent 2 × 5 = 10 students
Hence, the number of boys in the class is 10.

9. A wallet only contains £10 notes and £50 notes. The ratio of the number of £10 notes to the total number of notes is 4 : 13.
(a) Find the ratio of the number of £50 notes to the number of £10 notes.
(b) There are eight £10 notes. Find the total value of the money in the wallet.

Solution
(a) You are given that $\dfrac{\text{number of £10 notes}}{\text{total number of notes}} = \dfrac{4}{13}$.

The bar model below represents the information.

£10   £50

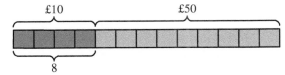

8

In the model, the number of £50 notes = 13 − 4
= 9 parts
Hence, the ratio of the number of £50 notes to the number of £10 notes = 9 : 4.

(b) If there are 8 £10 notes,
4 parts represent 8 notes
1 part represents 8 ÷ 4 = 2 notes
9 parts represent 2 × 9 = 18 notes
Hence, there are 8 £10 notes and 18 £50 notes in the wallet.
∴ the total value of the money in the wallet
= 8 × £10 + 18 × £50
= £80 + £900
= £980

Practice 7.3

Level 1   **GCSE Grade** **2⁺**

1. Write down an equivalent ratio for each of these ratios. Use bar models to explain your reasoning.
(a) 3 : 5   **(b)** 4 : 3
(c) 18 : 27   **(d)** 14 : 8

Solution
Note: There are many possible equivalent ratios for each of the given ratios.

(a)
3   5

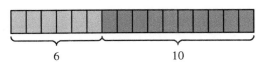

6   10

3 : 5 = 3 × 2 : 5 × 2
= 6 : 10

(b)
4   3

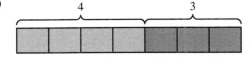

12   9

4 : 3 = 4 × 3 : 3 × 3
= 12 : 9

(c)
18   27

6   9

18 : 27 = 18 ÷ 3 : 27 ÷ 3
= 6 : 9

(d)

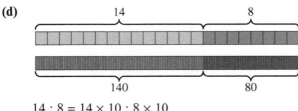

$$14 : 8 = 14 \times 10 : 8 \times 10$$
$$= 140 : 80$$

2. Reduce each ratio to its simplest form. Use bar models to explain your reasoning.

   (a) 5 : 10   (b) 15 : 21
   (c) 48 : 16   (d) 36 : 32

Solution

(a)

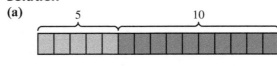

$$5 : 10 = 5 \div 5 : 10 \div 5$$
$$= 1 : 2$$

(b)

$$15 : 21 = 15 \div 3 : 21 \div 3$$
$$= 5 : 7$$

(c)

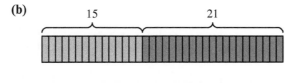

$$48 : 16 = 48 \div 16 : 16 \div 16$$
$$= 3 : 1$$

(d)

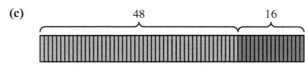
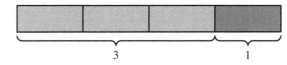

$$36 : 32 = 36 \div 4 : 32 : 4$$
$$= 9 : 8$$

3. Which of these pairs of ratios are equivalent?

   (a) 2 : 3 and 8 : 12   (b) 1 : 2 and 3 : 8
   (c) 7 : 10 and 28 : 40   (d) 8 : 7 and 40 : 35
   (e) 9 : 4 and 27 : 12   (f) 8 : 2 and 12 : 3

   Hint: A bar model might help you explain your reasoning.

Solution

(a) $8 : 12 = 8 \div 4 : 12 \div 4$
     $= 2 : 3$
     Hence, 2 : 3 and 8 : 12 are equivalent ratios.

(b) $1 : 2 = 1 \times 3 : 2 \times 3$
     $= 3 : 6$
     Since 1 : 2 ≠ 3 : 8, 1 : 2 and 3 : 8 are not equivalent ratios.

(c) $28 : 40 = 28 \div 4 : 40 \div 4$
     $= 7 : 10$
     Hence, 7 : 10 and 28 : 40 are equivalent ratios.

(d) $40 : 35 = 40 \div 5 : 35 \div 5$
     $= 8 : 7$
     Hence, 8 : 7 and 40 : 35 are equivalent ratios.

(e) $27 : 12 = 27 \div 3 : 12 \div 3$
     $= 9 : 4$
     Hence, 9 : 4 and 27 : 12 are equivalent ratios.

(f) $8 : 2 = 8 \div 2 : 2 \div 2$
     $= 4 : 1$
     $12 : 3 = 12 \div 3 : 3 \div 3$
     $= 4 : 1$
     Since 8 : 2 and 12 : 3 are both 4 : 1 in their simplest form, 8 : 2 and 12 : 3 are equivalent ratios.

4. Which might be the odd one out of 3 : 6, 3 : 9 and 6 : 12? Explain your choice.

Solution

$3 : 6 = 3 \div 3 : 6 \div 3 = 1 : 2$
$6 : 12 = 6 \div 6 : 12 \div 6 = 1 : 2$
$3 : 9 = 3 \div 3 : 9 \div 3 = 1 : 3$

3 : 9 can't be simplified to 1 : 2, therefore it is the odd one out.

Level 2   `GCSE Grade 3⁻/ 3`

5. There are 120 boys and 95 girls in a room. Find the ratio of the number of boys to the number of girls in its simplest form.

Solution

The ratio of the number of boys to the number of girls in the room
$= 120 : 95$
$= 120 \div 5 : 95 \div 5$
$= 24 : 19$

6. Mark has 64 stamps, John has 16 stamps and Peter has 4 stamps.
   (a) Find the following ratios and express them in their simplest form.
      (i) The number of John's stamps to the number of Mark's stamps,
      (ii) The number of Peter's stamps to the number of Mark's stamps,
      (iii) The number of Peter's stamps to the number of John's stamps.
   (b) Which two ratios in **(a)** are equal?

Solution
(a) **(i)** Ratio of John's stamps to Mark's stamps
      $= 16 : 64$
      $= 16 \div 16 : 64 \div 16$
      $= 1 : 4$
   (ii) Ratio of Peter's stamps to Mark's stamps
      $= 4 : 64$
      $= 4 \div 4 : 64 \div 4$
      $= 1 : 16$
   (iii) Ratio of Peter's stamps to John's stamps
      $= 4 : 16$
      $= 4 \div 4 : 16 \div 4$
      $= 1 : 4$

(b) The ratios in **(a)(i)** and **(a)(iii)** are equal.

7. The ratio of the number of children to the number of adults in a room is $42 : 48$.
   (a) Simplify the ratio.
   (b) If there are 70 children, find the number of adults.

Solution
(a) $42 : 48 = 42 \div 6 : 48 \div 6$
         $= 7 : 8$

(b) 7 parts represent 70 children
      1 part represents $70 \div 7 = 10$ children
      8 parts represent $8 \times 10 = 80$ adults
      Hence, there are 80 adults in the room.

8. The ratio of Isla's pocket money to Heather's pocket money is $84 : 154$.
   (a) Simplify the ratio.
   (b) If Isla has £18 a month, find the total amount of both their pocket money in a month.

Solution
(a) $84 : 154 = 84 \div 14 : 154 \div 14$
         $= 6 : 11$

(b) $6 + 11 = 17$ parts in total.
      6 parts represent £18
      1 part represents $18 \div 6 = £3$
      17 parts represent $3 \times 17 = £51$
      Hence, the total amount in a month is £51.

9. The ratio of Beth's height to Zac's height is $12 : 25$ and the ratio of Beth's height to Asha's height is $24 : 50$. Are Zac and Asha the same height? Explain your answer.

Solution
Express each ratio in its simplest form. Then compare the ratios.
Ratio of Beth's height to Zac's height = $12 : 25$.
Ratio of Beth's height to Asha's height
$= 24 : 50$
$= 24 \div 2 : 50 \div 2$
$= 12 : 25$.
The first number 12 in both ratios represents Beth's height and the second number is 25 in both ratios.
Hence, Zac and Asha are the same height.

Challenge 7

The ratio of the number of boys to the number of girls in a drama club is $2 : 3$. There are 18 boys. For a particular performance, another three boys join the club. Find the ratio of the number of boys to the number of girls now.

Solution
The bar model below represents the information.

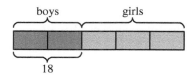

If there are 18 boys,
2 parts represent 18
1 part represents $18 \div 2 = 9$

3 parts represent $9 \times 3 = 27$
There are 27 girls.
When 3 boys join the club,
the number of boys now $= 18 + 3$
                                $= 21$
Hence, the ratio of the number of boys to the number of girls now is $21 : 27$
$= 21 \div 3 : 27 \div 3$
$= 7 : 9$.

Revision Exercise 7

1. Mr Taylor buys five adult tickets and four child tickets to watch a show with his family.
Find the ratio of
   (a) the number of adult tickets to the number of child tickets,
   (b) the number of child tickets to the total number of tickets.

Solution
(a) Ratio of the number of adult tickets to the number of child tickets = $5 : 4$.

(b) Total number of tickets = 5 + 4
$$= 9$$
Ratio of the number of child tickets to the total number of tickets = 4 : 9.

2. Write down the following ratios.
(a) The number of oranges to the number of apples.
(b) The number of apples to the number of bananas.
(c) The number of bananas to the total number of fruits.

Solution
(a) 1 : 2

(b) 2 : 3

(c) 3 : 6 = 1 : 2

3. **(a)** The ratio of basketballs to footballs in a store is 4 : 3. Express the number of basketballs as a fraction of the number of footballs.
(b) The ratio of occupied sears to the total number of seats in an aircraft is 5 : 8. Write down the number of occupied seats as a fraction of the total number of seats.

Solution
(a) $4 : 3 = \frac{4}{3}$ **(b)** $5 : 8 = \frac{5}{8}$

4. Find these ratios and express them in the simplest form.
(a) 45 cm to 200 cm **(b)** £3 to £12
(c) 30 minutes to 45 minutes **(d)** 125 g to 75 g

Solution
(a) 45 cm : 200 cm
= 45 : 200
= 45 ÷ 5 : 200 ÷ 5
= 9 : 40

(b) £3 : £12
= 3 : 12
= 3 ÷ 3 : 12 ÷ 3
= 1 : 4

(c) 30 minutes : 45 minutes
= 30 : 45
= 30 ÷ 15 : 45 ÷ 15
= 2 : 3

(d) 125 g: 75 g
= 125 : 75
= 125 ÷ 25 : 75 ÷ 25
= 5 : 3

5. Reduce each ratio to its simplest form. Show your reasoning.
(a) 4 : 12 **(b)** 18 : 24
(c) 55 : 45 **(d)** 35 : 21

Solution
(a) 4 : 12 = 4 ÷ 4 : 12 ÷ 4
= 1 : 3

(b) 18 : 24 = 18 ÷ 6 : 24 ÷ 6
= 3 : 4

(c) 55 : 45 = 55 ÷ 5 : 45 ÷ 5
= 11 : 9

(d) 35 : 21 = 35 ÷ 7 : 21 ÷ 7
= 5 : 3

6. Which of these pairs are equivalent ratios? Explain your answers.
(a) 3 : 4 and 15 : 20 **(b)** 24 : 30 and 4 : 5
(c) 9 : 2 and 18 : 6 **(d)** 30 : 20 and 21 : 14

Solution
(a) 15 : 20 = 15 ÷ 5 : 20 ÷ 5
= 3 : 4
Hence, 3 : 4 and 15 : 20 are equivalent ratios.

(b) 24 : 30 = 24 ÷ 6 : 30 ÷ 6
= 4 : 5
Hence, 24 : 30 and 4 : 5 are equivalent ratios.

(c) 18 : 6 = 18 ÷ 2 : 6 ÷ 2
= 9 : 3
Since 18 : 6 ≠ 9 : 2, 18 : 6 and 9 : 2 are not equivalent ratios.

(d) 30 : 20 = 30 ÷ 10 : 20 ÷ 10
= 3 : 2
21 : 14 = 21 ÷ 7 : 14 ÷ 7
= 3 : 2
Since 30 : 20 and 21 : 14 are both 3 : 2 in their simplest form, they are equivalent ratios.

7. A reaction uses 45 grams of chemical A, 60 grams of chemical B and 27 grams of chemical C. Find the ratio of
(a) the mass of chemical C to the mass of chemical B,
(b) the mass of chemical B to the mass of chemical A.
Give your answers in the simplest form.
Hint: Draw a bar model to help you.

Solution
The bar model below shows the situation.

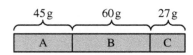

(a) Ratio of the mass of chemical C to the mass of chemical B
$= 27 : 60$
$= 27 \div 3 : 60 \div 3$
$= 9 : 20$

(b) Ratio of the mass of chemical B to the mass of chemical A
$= 60 : 45$
$= 60 \div 15 : 45 \div 15$
$= 4 : 3$

8. In a gas formed by nitrogen and oxygen, the ratio of the mass of nitrogen to the mass of oxygen is $7 : 16$.

GCSE Grade 3⁻

(a) Express the mass of oxygen as a fraction of the mass of nitrogen.

(b) If the mass of nitrogen is 21 grams, find the mass of oxygen.

Solution

You are given that $\dfrac{\text{mass of nitrogen}}{\text{mass of oxygen}} = \dfrac{7}{16}$.

(a) $\dfrac{\text{mass of oxygen}}{\text{mass of nitrogen}} = \dfrac{16}{7}$

(b)

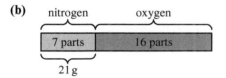

nitrogen | oxygen
7 parts | 16 parts
21 g

If the mass of nitrogen is 21 g,
7 parts represent 21 g
1 part represents $21 \div 7 = 3$ g
16 parts represent $3 \times 16 = 48$ g
Hence, the mass of oxygen is 48 grams.

9. Megan spends $\dfrac{9}{11}$ of her income and saves the rest.

GCSE Grade 3⁻

(a) Find the ratio of her spending to her income.

(b) Find the ratio of her spending to her savings.

(c) If Megan spends £540 a week, what are her savings in a week?

Solution

Given the fraction of income Megan spends,
$\dfrac{\text{spending}}{\text{income}} = \dfrac{9}{11}$.

(a) The ratio of her spending to her income
$= 9 : 11$.

(b) Assume that 11 equal parts represent her income, of which 9 parts represent her spending. Hence, $11 - 9 = 2$ parts represent her savings.
∴ the ratio of her spending to her savings
$= 9 : 2$.

(c) If Megan spends £540 a week,
9 parts represent £540
1 part represents $£540 \div 9 = £60$
2 parts represent $£60 \times 2 = £120$

Hence, Megan saves £120 a week.
Alternatively, use a bar model to help.

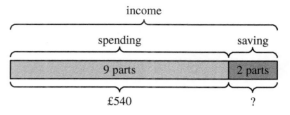

income
spending | saving
9 parts | 2 parts
£540 | ?

10. In a flat, the area of the bedroom is $10\,\text{m}^2$. The ratio of the area of the living room to the area of the bedroom is $3 : 1$. The ratio of the area of the bedroom to the area of the kitchen is $5 : 4$. Calculate

GCSE Grade 3

(a) the area of the living room,

(b) the area of the kitchen,

(c) the ratio of the area of the kitchen to the area of the living room, giving your answer in the simplest form.

Solution

(a)

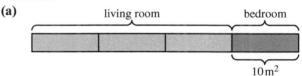

living room | bedroom
$10\,\text{m}^2$

If the area of the bedroom is $10\,\text{m}^2$,
1 part represents $10\,\text{m}^2$
3 parts represent $10 \times 3 = 30\,\text{m}^2$
Hence, the area of the living room is $30\,\text{m}^2$.

Alternatively, the area of the living room
$= 3 \times$ area of the bedroom
$= 3 \times 10$
$= 30\,\text{m}^2$

(b)

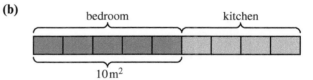

bedroom | kitchen
$10\,\text{m}^2$

5 parts represent $10\,\text{m}^2$
1 part represents $10 \div 5 = 2\,\text{m}^2$
4 parts represent $2 \times 4 = 8\,\text{m}^2$
Hence, the area of the kitchen is $8\,\text{m}^2$.

Alternatively,
$\dfrac{\text{area of the kitchen}}{\text{area of the bedroom}} = \dfrac{4}{5}$

∴ area of the kitchen $= \dfrac{4}{5}$ of area of the bedroom
$= \dfrac{4}{5} \times 10\,\text{m}^2$
$= 8\,\text{m}^2$

(c) Ratio of the area of the kitchen to the area of the living room $= 8\,\text{m}^2 : 30\,\text{m}^2$
$= 8 : 30$
$= 4 : 15$

Integrated Examples and Review Exercise 2

Try It!

1. There are 10 bars of chocolate. Four bars are dark chocolate and the rest are white chocolate. Find
   (a) the fraction of the bars that are dark chocolate,
   (b) the percentage of the bars that are dark chocolate,
   (c) the percentage of the bars that are white chocolate,
   (d) the ratio of the number of bars of dark chocolate to the number of bars of white chocolate, giving your answer in its simplest form.

   Hint: Use diagrams to explain your reasoning.

Solution
(a) Fraction of the bars that are dark chocolate
$$= \frac{4}{10}$$
$$= \frac{2}{5}$$

(b) Percentage of the bars that are dark chocolate
$$= \frac{2}{5} \times 100\%$$
$$= 40\%$$

(c) Number of the bars that are white chocolate
$$= 10 - 4$$
$$= 6$$
Hence, the percentage of the bars that are white chocolate
$$= \frac{6}{10} \times 100\%$$
$$= 60\%$$

Alternatively,
percentage of the bars that are white chocolate
= 100% − percentage of the bars that are dark chocolate
= 100% − 40%
= 60%

(d) Required ratio = 4 : 6
$$= 2 : 3$$

2. The mass of a fish is 0.918 kg. The mass of a turtle is 612 grams.
   (a) Write 0.918 in expanded form.
   (b) What value does the digit 1 represent in
      (i) 0.918, (ii) 612?
   (c) Express 0.918 kg in grams.
   (d) Find the ratio of the mass of the turtle to the mass of the fish.

Solution
(a) $0.918 = 9 \times \frac{1}{10} + 1 \times \frac{1}{100} + 8 \times \frac{1}{1000}$

(b) (i) The digit 1 in 0.918 represents $\frac{1}{100}$ or one hundredth.
   (ii) The digit 1 in 612 represents 10.

(c) 0.918 kg
   = 0.918 × 1000 grams
   = 918 grams

(d) Ratio of the mass of the turtle to the mass of the fish
   = 612 grams : 918 grams
   = 612 : 918
   = 612 ÷ 6 : 918 ÷ 6
   = 102 ÷ 3 : 153 ÷ 3
   = 34 : 51
   = 34 ÷ 17 : 51 ÷ 17
   = 2 : 3
   Alternatively,
   612 : 918
   = 612 ÷ 306 : 918 ÷ 306
   = 2 : 3

3. A bag of flour is divided into three portions, P, Q and R. Portion P is $\frac{7}{20}$ of the bag. Portion Q is 0.34 of the bag.
   (a) Which portion, P or Q, is smaller? Use a number line to represent your reasoning.
   (b) Copy and complete the bar model for the three portions.

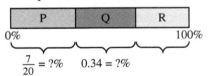

   What percentage of the whole bag is portion R?
   (c) If the mass of portion P is 140 grams, find the mass of portion R.

Solution
(a) Express $\frac{7}{20}$ as a decimal.
$$\frac{7}{20} = \frac{7 \times 5}{20 \times 5}$$
$$= \frac{35}{100}$$
$$= 0.35$$

∴ portion P is 0.35 of the bag and portion Q is 0.34 of the bag (given).

Since 4 < 5, 0.34 < 0.35.

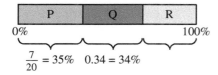

Hence, portion Q is smaller than portion P.

(b) From **(a)**, $\frac{7}{20} = 0.35$

$$= 0.35 \times 100\%$$
$$= 35\%$$

$$0.34 = 0.34 \times 100\%$$
$$= 34\%$$

Hence, the bar model is shown below.

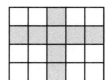

Portion R as a percentage of the whole bag
$$= 100\% - 35\% - 34\%$$
$$= 31\%$$

(c) Ratio of portion R to portion P = 31% : 35%
$$= 31 : 35$$

If the mass of portion P is 140 grams,
35 parts represent 140 g
1 part represents 140 ÷ 35 = 4 g
31 parts represent 4 × 31 = 124 g
Hence, the mass of portion R is 124 grams.

Review Exercise 2

1. **(a)** What fraction of the whole rectangle is shaded?

(b) Express this fraction as a decimal.

(c) Express this fraction as a percentage.

Solution

(a) Fraction of the whole rectangle that is shaded

$$= \frac{8}{20}$$

$$= \frac{2}{5}$$

(b) $\frac{2}{5} = \frac{2 \times 2}{5 \times 2}$

$$= \frac{4}{10}$$

$$= 0.4$$

(c) $\frac{2}{5} = \frac{2}{5} \times 100\%$

$$= 40\%$$

2. Calculate these values.

(a) $\frac{3}{8}$ of £56   **(b)** $\frac{11}{12}$ of 72 kg

Use a bar model to explain your reasoning.

Solution

(a)

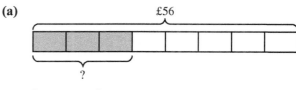

$\frac{3}{8}$ of £56 $= \frac{3}{8} \times 56$

$$= 3 \times 7$$
$$= £21$$

(b)

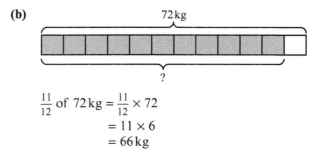

$\frac{11}{12}$ of 72 kg $= \frac{11}{12} \times 72$

$$= 11 \times 6$$
$$= 66 \text{ kg}$$

3. In a competition, Jane gets $\frac{4}{9}$ of the total prize. Zoe gets $\frac{2}{9}$ of the total prize.

(a) Who gets a greater prize? Explain your answer using a bar model.

(b) If the total prize is £10 800, find the amount of money that Jane wins.

Solution

(a)

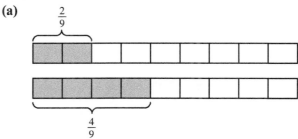

4 > 2
4 ninths > 2 ninths

$$\frac{4}{9} > \frac{2}{9}$$

Hence, Jane gets the greater prize.

(b) Amount of money that Jane wins

$$= \frac{4}{9} \text{ of £10 800}$$

$$= \frac{4}{9} \times 10\,800$$

$$= 4 \times 1200$$

$$= £4800$$

4. Cake A has a mass of $1\frac{4}{5}$ kg. Cake B has a mass of $1\frac{2}{7}$ kg.

(a) Express $1\frac{4}{5}$ and $1\frac{2}{7}$ as improper fractions.

(b) Which cake is heavier? Explain your answer.

Solution

(a)
$$1\frac{4}{5} = \frac{1 \times 5 + 4}{5}$$
$$= \frac{9}{5}$$
$$1\frac{2}{7} = \frac{1 \times 7 + 2}{7}$$
$$= \frac{9}{7}$$

(b) Both fractions, $\frac{9}{5}$ and $\frac{9}{7}$, have the same numerator. Looking at the denominators, $5 < 7$. Each part of a whole divided into 5 parts is bigger than each part of a whole divided into 7 parts.
$$\frac{1}{5} > \frac{1}{7}$$
$$\therefore \frac{9}{5} > \frac{9}{7}$$

Hence, cake A is heavier.

5. David runs 200 m in 25.37 seconds. Annabel runs the same race in 25.34 seconds.

(a) Write 25.37 in expanded form.

(b) What value does the digit 7 represent?

(c) Who is faster in the race?

Hint: Will the fastest person in a race take the shortest time or the longest time?

Solution

(a) $25.37 = 2 \times 10 + 5 \times 1 + 3 \times \frac{1}{10} + 7 \times \frac{1}{100}$

(b) The digit 7 represents the value $\frac{7}{100}$ or 7 hundredths.

(c) The two numbers, 25.37 and 25.34, have the same digits for their tens, ones and tenths places.
Since 4 hundredths < 7 hundredths,
$25.34 < 25.37$.
$\therefore$ Annabel takes less time than David.
Hence, Annabel is faster in the race.

6. Express

(a) 0.76 as a fraction, (b) 0.03 as a percentage,

(c) $3\frac{13}{20}$ as a decimal, (d) 49% as a decimal.

Solution

(a) $0.76 = \frac{76}{100}$
$$= \frac{76 \div 4}{100 \div 4}$$
$$= \frac{19}{25}$$

(b) $0.03 = 0.03 \times 100\%$
$$= 3\%$$

(c) $3\frac{13}{20} = 3\frac{13 \times 5}{20 \times 5}$
$$= 3\frac{65}{100}$$
$$= 3.65$$

(d) $49\% = \frac{49}{100}$
$$= 0.49$$

7. Convert

(a) 0.25 kg to grams,

(b) 1390 ml to litres,

(c) 465p to £,

(d) 36.5 m to cm.

Solution

(a) 0.25 kg
$= 0.25 \times 1000$ g
$= 250$ g

(b) 1390 ml
$= 1390 \div 1000$ litres
$= 1.39$ litres

(c) 465p
$= £(465 \div 100)$
$= £4.65$

(d) 36.5 m
$= 36.5 \times 100$ cm
$= 3650$ cm

8. (a) Write down the ratio of the price of the calculator to the price of the book, as represented by this bar model.

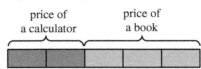

price of a calculator   price of a book

(b) The price of the book is £15. Find the price of the calculator.

Solution

(a) Ratio of the price of the calculator to the price of the book = 2 : 3.

(b) If the price of the book is £15,
3 parts represent £15
1 part represents £15 ÷ 3 = £5
2 parts represent £5 × 2 = £10
Hence, the price of the calculator is £10.

9. An aquarium tank has nine long-tailed goldfish and six short-tailed goldfish.

Find the ratio, in the simplest form, of
(a) the number of long-tailed goldfish to the number of short-tailed goldfish,
(b) the number of short-tailed goldfish to the number of long-tailed goldfish,
(c) the number of short-tailed goldfish to the total number of goldfish.

Solution
(a) The required ratio is 9 : 6
$$= 3 : 2$$

(b) The required ratio is 6 : 9
$$= 2 : 3$$

(c) Total number of goldfish
$$= 9 + 6$$
$$= 15$$
The required ratio is 6 : 15
$$= 2 : 5$$

10. (a) Find the value of the missing number if $\frac{16}{9}$ and $\frac{\square}{45}$ are equivalent fractions.
(b) The ratio of the width to the height of a TV is 16 : 9. The width of the TV is 112 cm. Work out the height of the TV.

Solution
(a) $\frac{16}{9} = \frac{16 \times 5}{9 \times 5}$
$$= \frac{80}{45}$$

$\frac{16}{9}$ and $\frac{80}{45}$ are equivalent fractions.

Hence, the missing number is 80.

(b) You are given that width of TV : height of TV = 16 : 9.

The bar model below shows the situation.

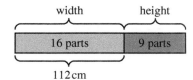

If the width is 112 cm,
16 parts represent 112 cm
1 part represents 112 ÷ 16 = 7 cm
9 parts represent 7 × 9 = 63 cm
Hence, the height of the TV is 63 cm.

11. (a) Copy the number line and plot the points representing 1.3 and $2\frac{1}{4}$ on it.

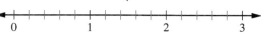

(b) Which of the two numbers is greater? Explain your answer.
(c) Express 1.3 as an improper fraction.
(d) Hence write 1.3 as a sum of two proper fractions. Can you do so in more than one way?
Hint: You may use a diagram of the improper fraction to explain your choices.

Solution
(a)

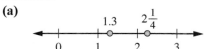

(b) $2\frac{1}{4}$ is to the right of 1.3 on the number line. Hence, $2\frac{1}{4} > 1.3$.

(c) $1.3 = 1\frac{3}{10}$
$$= \frac{13}{10}$$

(d) You can do so in multiple ways. Examples include:

$\frac{13}{10} = \frac{4}{10} + \frac{9}{10}$
$$= \frac{2}{5} + \frac{9}{10}$$

$\frac{13}{10} = \frac{5}{10} + \frac{8}{10}$
$$= \frac{1}{2} + \frac{4}{5}$$

$\frac{13}{10} = \frac{6}{10} + \frac{7}{10}$
$$= \frac{3}{5} + \frac{7}{10}$$

Some possible ways of writing 1.3 as a sum of two proper fractions are

$1.3 = \frac{2}{5} + \frac{9}{10}$,

$1.3 = \frac{1}{2} + \frac{4}{5}$ and

$1.3 = \frac{3}{5} + \frac{7}{10}$.

12. The price of a jacket is £150. The price of a skirt is $\frac{2}{3}$ of the price of the jacket. The price of a handbag is 30% of the price of the jacket. Work out
(a) the price of the skirt,
(b) the price of the handbag,
(c) the ratio of the price of the skirt to the price of the handbag, giving your answer in its simplest form.

Solution

(a) The price of the skirt

$$= \frac{2}{3} \text{ of } £150$$

$$= \frac{2}{3} \times £150$$

$$= £100$$

(b) The price of the handbag
$$= 30\% \text{ of } £150$$

$$= \frac{30}{100} \times 150$$

$$= £45$$

(c) Ratio of the price of the skirt to the price of the handbag
$$= £100 : £45$$
$$= 100 : 45$$
$$= 20 : 9$$

13. (a) The height of a tulip is $\frac{3}{7}$ of 56 cm. Find the tulip's height.

(b) The height of a rose is 75% of 60 cm. Find the rose's height.

(c) Find the ratio of the tulip's height to the rose's height, giving your answer in the simplest form.

Solution

(a) Height of the tulip
$$= \frac{3}{7} \text{ of } 56 \text{ cm}$$

$$= \frac{3}{7} \times 56$$

$$= 24 \text{ cm}$$

(b) Height of the rose
$$= 75\% \text{ of } 60 \text{ cm}$$

$$= \frac{75}{100} \times 60$$

$$= 45 \text{ cm}$$

(c) The required ratio is
$$24 \text{ cm} : 45 \text{ cm}$$
$$= 24 : 45$$
$$= 8 : 15$$

14. The ratio of the number of juniors to the number of seniors in a school choir is 10 : 15.

(a) Find the ratio of the number of seniors to the number of juniors in the simplest form.

(b) Find the percentage of seniors in the choir.

(c) If the choir has 60 students, find the number of seniors in the choir.

Solution

(a) Ratio of the number of seniors to the number of juniors = 15 : 10
$$= 3 : 2$$

(b) Ratio of the number of seniors to the number of students in the choir
$$= 3 : (3 + 2)$$
$$= 3 : 5$$

$$\therefore \frac{\text{number of seniors}}{\text{number of students}} = \frac{3}{5}$$

Hence, the percentage of seniors in the choir

$$= \frac{3}{5} \times 100\%$$

$$= 60\%$$

(c) Number of seniors in the choir = 60% of 60

$$= \frac{60}{100} \times 60$$

$$= 36$$

15. In a gym, the ratio of the number of 3 kg dumbbells to the number of 5 kg dumbbells is 9 : 4. The number of 5 kg dumbbells is 12. Find

(a) the number of 3 kg dumbbells,

(b) the total mass of all the dumbbells.

Solution

(a)

3 kg dumbbells   5 kg dumbbells

9 parts   4 parts

12

4 parts represent 12 dumbbells
1 part represents 12 ÷ 4 = 3 dumbbells
9 parts represent 3 × 9 = 27 dumbbells
Hence, there are 27 3 kg dumbbells.
Alternatively, from the given ratio

$$\frac{\text{number of 3 kg dumbbells}}{\text{number of 5 kg dumbbells}} = \frac{9}{4},$$

number of 3 kg dumbbells = $\frac{9}{4}$ of number of 5 kg dumbbells

$$= \frac{9}{4} \times 12$$

$$= 27$$

(b) Total mass of all the dumbbells
$$= 27 \times 3 \text{ kg} + 12 \times 5 \text{ kg}$$
$$= 81 + 60$$
$$= 141 \text{ kg}$$

Measures and Angles

Class Activity 1

Objective: To check understanding of how to draw and measure angles.

1. Lauren is asked to measure $\angle ABC$. Her steps are shown below.
   Step 1   *Step 2*

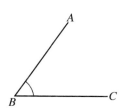 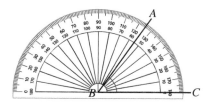

125°

$\angle ABC = 125°$

Is Lauren's answer right? What feedback would you give her?

Lauren's answer is not correct. Since line segment *BC* lies on the zero line, Lauren should read the size of the angle anticlockwise using the inner scale. $\angle ABC = 55°$

2. Toby is asked to measure $\angle DEF$. His steps are shown below.
   Step 1   *Step 2*

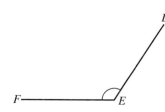 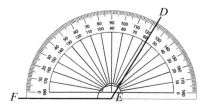 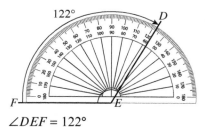

122°

$\angle DEF = 122°$

Is Toby's answer right? What feedback would you give him?

Toby's answer is not correct. Toby should place the centre of the protractor at point *E* for a more accurate answer.

3. Ethan is asked to draw $\angle TUV = 190°$. His steps are shown below.
   Step 1   *Step 2*   *Step 3*

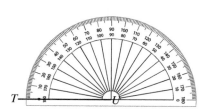 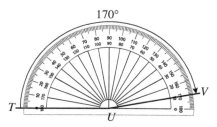 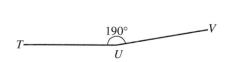

170°

190°

Is Ethan's answer right? What feedback would you give him?

Ethan's answer is not correct. In the third step, Toby has labelled the 'inside' angle when it is the larger 'outside' angle that has the value of 190°.

Class Activity 2

Objective: To identify angles of different sizes.

Look at the road sign below. There are a number of angles in the sign.

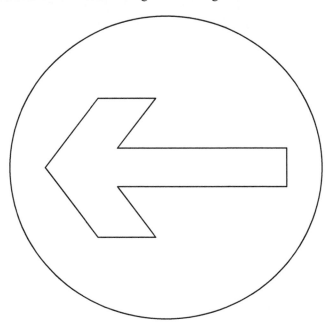

Tasks

1. Copy the arrow and label each of its corners with a letter.

2. Sort the corners into different groups, using your labels to help show you which corners are in the same group.

3. Compare your results with a classmate. Did you use the same method of grouping? Can you think of other ways to group the corners?

   Student's answer
   _____

Class Activity 3

Objective: To explore angles in shapes.

Work in pairs to answer these questions.

1. Can you draw a 3-sided shape with two acute angles? If so, draw the shape and label the angles. If not, explain why you can't.

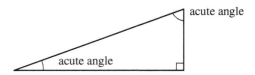

   acute angle

   acute angle

2. Can you draw a 3-sided shape with two obtuse angles? If so, draw the shape and label the angles. If not, explain why you can't.

   The angles in a 3-sided shape add to 180°. Therefore, it can't be possible to have a 3-sided shape with two obtuse angles.
   _____

3. Can you draw a 4-sided shape with two obtuse angles? If so, draw the shape and label the angles. If not, explain why you can't.

Obtuse angle

Obtuse angle

4. Can you draw a 4-sided shape with a reflex angle? If so, draw the shape and label the angles. If not, explain why you can't.

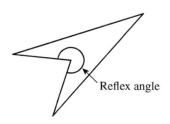

Reflex angle

Class Activity 4

Objective: To find the relationship between angles that form a right angle, a straight line or a full turn.

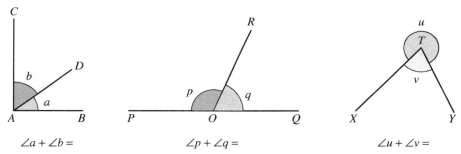

$\angle a + \angle b =$ $\angle p + \angle q =$ $\angle u + \angle v =$

1. (a) Use geometry software to create a right angle BAC.
(b) Draw a line AD to split the right angle into two angles a and b.
(c) Measure angle a and angle b. Work out their sum.
(d) Drag the point D around and observe the change in the values in **(c)**.
(e) What can you say about $\angle a + \angle b$?

$\angle a + \angle b = 90°$

2. (a) Use geometry software to create a straight line POQ.
(b) Draw a line OR to form two angles p and q as shown.
(c) Measure angle p and angle q. Work out their sum.
(d) Drag the point R around and observe the change in the values in **(c)**.
(e) What can you say about $\angle p + \angle q$?

$\angle p + \angle q = 180°$

3. (a) Use geometry software to draw two lines TX and TY to create two angles u and v as shown.
(b) Measure angle u and angle v. Work out their sum.
(c) Drag the point X or Y around and observe the change in the values in **(b)**.
(d) What can you say about $\angle u + \angle v$?

$\angle u + \angle v = 360°$

Try It!

Section 8.1

1. Measure $\angle ABC$ with a protractor and write down its size.

   Hint: You will need to rotate the protractor or the page in order to measure the angle.

   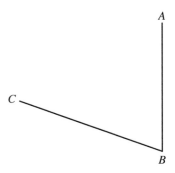

   Solution

   $\angle ABC = 70°$

2. Measure $\angle PQR$ with a protractor and write down its size.

   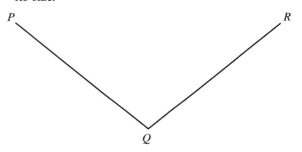

   Solution

   $\angle PQR = 100°$

3. Find the size of the marked angle PQR.

   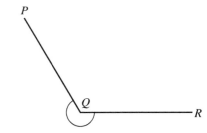

   Solution

   $\angle PQR = 240°$

4. Use a protractor to draw an angle of 126°.

   Solution

   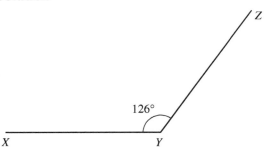

Section 8.2

5. Identify the types of angles labelled in the diagram.

   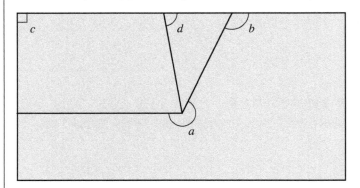

   Solution

   $\angle a$ is more than a straight line but less than a full turn, so $\angle a$ is a reflex angle.

   $\angle b$ is more than a right angle but less than a straight line, so $\angle b$ is an obtuse angle.

   $\angle c$ is equal to 90°, so $\angle c$ is a right angle.

   $\angle d$ is less than a right angle, so $\angle d$ is an acute angle.

Section 8.3

6. Given that $\angle ABC$ is a right angle and $\angle DBC = 52°$, find $\angle ABD$.

   Hint: Look at your diagram. Which angles are known? Which unknown angle are you going to find? What is the relationship between the unknown angle and the known angles?

   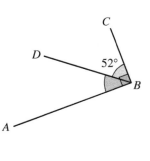

   Draw a bar model to help you.

Solution

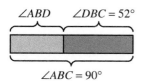

$\angle ABC = 90°$

$\angle ABD + 52° = 90°$ (Angles in a right angle
$\angle ABD = 90° - 52°$ add up to 90°.)
       $= 38°$

7. KLM is a straight line and $\angle NLM = 115°$.
Calculate $\angle KLN$.

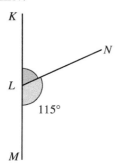

Hint: Observe the angles in the diagram as you
read the question.

Solution

$\angle KLN + 115° = 180°$ (Angles on a straight line add
                 up to 180°.)
$\angle KLN = 180° - 115°$
        $= 65°$

8. In the diagram, $\angle COD = 43°$. Work out the size
of $\angle y$.

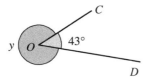

Solution

$\angle y + 43° = 360°$ (Angles at a point add up to 360°.)
$\angle y = 360° - 43°$
     $= 317°$

9. (a) How many degrees are there in a half turn?
Draw a bar model to help you.
(b) How many 45° angles are in a half turn?

Solution

(a) In the diagram, $\angle x$ is a half turn.

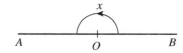

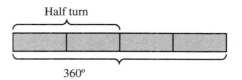

Half turn $= \dfrac{1}{2}$ of one full turn

        $= \dfrac{1}{2} \times 360°$

        $= 180°$

(b) Number of 45° angles in a half turn
     $= 180° \div 45°$
     $= 4$

Practice 8.1

Level 1   **GCSE Grade** 2^- / 2

1. Use a protractor to measure each angle and state its
size.

(a)

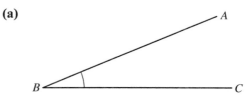

(b)

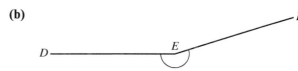

(c)

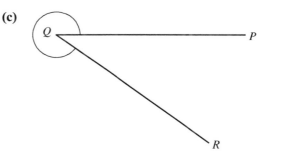

(d)

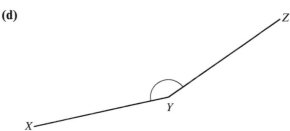

Solution

(a) $\angle ABC = 23°$
(b) Reflex $\angle DEF = 198°$
(c) Reflex $\angle PQR = 324°$
(d) $\angle XYZ = 158°$

2. Using a ruler and a protractor, draw these angles on separate diagrams.
   (a) 56° **(b)** 90°
   (c) 164° **(d)** 175°

   Solution
   (a)

   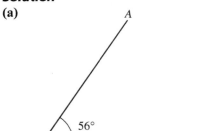

   (b)

   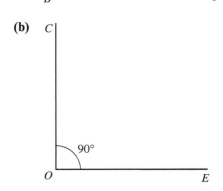

   (c)

   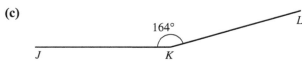

   (d)

   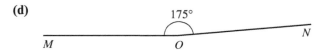

Level 2 GCSE Grade **2** / **2⁺**

3. Use a protractor to measure the size of each angle indicated in the diagram.
   Hint: You can turn the book to help you measure the angles comfortably.

   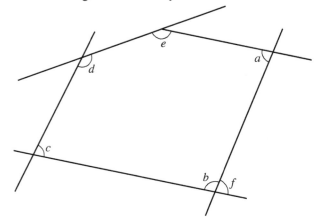

Solution
$\angle a = 80°$, $\angle b = 100°$, $\angle c = 77°$, $\angle d = 136°$,
$\angle e = 149°$, $\angle f = 80°$

4. Using a ruler and protractor, draw these angles on separate diagrams.
   (a) 190° **(b)** 220°
   (c) 318° **(d)** 347°

   Solution
   (a)

   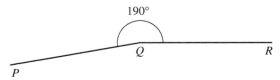

   (b)

   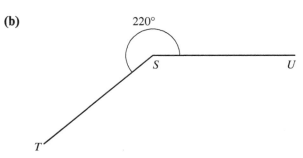

   (c) $360° − 318° = 42°$

   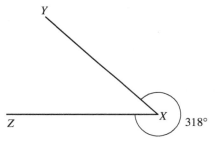

   (d) $360° − 347° = 13°$

   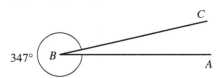

Practice 8.2

Level 1 GCSE Grade **1⁺** / **2⁻**

1. Copy and complete the table by stating whether the given angles are acute, obtuse or reflex.

Size of angle	36°	72°	95°	107°	182°	242°
Type of angle						

Solution

Size of angle	Type of angle
36°	acute
72°	acute
95°	obtuse
107°	obtuse
182°	reflex
242°	reflex

2. Robert says that 'every angle is either acute, obtuse or reflex'. Do you agree with Robert? Explain your answer.

Solution

Robert is not correct. For example, a 90° angle is not acute or obtuse; it is a right angle.

Level 2   GCSE Grade **2 / 2⁺**

3. Identify the stated type of angle in each of these objects by tracing or sketching the object and marking the angle.

(a)

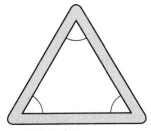

Acute angle

(b)

Right angle

(c)

Obtuse angle

(d)

Reflex angle

Solution

(a)

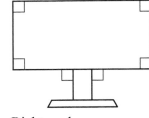

Acute angle

(b)

Right angle

(c)

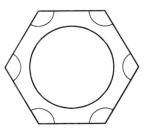

Obtuse angle

(d)

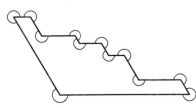

Reflex angle

4. Using a ruler and a protractor, draw an example of each of these types of angles. State the size of each angle you have drawn.

(a) Acute angle   **(b)** Right angle
(c) Obtuse angle   **(d)** Reflex angle

Solution

(a) Acute angle (less than 90°)

44°

(b) Right angle = 90°

90°

(c) Obtuse angle (more than 90° but less than 180°)

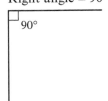

123°

(d) Reflex angle (more than 180° but less than 360°)

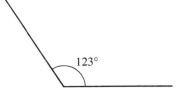

298°

Practice 8.3

State the geometrical reasoning in your working.

Level 1 GCSE Grade **2⁺**

1. Work out the size of the angle x in each diagram.
   Hint: You may draw bar models to help you.

   (a)

   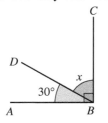

   (b)

   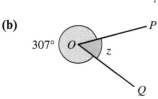

   Solution

   (a) $\angle x + 30° = 90°$ (Angles in a right angle add up to 90°.)
   $\angle x = 90° - 30°$
   $\quad = 60°$

   (b) $\angle x + 64° = 90°$ (Angles in a right angle add up to 90°.)
   $\angle x = 90° - 64°$
   $\quad = 26°$

2. Work out the size of the angle y in each diagram, where AOB is a straight line.

   Hint: You may draw bar models to help you.

   (a)

   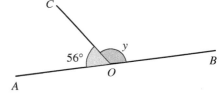

   (b)

   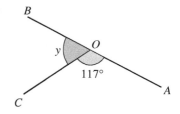

   Solution

   (a) $\angle y + 56° = 180°$ (Angles on a straight line add up to 180°.)
   $\angle y = 180° - 56°$
   $\quad = 124°$

   (b) $\angle y + 117° = 180°$ (Angles on a straight line add up to 180°.)
   $\angle y = 180° - 117°$
   $\quad = 63°$

3. Work out the size of the angle z in each diagram.
   Hint: You may draw bar models to help you.

   (a)

   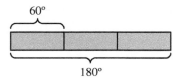

   (b)

   Solution

   (a) $\angle z + 102° = 360°$ (Angles at a point add up to 360°.)
   $\angle z = 360° - 102°$
   $\quad = 258°$

   (b) $\angle z + 307° = 360°$ (Angles at a point add up to 360°.)
   $\angle z = 360° - 307°$
   $\quad = 53°$

Level 2 GCSE Grade **3⁻/3**

4. Find the number of 60° angles in a half turn. Draw a bar model to help you.

   Solution

   One half turn = 180°
   ∴ number of 60° angles in a half turn
   $= 180° ÷ 60°$
   $= 3$

5. The diagram shows a right-angle tool, in which $\angle ABC = 90°$ and $\angle ABD = 45°$. Find $\angle CBD$.

   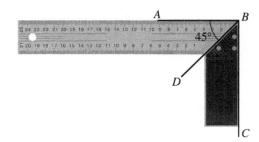

Solution

∠CBD + ∠ABD = ∠ABC (given)
∠CBD + 45° = 90°
∠CBD = 90° − 45°
= 45°

6. The diagram shows some dovetail joints in a drawer. *ABC* is a straight line and ∠*ABD* = 78°. Find ∠*CBD*.

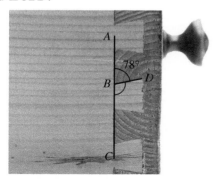

Solution

∠CBD + 78° = 180° (Angles on a straight line add up to 180°.)
∠CBD = 180° − 78°
= 102°

7. The diagram shows a roof top, in which ∠*PTQ* = 129°. Calculate reflex ∠*PTQ*.

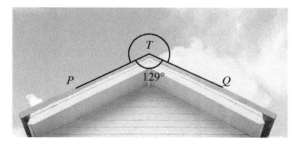

Solution

Reflex ∠PTQ + 129° = 360° (Angles at a point add up to 360°.)
Reflex ∠PTQ = 360° − 129°
= 231°

8. Fred is thinking of an angle. It is acute. It is also a multiple of 20°. Twice the angle is an obtuse angle. What angles could Fred be thinking of?

Solution

Acute angles which are multiples of 20° are 20°, 40°, 60° and 80°.
Two times each of these angles are 40°, 80°, 120° and 160°.
Only 120° and 160° are obtuse angles.
Hence, Fred could be thinking of 60° or 80°.

Challenge 8

 Find the angle that

GCSE Grade 3

(a) the minute hand of a clock rotates in
   (i) 1 hour,
   (ii) 25 minutes.

(b) the second hand of a clock rotates in 1 second.

Solution

(a) (i) The minute hand of a clock makes a complete full turn in one hour. Hence, the angle is 360°.

   (ii) 25 minutes as a fraction of one hour
   $= \dfrac{25 \text{ minutes}}{60 \text{ minutes}}$
   $= \dfrac{25}{60}$
   $= \dfrac{5}{12}$

   Angle made by the minute hand in 1 hour
   = 360°
   ∴ angle made in $\dfrac{5}{12}$ of an hour $= \dfrac{5}{12} \times 360°$
   $= 5 \times 30°$
   $= 150°$

(b) The second hand of a clock makes one full turn in one minute (60 seconds) i.e. the angle made by the second hand in 60 seconds = 360°.
   ∴ the angle made in 1 second = 360° ÷ 60
   = 6°
   Hence, the angle that the second hand of a clock rotates in one second is 6°.

Revision Exercise 8

1. Measure the sizes of these angles.

GCSE Grade 2⁺

(a)    (b)

(c)    (d)

Solution

(a) 124°
(b) 44°
(c) 141°
(d) 270°

2. Using a ruler and a protractor, draw a separate diagram for each angle.

(a) 108°   **(b)** 29°
(c) 341°   **(d)** 275°

Solution

(a)

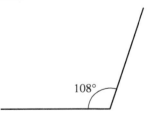

108°

(b)

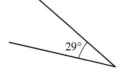

29°

(c)

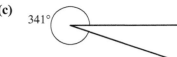

341°

(d)

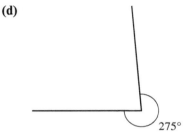

275°

3. Identify the type of each angle.

(a)   **(b)**

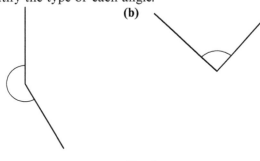

(c)   **(d)**

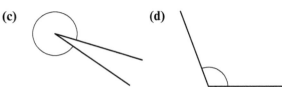

Solution

(a) Reflex angle

(b) Acute angle

(c) Reflex angle

(d) Obtuse angle

4. In each of these diagrams, work out the size of the missing angles. Give geometrical reasoning for your steps.

(a)   **(b)**

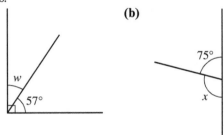

(c)

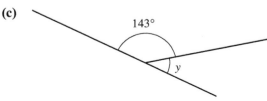

(d)

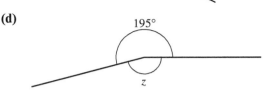

Solution

(a) $\angle w + 57° = 90°$ (Angles in a right angle add
     $\angle w = 33°$ up to 90°.)

(b) $\angle x + 75° = 180°$ (Angles on a straight line add
     $\angle x = 105°$ up to 180°.)

(c) $\angle y + 143° = 180°$ (Angles on a straight line add
     $\angle y = 37°$ up to 180°.)

(d) $\angle z + 195° = 360°$ (Angles at a point add
     $\angle z = 165°$ up to 360°.)

5. Are the following statements true or false? Explain your answers.

(a) 3° is an example of an acute angle.
(b) 182° is an example of an obtuse angle.
(c) A reflex angle is more than 270° and less than 360°.

Solution

(a) 3° is less than 90°. 3° is an example of an acute angle. (True)

(b) 182° is more than 180°. An obtuse angle is more than 90° but less than 180°.
182° is not an example of an obtuse angle. (False)

(c) A reflex angle is more than 180° and less than 360°. (False)

6. $\angle x$ is more than 100° but less than 360°. Do you have enough information to identify the type of this angle? Explain your answer.

Solution

obtuse   reflex

100°   180°   360°

If an angle is more than 100° but less than 180°, it is an obtuse angle.

If an angle is more than 180° but less than 360°, it is a reflex angle.

So, there is not enough information to identify the type of the angle.

7. The two fingers form an angle AVB of 30°. What is the size of reflex $\angle AVB$?

Solution

Reflex $\angle AVB + 30° = 360°$ (Angles at a point add up to 360°.)

$$\text{Reflex } \angle AVB = 360° - 30°$$
$$= 330°$$

8. A wooden plank is cut along the lines BE and CE. ABC is a straight line, $\angle ACD = 90°$, $\angle EBC = 40°$ and $\angle BCE = 49°$. Calculate

(a) $\angle x$,

(b) $\angle y$.

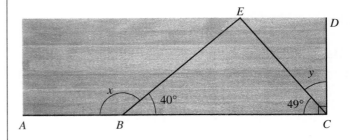

Solution

(a) $\angle x + 40° = 180°$ (Angles on a straight line
     $\angle x = 180° - 40°$ add up to 180°.)
         $= 140°$

(b) $\angle y + 49° = 90°$ (given)   (Angles in a right angle
     $\angle y = 90° - 49°$ add up to 90°.)
         $= 41°$

9. Find the multiples of 45° which are reflex angles.

Solution

Angles which are multiples of 45° and are less than 360° are

45°, 90°, 135°, 180°, 225°, 270°, 315°, 360°.

              more than 180° but less than 360°

Hence, the multiples of 45° which are reflex angles are 225°, 270° and 315°.

Symmetry

Class Activity 1

Objective: To identify objects that have reflection symmetry.

1. Look at these objects. Which objects have reflection symmetry? If an object has reflection symmetry, sketch it and draw its line or lines of symmetry.

   (a) Butterfly

   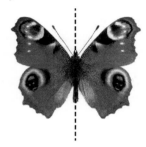

   Number of lines of symmetry: ___1___

   (b) Domino

   Number of lines of symmetry: ___0___

   (c) Propeller

   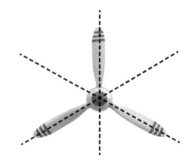

   Number of lines of symmetry: ___3___

   (d) Cracker

   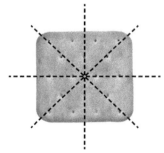

   Number of lines of symmetry: ___4___

2. Look around your classroom and identify two plane figures that have reflection symmetry. Sketch each shape with its line or lines of symmetry.
   Examples include:

   Number of line(s) of symmetry: ___1___

   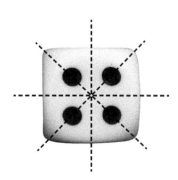

   Number of line(s) of symmetry: ___4___

Class Activity 2

Objective: To explore reflection symmetry.

Resources: Geometry software, tracing paper.

1. (a) Use geometry software to draw a vertical line in the centre of the screen. This line will be a line of symmetry. See Diagram 1.

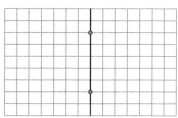

Diagram 1

(b) Use line tools to draw a simple design on the right of the line. See Diagram 2.

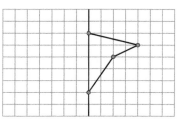

Diagram 2

(c) Use the reflection symmetry tool to reflect the design in the line to get its image on the left. See Diagram 3.

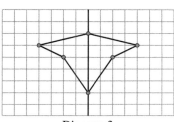

Diagram 3

(d) Create another design by repeating Steps (a) to (c).

Student's own design.

(e) What is different about your two designs? What is the same?

Both designs have the same line of symmetry.

2.

Diagram 4

Diagram 5

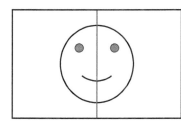

Diagram 6

(a) Fold the tracing paper into two halves. See Diagram 4.

(b) Draw your own design on one half. An example is shown in Diagram 5.

(c) Flip over the paper and copy your design on to the other half. This is called the image of your design.

(d) Open the paper and lie it flat. See Diagram 6.

(e) What do you notice about your design and its image?

It has at least one line of symmetry.

Class Activity 3

Objective: To determine the order of rotation symmetry.

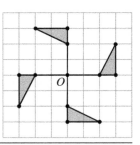

1. Draw the diagram consisting of four flags using geometry software.

2. Does the diagram have reflection symmetry?

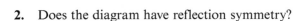

   There is no reflection symmetry, this diagram has no lines of symmetry.

3. Copy the table and complete it by using the rotation tool to rotate the diagram about a centre of rotation at point *O*.

Angle of rotation	Does the image map onto the original? (Yes/No)
30° anticlockwise about point *O*	No
45° anticlockwise about point *O*	No
90° anticlockwise about point *O*	Yes

4. Using trial and error, find all angles up to rotation 360° about the point *O*, where the image maps onto itself. Continue the table above to show what you have found.

Angle of rotation	Does the image map onto the original? (Yes/No)
90° anticlockwise about point *O*	Yes
180° anticlockwise about point *O*	Yes
270° anticlockwise about point *O*	Yes
360° anticlockwise about point *O*	Yes

5. What is the order of rotation symmetry of the diagram about point *O*?

   4

6. Can you draw a diagram with flags that has rotation symmetry of order 2 and no reflection symmetry? Mark the centre of rotation on your diagram.
   Example answer:

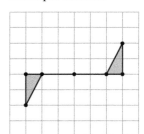

7. Can you draw a diagram with flags that has rotation symmetry of order 3 and no reflection symmetry? Mark the centre of rotation on your diagram.
   Example answer:

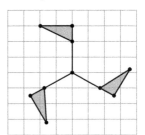

8. Can you draw a diagram with flags that has rotation symmetry of order 4 and 4 lines of symmetry? Mark the centre of rotation on your diagram.

No, it is not possible to draw a shape with flags that has 4 lines of symmetry and rotation symmetry of order 4.

Try It!

Section 9.1

1. How many lines of symmetry does each of these following regular polygons have?

(a)

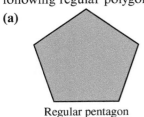

Regular pentagon

(b)

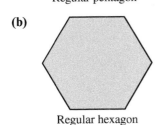

Regular hexagon

Solution

(a)

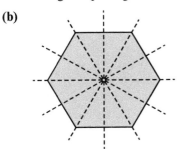

A regular pentagon has 5 lines of symmetry.

(b)

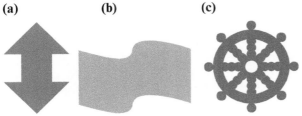

A regular hexagon has 6 lines of symmetry.

2. How many lines of symmetry does each of these figures have?

(a)　　　　**(b)**　　　　**(c)**

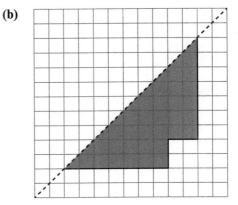

Solution

(a)

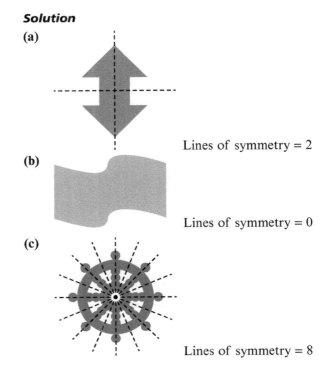

Lines of symmetry = 2

(b)

Lines of symmetry = 0

(c)

Lines of symmetry = 8

3. Copy and complete these drawings so that they are symmetrical about the dotted line. Do your new shapes have any other lines of symmetry?

(a)

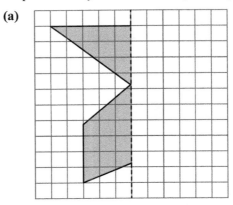

(b)

211

Solution

(a)

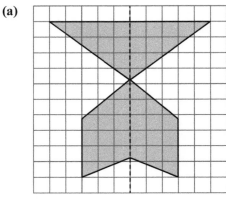

(b)

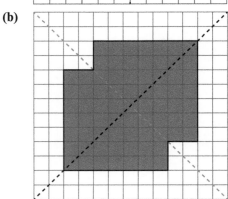

Shape **(a)** has no other lines of symmetry.
Shape **(b)** has 1 more line of symmetry,
as shown.

Section 9.2

4. What is the order of rotation symmetry of each of
these shapes?

(a)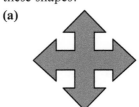

Four-arrow shape

(b)

Single arrow

(c)

Car logo

(d)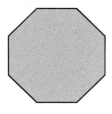

Regular octagon

Solution

(a) Order of rotation symmetry = 4

(b) No rotation symmetry

(c) Order of rotation symmetry = 3

(d) Order of rotation symmetry = 8

5. For each of these figures, state the number of lines
of symmetry and the order of rotation symmetry.

(a)

(b)

(c) B

Solution

(a) Number of lines of symmetry = 6
Order of rotation symmetry = 6

(b) Number of lines of symmetry = 0
Order of rotation symmetry = 2

(c) Number of lines of symmetry = 1
No rotation symmetry

Practice 9.1

Level 1   **GCSE Grade 1**

1. Copy each figure and draw its line or lines of
symmetry. You may use tracing paper. State how
many lines of symmetry each figure has.

(a)   **(b)**   **(c)**

Solution

(a)

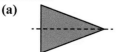

Number of lines of symmetry = 1

(b)

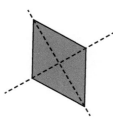

Number of lines of symmetry = 2

(c)

Number of lines of symmetry = 5

2. Write each letter and draw its line(s) of symmetry.

(a)  (b) (c)

Solution

(a)

Number of lines of symmetry = 2

(b)

Number of lines of symmetry = 1

(c)

Number of lines of symmetry = 2

3. How many (capital) letters of the alphabet have at least one line of symmetry?

Solution

16 letters have at least one line of symmetry: A, B, C, D, E, H, I, K, M, O, T, U, V, W, X, Y

4. State the number of lines of symmetry of each road sign.

(a) (b) (c)

Solution

(a)

Number of lines of symmetry = 1

(b)

Number of lines of symmetry = 4

(c)

Number of lines of symmetry = 0

5. Copy each figure and draw its line or lines of symmetry. State how many lines of symmetry each figure has.

(a) (b)

(c)

Solution

(a)

Number of lines of symmetry = 1

(b)

Number of lines of symmetry = 1

(c)

Number of lines of symmetry = 8

6. Write a three-letter word using capital letters. The word should have one line of symmetry.
Hint: For example, BOX.

Solution
Possible answers that have one line of symmetry include:
BEE,
HEX,
HOB,
COB,
BED,
MUM,
TUT.

7. What is the largest number you can write in digits which has one line of symmetry and in which every digit is different?

Solution

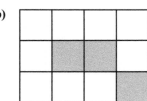

Solution
(a)

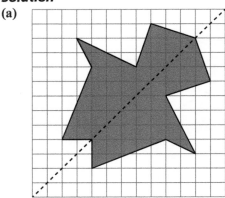

(b)

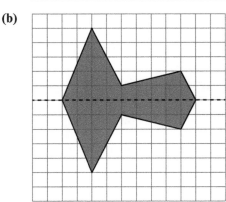

Level 2   GCSE Grade **1⁺**

8. Copy and complete these drawings so that they are symmetrical about the dotted line.
(a)

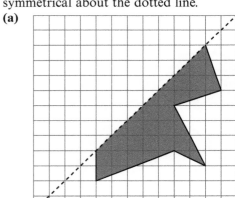

(b)

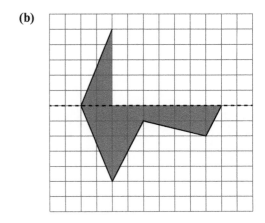

9. Copy each figure and shade one small square so that the figure will have only one line of symmetry. Draw the line of symmetry. Is there more than one choice of square?

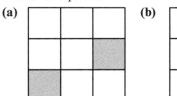

Solution

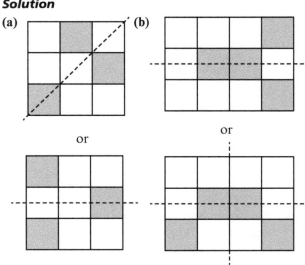

Both part **(a)** and **(b)** have two different options for shading one square.

10. Can you draw a four sided shape with the following numbers of lines of symmetry? **(a)** 0, **(b)** 1, **(c)** 2, **(d)** 3, **(e)** 4.

Solution

(a)
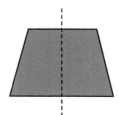

(b)
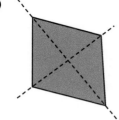

(c)
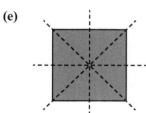

(d) It is not possible to draw a shape with four sides that has three lines of symmetry.

(e)

Several of these parts have other solutions; these are an example of students' diagrams.

Practice 9.2

Level 1 `GCSE Grade 2⁺`

Use tracing paper to help you work out the order of rotation symmetry of each figure.

1. For each of these figures, state the order of rotation symmetry.
Hint: Remember that equal numbers of dashes at the centre of each side of a shape mean that the sides are of equal length.

(a) **(b)** **(c)**

Solution
(a) Order of rotation symmetry = 4

(b) Order of rotation symmetry = 2

(c) No rotation symmetry

2. For each of these figures, state the order of rotation symmetry.

(a) **(b)** **(c)**

Solution
(a) Order of rotation symmetry = 2

(b) Order of rotation symmetry = 2

(c) Order of rotation symmetry = 5

3. State the number of lines of symmetry and the order of rotation symmetry for each figure.

(a) **(b)** **(c)**
  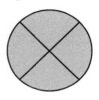

Solution
(a) Number of lines of symmetry = 2
Order of rotation symmetry = 2

(b) Number of lines of symmetry = 4
Order of rotation symmetry = 4

(c) Number of lines of symmetry = 4
Order of rotation symmetry = 4

4. State the order of rotation symmetry of each letter.

(a) **(b)** **(c)**

Solution
(a) No rotation symmetry

(b) Order of rotation symmetry = 2

(c) Order of rotation symmetry = 2

5. State the number of lines of symmetry and the order of rotation symmetry of each logo.

(a) Recycle **(b)** Railway **(c)** Radioactive

Solution

(a) Number of lines of symmetry = 0
Order of rotation symmetry = 3

(b) Number of lines of symmetry = 0
Order of rotation symmetry = 2

(c) Number of lines of symmetry = 3
Order of rotation symmetry = 3

6. Copy each figure twice.

(i) **(ii)**

(iii)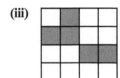

(a) Shade one small square on each figure so that the figure has rotation symmetry.

(b) On which of the figures can you shade one small square so that the figure has rotation symmetry but not reflection symmetry?

(c) Shade two small squares on each figure so that there is reflection symmetry but no rotation symmetry.

Solution

(a) (i) **(ii)**

(iii)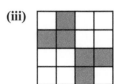

(b) In part **(a)**, figure **(ii)** has rotation symmetry but not reflection symmetry after one small square is shaded.

(c) (i) **(ii)**

(iii)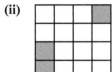

These are just one example of how this question could be answered. There are multiple answers for each part.

7. Use some arrows ⟶ to create a shape which has
(a) rotation symmetry of order 3 but no reflection symmetry,
(b) rotation symmetry and reflection symmetry,
(c) neither reflection symmetry nor rotation symmetry.

Solution
Accept any correct shapes.

8. Use drawing software to create a logo which has rotation symmetry of order
(a) 2, **(b)** 3, **(c)** 4.

Solution
Accept any correct shapes.

Challenge 9

GCSE Grade 3 The figure shows a regular hexagon with six identical triangles. Each triangle has equal sides and angles.

Use tracing paper to copy this figure four times. On each figure, shade exactly two triangles so that the resulting figure will have
(a) one line of symmetry,
(b) two lines of symmetry,
(c) rotation symmetry of order 3,
(d) reflection symmetry but no rotation symmetry.

Solution

(a)

(b)

(c) It is not possible to shade only two triangles to make a figure that has rotation symmetry of order 3.

(d)

These are just one example of how this question could be answered. There are multiple answers for parts **(a)**, **(b)** and **(d)**.

Revision Exercise 9

1. Using tracing paper copy each shape and draw its line or lines of symmetry.

(a)   (b)    (c)

Solution

(a) 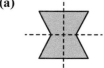   (b)   (c)

2. Write down the order of rotation symmetry of each shape.

(a)    (b)   (c)

Solution

(a) Order of rotation symmetry = 2

(b) Order of rotation symmetry = 4

(c) Order of rotation symmetry = 3

3. For each of these figures, state the number of lines of symmetry and the order of rotation symmetry.

(a)   (b)   (c)

Solution

(a) Number of lines of symmetry = 0
Order of rotation symmetry = 2

(b) Number of lines of symmetry = 4
Order of rotation symmetry = 4

(c) Number of lines of symmetry = 4
Order of rotation symmetry = 4

4. Which letter or letters from the word **SWIFT** have

(a) reflection symmetry only,
(b) rotation symmetry only,
(c) both reflection and rotation symmetry,
(d) no symmetry?

Solution

(a) W, T   (b) S

(c) I   (d) F

5. For each item, if it has reflection symmetry, write down its number of lines of symmetry. If it has rotation symmetry, write down its order of rotation symmetry.

(a) Photo frame (b) Circular dish (c) Fork

Solution

(a) Number of lines of symmetry = 2
Order of rotation symmetry = 2

(b) Number of lines of symmetry = 8
Order of rotation symmetry = 8

(c) Number of lines of symmetry = 1
No rotation symmetry

6. Describe the symmetry of these signs.

(a) Peace   (b) Danger   (c) Pharmacy

Solution

(a) The peace sign has one line of symmetry. It has no rotation symmetry.

(b) The danger sign has one line of symmetry. It has no rotation symmetry.

(c) The pharmacy sign has 4 lines of symmetry. It has rotation symmetry of order 4.

7. Copy and complete these drawings so that they are symmetrical about the dotted line. State the order of rotation symmetry of each completed figure.

(a)

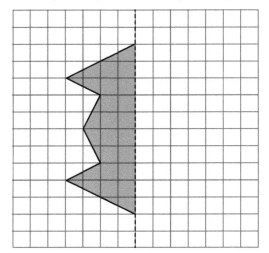

(b)

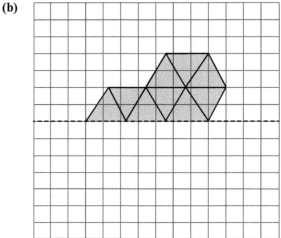

(b)

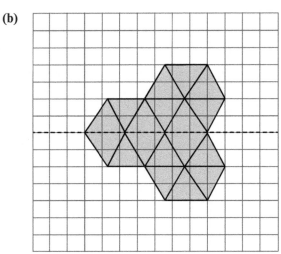

Order of rotation symmetry = 3

8. Copy and complete this drawing so that it is symmetrical about the dotted line. State whether the completed figure has rotation symmetry.

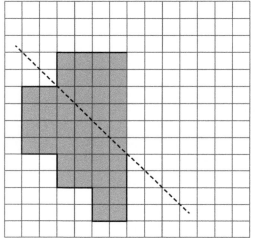

Solution

(a)

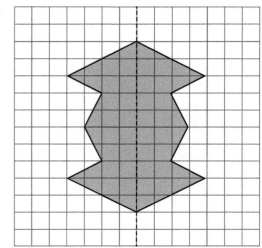

Order of rotation symmetry = 2

Solution

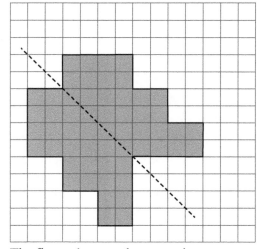

The figure does not have rotation symmetry.

Perimeter and Area of Rectangles, Squares and Triangles

Class Activity 1

Objective: To investigate the outlines of different shapes.

1. Measure the length and width of this textbook. Copy and complete the table below.

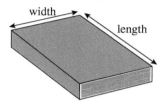

Book length	cm
Book width	cm
Length of outline = length + length + width + width	cm
2 × length + 2 × width	cm

Student's own answers.

2. Draw around the outline of the book. Put a drawing pin in each corner of the outline and then take a piece of string and lay it over the outline. Make sure the start and end of the string meet, with no overlap and no gaps. Cut the string so that it is the same length as the length of the outline.

   (a) Make a shape using the string as the outline on a piece of card. Fix the corners of the shape by sticking some drawing pins on the card. Sketch the shape. Make more shapes in this way. What is the relationship between these shapes and the outline of the book?

   The outline of each shape has the same length as the outline of the book.

   (b) Form a square using the string. What is the length of each side of the square?

   Student's own answers.

   (c) Form an equilateral triangle using the string. What is the length of each side of the triangle?

   Student's own answers.

Class Activity 2

Objective: To understand the concept of area of squares and rectangles.

A shopping centre is organising an indoor market.

The area allocated for each stall is a 2 m by 1 m rectangle. The floor plan of the space used for the indoor market is shown below. Every square on the plan represents an actual length of 1 m by 1 m.

Existing shop units											Existing shop units

Fountain area

Stalls can only be set up in the grey shaded area around the middle - they can't be placed over the fountain or over the green area, where there are shops already.

There should be a distance of 1 m between the stalls, the fountain area and the existing shops, and stalls must be placed directly over the grey squares (without overlapping the lines). The rental fee for each stall is £50.

1. Imagine you own the shopping centre. Discuss with your classmates how you can place as many stalls as possible so that you can charge the most rent. Copy the diagram and then draw the stalls on it to show your final layout.

    For example:

    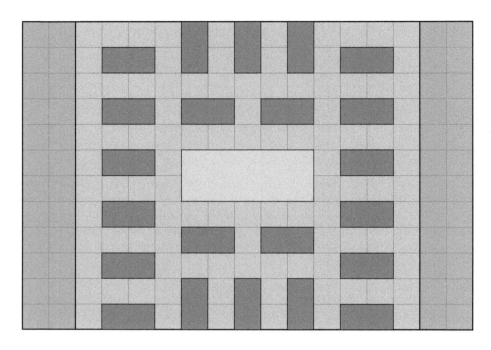

2. Repeat Question **1** using all the same rules as before, except the stalls can be any shape of area exactly 5 m^2. One example below. Answers should have a total of 10 stalls, but the orientation of the stalls may vary.

    For example:

    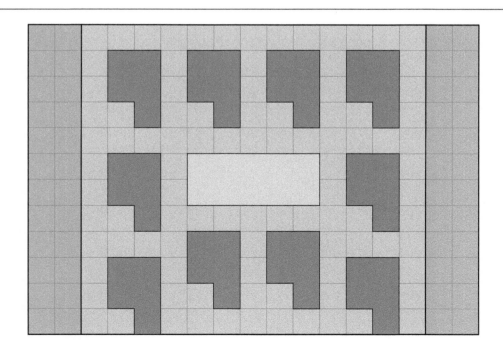

Class Activity 3

Objective: To explore the area of a triangle.

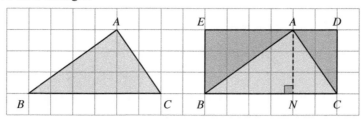

1. **(a)** Using a ruler, draw triangle *ABC* on a piece of square grid paper.
   (b) Draw a rectangle *EBCD* around *ABC* as shown. Cut out *EBCD*.
   (c) Fold along the line *AB*. Then fold along the line *AC*.
   (i) What is the relationship between triangles *ABN* and *BAE*?

   The triangles are identical.

   (ii) What is the relationship between triangles *CAN* and *CAD*?

   The triangles are identical.

   (iii) What can you say about the area of triangle *ABC* and the area of the rectangle *EBCD*? Explain your answer.

   Triangles *ABN* and *BAE* have the same area as they are identical, and triangles *CAN* and *CAD* have the same area as they are identical. Therefore, the area of triangle *ABC* is half the area of the rectangle *EBCD*.

2. Draw three more triangles and repeat the steps above. See if you notice the same results when you draw different types of triangles.

   Student's own answer.

3.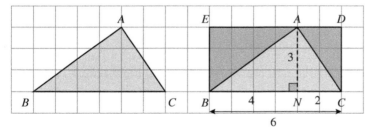

   If $\triangle ABC$ has lengths $BC = 6\,\text{cm}$ and $AN = 3\,\text{cm}$.
   (a) Area of *EBCD* = length × width

   $$= \underline{\hspace{1cm}} \times \underline{\hspace{1cm}}$$
   $$= \underline{\hspace{1cm}} \text{cm}^2$$

   Area of *EBCD* = length × width
   $$= 6 \times 3$$
   $$= 18\,\text{cm}^2$$

   (b) Area of $\triangle ABC = \frac{1}{2} \times$ area of the rectangle

   $$= \frac{1}{2} \times \underline{\hspace{1cm}}$$
   $$= \underline{\hspace{1cm}} \text{cm}^2$$

   Area of $\triangle ABC = \frac{1}{2} \times$ area of the rectangle
   $$= \frac{1}{2} \times 18$$
   $$= 9\,\text{cm}^2$$

4.

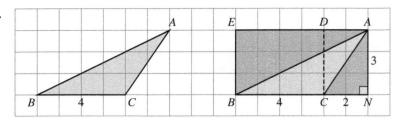

The diagram shows a triangle ABC with $BC = 4\,$cm and $AN = 3\,$cm. The rectangle $AEBN$ is added to it in order to find the area of the triangle. Copy and complete the working below.

(a) Area of $\triangle ABN = \dfrac{1}{2} \times$ area of the rectangle $AEBN$

$$= \dfrac{1}{2} \times BN \times \underline{\qquad}$$

$$= \dfrac{1}{2} \times 6 \times \underline{\qquad}$$

$$= \underline{\qquad}\ \text{cm}^2$$

Area of $\triangle ABN = \dfrac{1}{2} \times$ area of the rectangle $AEBN$

$$= \dfrac{1}{2} \times BN \times AN$$

$$= \dfrac{1}{2} \times 6 \times 3$$

$$= 9\,\text{cm}^2$$

(b) Area of $\triangle ACN = \dfrac{1}{2} \times$ area of the rectangle

$$= \dfrac{1}{2} \times CN \times \underline{\qquad}$$

$$= \dfrac{1}{2} \times 2 \times \underline{\qquad}$$

$$= \underline{\qquad}\ \text{cm}^2$$

Area of $\triangle ACN = \dfrac{1}{2} \times$ area of the rectangle $ADCN$

$$= \dfrac{1}{2} \times CN \times AN$$

$$= \dfrac{1}{2} \times 2 \times 3$$

$$= 3\,\text{cm}^2$$

(c) Area of $\triangle ABC =$ Area of $\triangle ABN - \underline{\qquad\qquad}$

$$= \underline{\qquad} - \underline{\qquad}$$

$$= \underline{\qquad}\ \text{cm}^2$$

Area of $\triangle ABC =$ Area of $\triangle ABN -$ Area of $\triangle ACN$

$$= 9 - 3$$

$$= 6\,\text{cm}^2$$

(d) How can you work out the area of $\triangle ABC$ using the lengths of BC and AN directly?

Area of $\triangle ABC = \dfrac{1}{2} \times BC \times AN$

Class Activity 4

Objective: To identify the base and the perpendicular height in a triangle.

1. Identify two different possible bases on each triangle and the corresponding perpendicular height to each base.

(a)

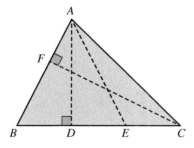

If the base is *AB* then the perpendicular height is *FC*.
If the base is *BC* then the perpendicular height is *DA*.

(b)

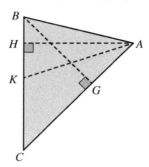

If the base is *BC* then the perpendicular height is *HA*.
If the base is *AC* then the perpendicular height is *GB*.

(c)

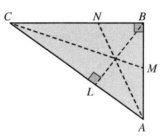

If the base is *CA* then the perpendicular height is *LB*.
If the base is *CB* then the perpendicular height is *BA*.

(d)

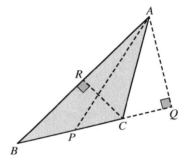

If the base is *AB* then the perpendicular height is *RC*.
If the base is *BQ* then the perpendicular height is *QA*.

2. Use tracing paper to copy each triangle *PQR* and draw the perpendicular height to the base *PQ*.

(a)

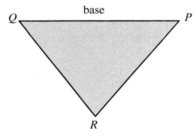

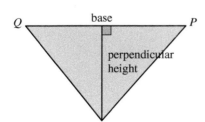

(b)

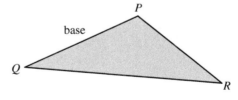

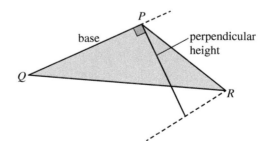

3. For each triangle identify the base corresponding to the perpendicular height XN.

(a)

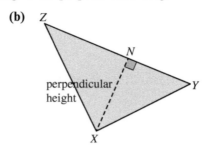

Base = *NY*

(b)

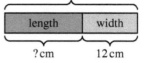

Base = *ZY*

Try It!

Section 10.1

1. Find the perimeter of each of these figures.

   (a)

   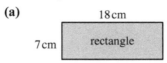

   18 cm

   7 cm — rectangle

   (b)

   16 cm

   square

   Solution

   (a) Perimeter of rectangle = 2 × (18 + 7)
   $$= 50 \text{ cm}$$

   (b) Perimeter of square = 4 × 16
   $$= 64 \text{ cm}$$

2. Given the perimeter, find the unknown length in each of these figures.

   (a) Perimeter = 84 cm

   ? cm

   rectangle   12 cm

   (b) Perimeter = 76 m

   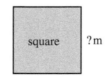

   square   ? m

   Solution

   (a) Draw a bar model to show the perimeter of the rectangle:

   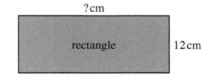

   Perimeter = 84

length	width	length	width
? cm	12 cm	? cm	12 cm

Taking only half of this:

Half of perimeter = 84 ÷ 2 = 42 cm

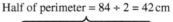

length	width
? cm	12 cm

Length + width = 42
Length + 12 = 42
Length = 42 − width
$$= 42 - 12$$
$$= 30 \text{ cm}$$

(b) Using a bar model to show the perimeter of the square:

Perimeter = 76 cm

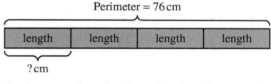

length	length	length	length
? cm			

Perimeter = length + length + length + length
4 × length = 76
Length = 76 ÷ 4
$$= 19 \text{ m}$$

3. A school playground is shaped like a rectangle and measures 50 m by 25 m. A child walks all the way around the outer edge of the playground. Calculate the total distance the child has walked.

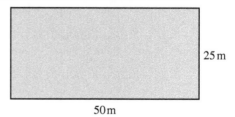

25 m

50 m

Solution

Perimeter of the playground = 2 × (50 + 25)
$$= 150 \text{ m}$$

Therefore, the total distance walked by the child is 150 m.

Section 10.2

4. A rectangular carpet measures 5 m by 3 m. Find the perimeter and area of the carpet.

Solution
Perimeter of the carpet $= 2 \times (5 + 3)$
$$= 16\,\text{m}$$
Area of the carpet $= \text{length} \times \text{width}$
$$= 5 \times 3$$
$$= 15\,\text{m}^2$$

5. A tile in the shape of a square has a length of 40 cm. A wall is covered completely with 100 of these tiles. What is the area of the wall?

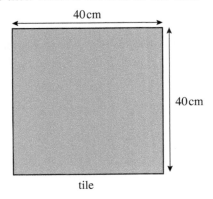
tile

Solution
Area of one tile $= \text{length} \times \text{length}$
$$= 40 \times 40$$
$$= 1600\,\text{cm}^2$$
Area of 100 tiles $= 1600 \times 100$
$$= 160\,000\,\text{cm}^2$$

Therefore, the area of the wall is $160\,000\,\text{cm}^2$.

6. The top face of a rectangular box has a width of 8 cm. If the area of the top face is 80 cm², find the length of the face.

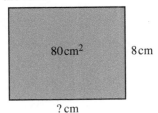
? cm

Solution
Area of rectangular face $= \text{length} \times \text{width}$
$$80\,\text{cm}^2 = \text{length} \times 8\,\text{cm}$$
$$\text{length} = 80 \div 8$$
$$= 10\,\text{cm}$$

Section 10.3

7. The perimeter of this triangle is 38 cm. How long is the missing side?

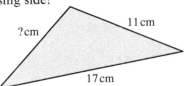

Solution
Perimeter of triangle = sum of the lengths of its three sides
$$38 = ? + 11 + 17$$
Therefore, the missing side $= 38 - 11 - 17$
$$= 10\,\text{cm}$$

8. (a) One face of a building is an equilateral triangle of side length 80 m. Find the perimeter of the face.

(b) An isosceles triangle has a perimeter of 36 cm. The unequal side is 10 cm long. How long are the two equal sides?

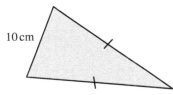

Solution
(a) The side of the building is an equilateral triangle so,
Perimeter $= 3 \times \text{one side}$
$$= 3 \times 80$$
$$= 240\,\text{m}$$

(b) For an isosceles triangle,
Perimeter $= (2 \times \text{one side}) + \text{the third side}$
$$36 = (2 \times \text{side}) + 10$$
$$2 \times \text{side} = 36 - 10$$
$$= 26$$
Each of the two equal sides $= 26 \div 2$
$$= 13\,\text{cm}$$

9. Find the area of each of these triangles.

(a)   **(b)**

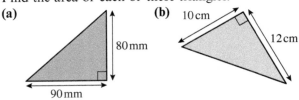

Solution
(a) Area of triangle $= \dfrac{1}{2} \times \text{base} \times \text{perpendicular height}$
$$= \dfrac{1}{2} \times 90 \times 80$$
$$= 3600\,\text{mm}^2$$

(b) Area of triangle $= \frac{1}{2} \times$ base $\times$ perpendicular height

$$= \frac{1}{2} \times 10 \times 12$$
$$= 60\,\text{cm}^2$$

10. (a) Find the area of this triangle.

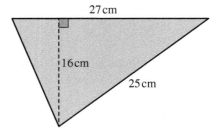

(b) Serena thinks that the area of $\triangle ABC$ is given by $\frac{1}{2} \times 3 \times 7$. Her sister Venus thinks that actually it's given by $\frac{1}{2} \times 5 \times 7$.

Which of the sisters do you think is right? Explain why the other one is wrong.

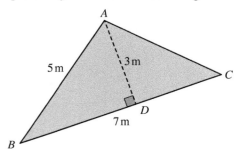

Solution

(a) Area of the triangle $= \frac{1}{2} \times$ base $\times$ perpendicular height

$$= \frac{1}{2} \times 27 \times 16$$
$$= 216\,\text{cm}^2$$

(b) You need to use the base and the perpendicular height to calculate the area of a triangle.
If the base of the triangle is $7\,\text{cm}$, then the perpendicular height must make a right angle with this side. So the perpendicular height is $3\,\text{cm}$, not $5\,\text{cm}$. So Serena is correct.

11. (a) Find the area of this shaded triangle.

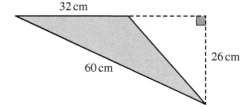

(b) The area of $\triangle PQR$ is $60\,\text{cm}^2$.
$PR = 8\,\text{cm}$.
Find the length of QR.

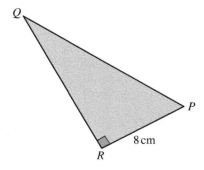

Solution

(a) Area of triangle $= \frac{1}{2} \times$ base $\times$ perpendicular height

$$= \frac{1}{2} \times 32 \times 26$$
$$= 416\,\text{cm}^2$$

(b) Area of $\triangle PQR = \frac{1}{2} \times QR \times PR$

$$60 = \frac{1}{2} \times QR \times 8$$
$$60 = 4 \times QR$$
$$QR = 60 \div 4$$
$$= 15\,\text{cm}$$

12. The balcony of a flat has an area of paving and an area of fake grass, represented by $\triangle ABC$. The grass has an area of $480\,\text{m}^2$. Find the unknown length, BC.

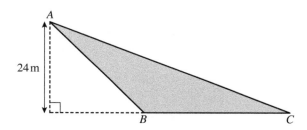

Solution

Area of triangular grass $= \frac{1}{2} \times$ base $\times$ perpendicular height

$$480 = \frac{1}{2} \times BC \times 24$$
$$= \frac{1}{2} \times 24 \times BC$$
$$= 12 \times BC$$
$$BC = 480 \div 12$$
$$= 40\,\text{m}$$

The required length is $40\,\text{m}$.

Practice 10.1

1. Find the perimeter of each of these figures. Draw a bar model to explain your reasoning.

(a)

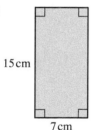

15 cm

7 cm

(b)

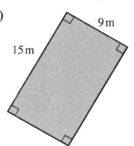

9 m

15 m

(c)

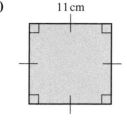

11 cm

Solution

(a) Perimeter of rectangle = 2 × (15 + 7)
= 44 cm

(b) Perimeter of rectangle = 2 × (15 + 9)
= 48 m

(c) Perimeter of square = 4 × 11
= 44 cm

2. Find the length of the unknown side in each of these figures. Draw a bar model to explain your reasoning.

(a)

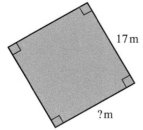

17 m

? m

Perimeter = 64 m

(b)

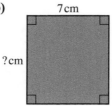

7 cm

? cm

Perimeter = 32 cm

(c)

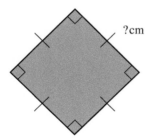

? cm

Perimeter = 68 m

Solution

(a) Perimeter of rectangle = 2 × (length + width)

$$\text{Length} + \text{width} = \frac{\text{perimeter of rectangle}}{2}$$
$$= \frac{64}{2}$$
$$= 32\,\text{m}$$

Length = 32 − width
= 32 − 17
= 15 cm

(b) Perimeter of rectangle = 2 × (length + width)

$$\text{Length} + \text{width} = \frac{\text{perimeter of rectangle}}{2}$$
$$= \frac{32}{2}$$
$$= 16\,\text{cm}$$

Length = 16 − width
= 16 − 7
= 9 cm

(c) $$\text{Length} = \frac{\text{perimeter of square}}{4}$$
$$= \frac{68}{4}$$
$$= 17\,\text{cm}$$

If the question does not have a diagram, it can help you visualise the problem if you draw your own diagram.

3. A rectangular football pitch measures 105 m by 68 m. Work out the perimeter of the football pitch.

Solution

Perimeter of football pitch = 2 × (105 + 68)
= 346 m

4. A rectangular vegetable plot has a perimeter of 80 m and a length of 30 m. Find the width of the plot.

Solution

Perimeter of vegetable plot = 2 × (length + width)

$$80 = 2 \times (30 + \text{width})$$
$$\text{Width} + 30 = \frac{80}{2}$$
$$= 40\,\text{m}$$
$$\text{Width} = 40 - 30$$
$$= 10\,\text{m}$$

5. A piece of wire is bent into the shape of a square of side length 24 cm. What is the length of the piece of wire?

Solution
Length of wire = perimeter of square formed
$$= 24 \times 4$$
$$= 96 \, cm$$

6. Two square bathroom tiles are placed next to each other and have a perimeter of 96 cm. Find the side length of one bathroom tile.

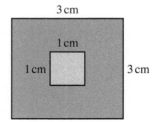

Perimeter = 96 cm

Solution
Perimeter of two tiles = 6 × side length = 96 cm
Side length = 96 ÷ 6
$$= 16 \, cm$$

7. A shopping centre has a square fountain with a statue on a square platform in the middle. The fountain measures 3 m by 3 m and the platform measures 1 m by 1 m.

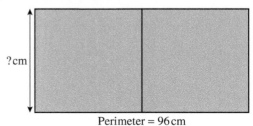

Kourtney says that the perimeter of the fountain is 16 m. Kylie says that the perimeter is 8 m. Kendall says that it's 12 m. Who do you agree with, and why?

Solution
The perimeter of the fountain is the perimeter of the outer edge of the square (the square platform is part of the fountain).

Perimeter = 3 + 3 + 3 + 3 = 12 m
Therefore, Kendall is correct.

Practice 10.2

Level 1   **GCSE Grade** 1^+/2^-

1. Find the area of each of these figures.

(a)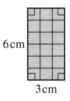

6 cm

3 cm

(b)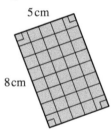

5 cm

8 cm

(c)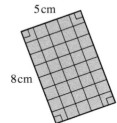

5 cm

8 cm

(d)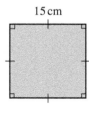

15 cm

Solution
(a) Area of rectangle = length × width
$$= 6 \times 3$$
$$= 18 \, cm^2$$

(b) Area of rectangle = length × width
$$= 8 \times 5$$
$$= 40 \, m^2$$

(c) Area of rectangle = length × width
$$= 16 \times 8$$
$$= 128 \, m^2$$

(d) Area of square = length × length
$$= 15 \times 15$$
$$= 225 \, cm^2$$

2. Find the length of the unknown side in each of these rectangles.

(a)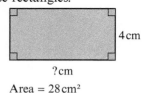

4 cm

? cm

Area = 28 cm²

(b)

6 cm

? cm

Area = 108 m²

(c)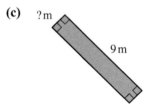

? m

9 m

Area = 18 m²

Solution

(a) Area of rectangle = length × width
$$28 = \text{length} \times 4$$
$$\text{Length} = 28 \div 4$$
$$\text{Length} = 7\,\text{cm}$$

(b) Area of rectangle = length × width
$$108 = \text{length} \times 6$$
$$\text{Length} = 108 \div 6$$
$$= 18\,\text{cm}$$

(c) Area of rectangle = length × width
$$18 = 9 \times \text{width}$$
$$\text{Width} = 18 \div 9$$
$$= 2\,\text{m}$$

Level 2 | GCSE Grade 2 / 2⁺

Remember you can draw a diagram if it helps you to visualise the question.

3. The length of a square card is 14 cm. Find the area of the card.

Solution

Area of the card = length × length
$$= 14 \times 14$$
$$= 196\,\text{cm}^2$$

4. A rectangle has length 15 m and you want to find its width. Its area is 75 m². Copy and complete this calculation:

Width = _____ ÷ _____

= _____

Solution

Width = 75 ÷ 15
$$= 5\,\text{m}$$

5. The rectangular cover of a textbook has an area of 432 cm². Find the length of the cover if the width is 18 cm.

Solution

Area of cover = length × width
$$432 = \text{length} \times 18$$
$$\text{Length} = 432 \div 18$$
$$= 24\,\text{cm}$$

6. A rectangular wall tile is 25 cm by 10 cm. It takes 240 of these tiles to tile a wall. What is the area of the wall?

Solution

Area of one wall tile = length × width
$$= 25 \times 10$$
$$= 250\,\text{cm}^2$$

Area of 240 wall tiles = 240 × 250
$$= 60\,000\,\text{cm}^2$$

7. A square plot of land is worth £2000 per square metre. The length of the plot of land is 10 m. Logan thinks the land is worth £20 000, but Jake thinks it's worth £200 000. Which of them do you think is correct, and why?

Solution

Area of the piece of land = length × length
$$= 10 \times 10$$
$$= 100\,\text{m}^2$$

Cost of the piece of land = 2000 × 100
$$= £200\,000$$

Therefore, Jake is correct, the land is worth £200 000.

8. A living room is 10 m by 6 m. The cost of carpet is £34 per square metre. What is the cost of carpet for the whole living room?

Solution

Area of the floor = length × width
$$= 10 \times 6$$
$$= 60\,\text{m}^2$$

Cost of carpet for 1 m² = £34
Cost of carpet for 60 m² = 34 × 60
$$= £2040$$

Practice 10.3

Level 1 | GCSE Grade 1⁺ / 2⁺

1. Find the perimeter of each triangle.

(a)

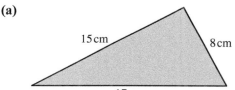

(b)

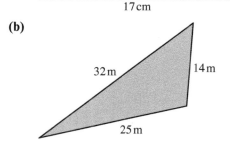

Solution

(a) Perimeter of the triangle = 15 + 8 + 17
$$= 40\,\text{cm}$$

(b) Perimeter of the triangle = 32 + 14 + 25
$$= 71\,\text{m}$$

2. Find the area of the rectangle and the shaded triangle in each diagram.

(a)

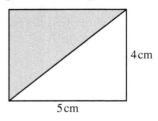

4 cm

5 cm

(b)

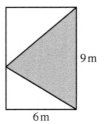

9 m

6 m

(d)

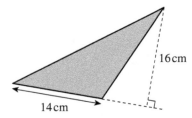

16 cm

14 cm

Solution

(a) Area of triangle

$$= \frac{1}{2} \times \text{base} \times \text{perpendicular height}$$

$$= \frac{1}{2} \times 6 \times 4$$

$$= 12 \, \text{m}^2$$

(b) Area of triangle $= \frac{1}{2} \times$ base $\times$ perpendicular height

$$= \frac{1}{2} \times 32 \times 12$$

$$= 192 \, \text{m}^2$$

(c) Area of triangle $= \frac{1}{2} \times$ base $\times$ perpendicular height

$$= \frac{1}{2} \times 16 \times 22$$

$$= 176 \, \text{cm}^2$$

(d) Area of triangle $= \frac{1}{2} \times$ base $\times$ perpendicular height

$$= \frac{1}{2} \times 14 \times 16$$

$$= 112 \, \text{cm}^2$$

Solution

(a) Area of the rectangle = length × width

$$= 4 \times 5$$

$$= 20 \, \text{cm}^2$$

Area of the triangle $= \frac{1}{2} \times$ area of the rectangle

$$= \frac{1}{2} \times 20$$

$$= 10 \, \text{cm}^2$$

(b) Area of the rectangle = length × width

$$= 9 \times 6$$

$$= 54 \, \text{m}^2$$

Area of the triangle $= \frac{1}{2} \times$ area of the rectangle

$$= \frac{1}{2} \times 54$$

$$= 27 \, \text{m}^2$$

3. Find the area of each shaded triangle.

(a)

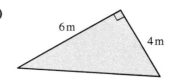

6 m

4 m

(b)

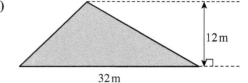

12 m

32 m

(c)

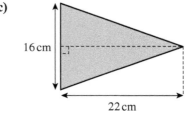

16 cm

22 cm

Level 2

4. Find the perimeter and area of each triangle.

(a)

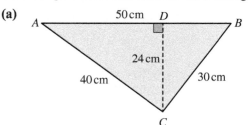

50 cm D

A B

24 cm

40 cm   30 cm

C

(b)

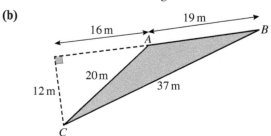

19 m

16 m

A B

12 m   20 m   37 m

C

Solution

(a) Perimeter of the triangle = 40 + 30 + 50
$$= 120\,\text{cm}$$

Area of the triangle $= \frac{1}{2} \times$ base
$$\times \text{ perpendicular height}$$
$$= \frac{1}{2} \times 50 \times 24$$
$$= 600\,\text{cm}^2$$

(b) Perimeter of the triangle = 19 + 20 + 37
$$= 76\,\text{m}$$

Area of the triangle $= \frac{1}{2} \times$ base
$$\times \text{ perpendicular height}$$
$$= \frac{1}{2} \times 19 \times 12$$
$$= 114\,\text{m}^2$$

5. ΔXYZ represents a view of an ice cream cone. Find the perimeter and area of the triangle.

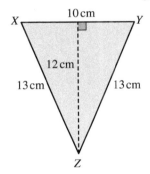

Solution

Perimeter of the triangle = 13 + 13 + 10
$$= 36\,\text{cm}$$

Area of the triangle $= \frac{1}{2} \times$ base
$$\times \text{ perpendicular height}$$
$$= \frac{1}{2} \times 10 \times 12$$
$$= 60\,\text{cm}^2$$

6. A school wants to paint its new logo on the school playground. The logo is made up of a white, a red and a blue triangle as shown in the diagram.

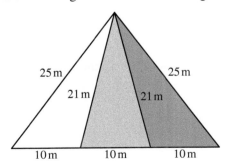

Vina thinks that the logo will need less blue paint than red and white paint, because the blue triangle has the same base but a smaller perimeter than the

other two. Hajrah disagrees, and thinks it will need the same amount of paint of each colour. Who do you agree with? Explain your answer.

Solution

Hajrah is correct, the same amount of paint is needed for each colour. The area of each triangle is found using the base and perpendicular height, which have the same values in each triangle.

7. ΔABC has a base length of 18 cm and an area of 63 cm². Find the perpendicular height of the triangle. **Hint:** Draw the triangle first.

Solution

Area of $\Delta ABC = \frac{1}{2} \times$ base $\times$ perpendicular height
$$63 = \frac{1}{2} \times 18 \times \text{ perpendicular height}$$
$$= 9 \times \text{ perpendicular height}$$

Perpendicular height = 63 ÷ 9
$$= 7\,\text{cm}$$

8. A triangular advertisement board has an area of 96 m² and a perpendicular height of 6 m. Find the base length of the board.

Hint: Draw the triangle first.

Solution

Area of triangle $= \frac{1}{2} \times$ base $\times$ perpendicular height
$$96 = \frac{1}{2} \times \text{ base} \times 6$$
$$= \frac{1}{2} \times 6 \times \text{ base}$$
$$= 3 \times \text{ base}$$
Base = 96 ÷ 3
$$= 32\,\text{m}$$

Challenge 10

GCSE Grade 3 Composite figures are made up of different shapes. The figure below is made up of a rectangle, a square and a triangle. Find the perimeter and the area of the composite figure.

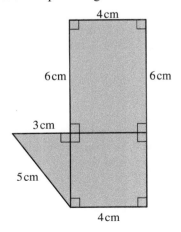

Solution

The perimeter is the total length of the outline of a closed figure.

Perimeter of composite figure = 4 + 6 + 4 + 4 + 5
                                          + 3 + 6
                                          = 32 cm

Area of rectangle = length × width
                          = 4 × 6
                          = 24 cm²

Area of square = length × length
                      = 4 × 4
                      = 16 cm²

Area of triangle = $\frac{1}{2}$ × base × height
                        = $\frac{1}{2}$ × 3 × 4
                        = 6 cm²

Total area of composite figure = Area of rectangle
                                          + area of square +
                                          area of triangle
                                          = 24 + 16 + 6
                                          = 46 cm²

Revision Exercise 10

1. Find the perimeter and area of each of these figures.

(a)

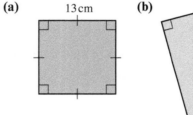
13 cm

(b)

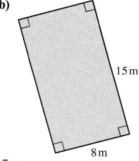
15 m
8 m

(c)

17 cm
5 cm

Solution

(a) The figure is a square
    ∴ each side is equal.
    Perimeter of the figure = sum of all sides
                                   = 13 + 13 + 13 + 13
                                   = 52 cm
    Area of the figure = 13 × 13
                              = 169 cm²

(b) The figure is a rectangle
    ∴ the opposite sides are equal to each other.
    Perimeter of the figure = 2 × (length + width)
                                   = 2 × (15 + 8)
                                   = 46 m
    Area of the figure = 15 × 8
                              = 120 cm²

(c) Perimeter of the figure = 2 × (17 + 5)
                                   = 44 cm
    Area of the figure = 17 × 5
                              = 85 cm²

2. For each figure, find the length of the unknown side.

GCSE Grade 2⁻

(a)

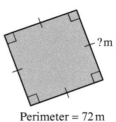
?m
Perimeter = 72 m

(b)

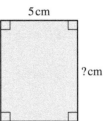
5 cm
?cm
Perimeter = 34 cm

(c)

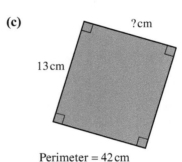
?cm
13 cm
Perimeter = 42 cm

Solution

(a) Length = $\frac{\text{perimeter of square}}{4}$
                  = $\frac{72}{4}$
                  = 18 m

(b) Perimeter of rectangle = 2 × (length + width)
    Length + width = $\frac{\text{perimeter of rectangle}}{2}$
                          = $\frac{34}{2}$
                          = 17 cm
    Length = 17 − width
                = 17 − 5
                = 12 cm

(c) Perimeter = 2 × (length + width)
    42 = 2 × (13 + width)
    Width = $\frac{42}{2}$ − 13
            = 8 cm

3. Find the length of the unknown side, *AB*, in each of these rectangles.

GCSE Grade 2⁻

(a)

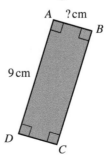
A   ?cm
B
9 cm
D
C
Area = 27 cm²

(b)

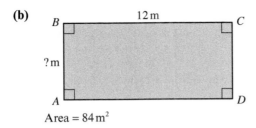

12 m

B ⌐———————⌐ C

? m

A ⌐_____⌐ D

Area = 84 m²

Solution

(a) Area of rectangle = length × width

$$27 = 9 \times AB$$
$$AB = 27 \div 9$$
$$= 3 \text{ cm}$$

(b) Area of rectangle = length × width

$$84 = 12 \times AB$$
$$AB = 84 \div 12$$
$$= 7 \text{ m}$$

4. Find the perimeter and area of each shaded triangle.

GCSE Grade 3⁻

(a)

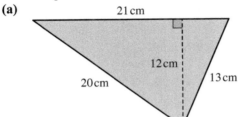

21 cm

12 cm

20 cm   13 cm

(b)

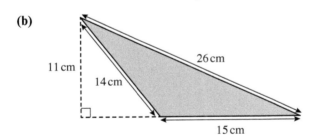

11 cm

14 cm   26 cm

15 cm

(c)

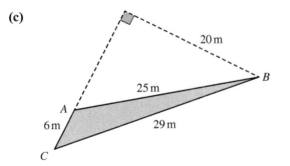

20 m

25 m

A   B

6 m   29 m

C

Solution

(a) Perimeter of triangle = sum of sides

$$= 21 + 20 + 13$$
$$= 54 \text{ cm}$$

Area of triangle = $\frac{1}{2}$ × base × perpendicular height

$$= \frac{1}{2} \times 21 \times 12$$
$$= 126 \text{ cm}^2$$

(b) Perimeter of triangle = sum of sides

$$= 26 + 14 + 15$$
$$= 55 \text{ cm}$$

Area of triangle = $\frac{1}{2}$ × base × perpendicular height

$$= \frac{1}{2} \times 15 \times 11$$
$$= 82.5 \text{ cm}^2$$

(c) Perimeter of triangle = sum of sides

$$= 25 + 29 + 6$$
$$= 60 \text{ m}$$

Area of triangle = $\frac{1}{2}$ × base × perpendicular height

$$= \frac{1}{2} \times 6 \times 20$$
$$= 60 \text{ m}^2$$

5. A rectangular playground has a perimeter of 222 m and a length of 75 m. Find the width of the playground.

GCSE Grade 2⁺

Solution

Perimeter = 2 × (length + width)

$$\text{Length + width} = \frac{\text{perimeter of rectangle}}{2}$$
$$= \frac{222}{2}$$
$$= 111 \text{ m}$$
$$\text{Width} = 111 - \text{length}$$
$$= 111 - 75$$
$$= 36 \text{ m}$$

6. A triangular banner has an area of 68 m² and a perpendicular height of 8 m. Find the length of the base of the banner.

GCSE Grade 3⁻

Solution

Area of banner = $\frac{1}{2}$ × base × perpendicular height

$$68 = \frac{1}{2} \times \text{base} \times 8$$
$$= \frac{8}{2} \times \text{base}$$
$$= 4 \times \text{base}$$
$$\text{Base} = 68 \div 4$$
$$= 17 \text{ m}$$

7. Arrange these shapes in orders of their areas from the smallest to the largest.

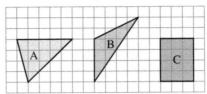

Solution

Area of shape $A = \frac{1}{2} \times$ base $\times$ perpendicular height

$$= \frac{1}{2} \times 5 \times 4$$

$$= 10 \text{ square units}$$

Area of shape $B = \frac{1}{2} \times$ base $\times$ perpendicular height

$$= \frac{1}{2} \times 4 \times 4$$

$$= 8 \text{ square units}$$

Area of shape $C = $ width $\times$ length

$$= 3 \times 4$$

$$= 12 \text{ square units}$$

Therefore, the areas from smallest to largest are B, A, C.

8. Samira has a rectangular garden $ABCD$. The path BD splits the garden into two triangles. She wants to know the perimeter of the rectangular garden. Eyal says that she just needs to measure the perimeter of triangle ABD and multiply it by 2. Do you think he's correct, and why?

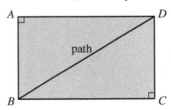

Solution

As the path is part of the rectangular garden, the perimeter is simply the perimeter of the rectangle itself. Therefore, Eyal is incorrect.
The path shouldn't be included at all.

9. The orange shaded area represents a wide path around a rectangular lawn, $PQRS$. Find the area of the path $ABCD$.

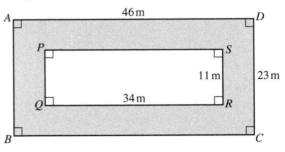

Solution

Area of $ABCD = 46 \times 23$

$$= 1058 \text{ m}^2$$

Area of $PQRS = 34 \times 11$

$$= 374 \text{ m}^2$$

Area of path $= 1058 - 374$

$$= 684 \text{ m}^2$$

Class Activity 1

Objective: To draw the nets of a cube. You will need a marker pen, a ruler and thin, square grid card.

1. Copy the figures shown onto thin, square grid card. Cut them out and try to fold them into cubes.

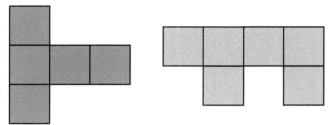

    Figure 1   Figure 2

    (a) Are you able to fold Figure 1 into a cube? Why?

    No. There are only five squares. The net would need another square to be folded into a complete cube.

    (b) Are you able to fold Figure 2 into a cube? Why?

    No. The two squares at the bottom would overlap.

2. Use the marker pen to draw the figure below.

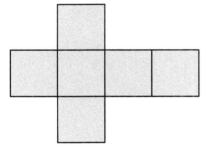

3. Cut out the figure and fold it into a cube.

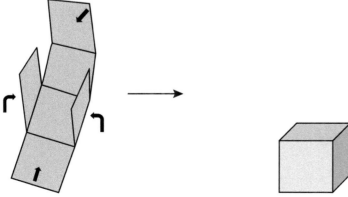

    (a) How many squares are there in the original figure?

(b) How many faces does the cube have?

6

4. Try drawing another two different nets of the cube on square grid paper. Compare your nets with your classmates. How many different nets have you found as a class?

Student's answer.

Class Activity 2

Objective: To draw a cube and a cuboid on paper. You will need a square grid, a pencil, an eraser and a ruler.

1. Using a ruler, draw a square with side length 4 cm on the paper.

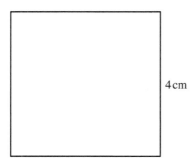

4 cm

2. On the same diagram, draw another identical square overlapping the first square.

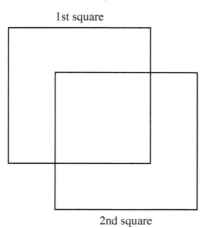

1st square

2nd square

3. Draw lines to join the four pairs of corners of the two squares, to form the image of a cube of edges 4 cm.

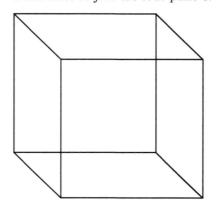

4. Now, using the same method, draw a cuboid with length 5 cm and height 2 cm.

5. For the cubes and cuboids you've drawn, count the edges and the vertices. Do you notice any similarities between them? Or any differences? Compare your answers with those of your classmates.

Student's answer.

Class Activity 3

Objective: To observe the relationship between the surface area of a solid and its net.

1. Collect some empty cardboard boxes of different shapes and sizes, cardboard inner rolls from kitchen towels or toilet rolls, and some tins of food such as soup.

2. Use a pair of scissors to cut along some edges of a closed box such that the shape formed is in one piece and can lie flat on your desk.

3. Compare the shape you have formed with your classmates' shapes. If two or more of you started with the same box, what is different and what is the same about the shapes you have formed? Do they have the same area? Explain your answer.

Student's answer.

4. The flat shape you have formed is a net of the box. Explain why this is so.

A net is a flat, 2D figure that can be folded to form a three-dimensional shape. The shape formed can be folded to form a box.

5. What is the relationship between the area of the net and the surface area of the box?

The area of the net and the surface area of the box are the same.

6. Cut an open box, such as a gift box without its lid, in a similar way.

7. What is the same and what is different about the nets of a closed box and an open box?

The net of a closed box and an open box will be the same, but with one face (the lid of the box) missing.

8. Cut the paper label of a soup can along a straight line from the top to the bottom. Lie the label flat on your desk. What shape do you get?

The net of the paper label of a soup can is in the shape of a rectangle.

Class Activity 4

Objective: To use the nets of a cube and a cuboid to find their surface areas.

1. Look at this figure that is made out of six squares. Copy and complete the sentences.

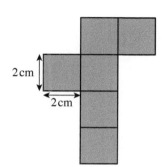

2 cm

2 cm

(a) This is the net of a _____cube_____.

(b) Calculate the area of each square face of the net.
    Area of each square face = _____4_____ cm^2

(c) Surface area of the cube formed by this
    net = _____24_____ cm^2

2. Look at this figure then copy and complete the sentences.

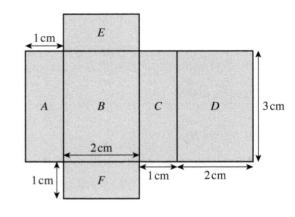

   (a) This is the net of a _____cuboid_____.

   (b) Calculate the area of each face of the net.

   Area of A = _____3_____ cm²

   Area of C = _____3_____ cm²

   Area of B = _____6_____ cm²

   Area of D = _____6_____ cm²

   Area of E = _____2_____ cm²

   Area of F = _____2_____ cm²

   (c) Surface area of the cuboid formed by this net = _____22_____ cm²

Class Activity 5

Objective: To calculate surface area and volume in real-world situations.

A production engineer designs a corn flakes box of length 18 cm, width 6 cm and height 25 cm.

1. Calculate the surface area of the box.

Total surface area of the box = $2 \times 18 \times 6 + 2 \times 6 \times 25 + 2 \times 25 \times 18 = 216 + 300 + 900 = 1416$ cm²

2. The cost of the cardboard for the box is 2 pence per 100 cm².

   Work out the cardboard cost of the box. Give your answer to the nearest 10 pence. There are flaps inside the box so that the sides can be glued together. How much do you think this would affect your calculation of the cost of the cardboard needed to make the box? Discuss this with your classmates.

   The cost of the cardboard = $(1416 \div 100) \times 2p = 28.32p = 30p$ (to the nearest 10 pence). The flaps would mean more cardboard is required, adding

   to the cost. However, this would only have a small effect on the calculation.

3. What is the maximum volume of corn flakes that can be put into the box?

   Volume of the box = length × width × height = $18 \times 6 \times 25 = 2700$ cm³

Try It!

Section 11.1

1. Draw each of these figures with pencil and square grid paper. Draw the figures larger to make cutting out easier. Predict which one(s) will not form a cube when folded, and explain your reasoning. Now cut out the figures and fold them. Was your prediction correct?

(a)

(b)

(c)

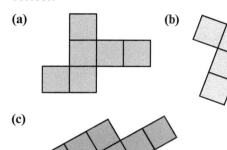

Solution

The figure that will not form a cube is **(b)**. This is because the bottom-most and right-most flaps will overlap.

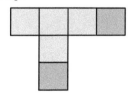

2. Each of these figures shows a student's drawing for the net of a cuboid. For each one, predict whether it would form a cuboid when folded, explaining your reasoning. If the drawing is not a net, how could you make it a net?

Diagram A

Diagram B

Solution

(a) It will not form a cuboid because it has only 5 faces while a cuboid has 6 faces. A fix would be to add another small square face on the rightmost side of the figure.

(b) It will form a cuboid.

Section 11.2

3. A toy-box is shaped like a cube, with sides of length 1 m.
   (a) Find the surface area of the toy-box.
   (b) The top face of the box is a removable lid. What is the surface area of the toy-box with the lid removed?

Solution

(a) Calculate the area of 1 square face.
   Area of 1 face = 1 × 1
   $$= 1\,m^2$$
   There are 6 identical faces on a toy box-shaped like a cube.
   ∴ Surface area of the cube = 6 × 1
   $$= 6\,m^2$$

(b) The surface area of the toy-box with the lid removed is the surface area of the toy-box with one face removed.
   Surface area with lid removed = 6 − 1
   $$= 5\,m^2$$

4. Here is a cuboid.

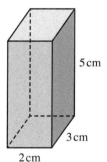

5 cm

3 cm

2 cm

(a) Draw a net of this cuboid.
(b) Work out the surface area of the cuboid.
(c) Draw a second net for the cuboid. Does it have the same surface area as the first? Explain your reasoning.

Solution

(a)

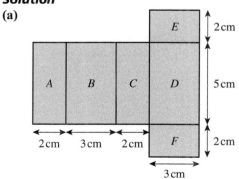

(b) Areas of rectangles *A*, *B*, *C* and *D*
   = (2 + 3 + 2 + 3) × 5
   = 50 cm²
   Areas of rectangles *E* and *F* = 2 × (3 × 2)
   = 12 cm²
   Total surface area of the cuboid = 50 + 12
   = 62 cm²

239

Note: The other method described in the Student Book, that sums the pairs of rectangles of the same dimensions, could be used instead. This also applies to all the following cuboid surface area questions.

(c) All nets of the cuboid will have the same surface area.

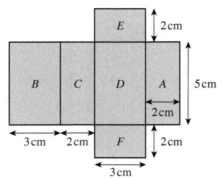

3 cm   2 cm   F   2 cm

3 cm

5. A closed gift box is made in the shape of a cube. The surface area of the box, including its lid, is 216 cm².

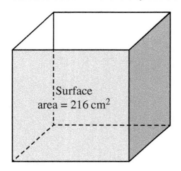

Surface area = 216 cm²

(a) Find the area of one face of the box.
(b) The lid of the box is taken off to open the box. Draw a net of the open box and calculate its surface area.
(c) Compare your net with your classmates' nets and calculations. Do your answers agree?

Solution
(a) Open up the cube to see its net. Since the top is not open, there are 6 faces.

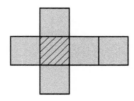

The area of one square face = 216 ÷ 6
$$= 36 \text{ cm}^2$$

(b)

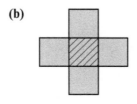

The surface area is found by taking away one face.
New surface area = 216 − 36
$$= 180 \text{ cm}^2$$

(c) Student's answer.

Section 11.3

6. A jewellery box is a cuboid with dimensions 4 cm by 5 cm by 3 cm.

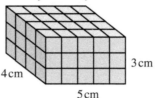

3 cm

4 cm

5 cm

(a) Decide how you want to slice the box into slices that are 1 cm thick. Draw or create the slices using interlocking cubes. Work out the total number of small cubes in each slice, and hence the total number of small cubes in all the slices. Compare your answers with your classmates.
(b) Hence find the volume of the box.
(c) Can you see a quicker calculation to work out the total number of small cubes and hence the volume of the box?

Solution
(a) We cut the cuboid into three slices, and each slice is 1 cm thick, for example:

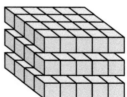

(b) From the above example:
Number of small cubes in one slice = 5 × 4
$$= 20$$
Number of small cubes in three slices = 20 × 3
$$= 60$$
So the volume of the jewellery box = 60 cm³

(c) You can multiply the three dimensions (length, width and height) together to get the same result.

7. A wooden block is in the shape of a cube with length 7 cm. Find the volume of the block.

Solution
The base of the cube is a square.
Base area = 7 × 7
$$= 49 \text{ cm}^2$$
Volume of the wooden block = base area × height
$$= 49 \times 7$$
$$= 343 \text{ cm}^3$$

8. An empty shoe box is in the shape of a cuboid. What is the volume of the shoe box?

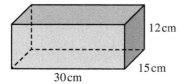

12 cm
15 cm
30 cm

Solution

The base of the shoe box is a rectangle.
Volume of the shoe box = base area × height
$$= 30 \times 15 \times 12$$
$$= 5400 \, \text{cm}^3$$

9. A rectangular tank of length 4 m is filled with water. The depth of the water is 3 m. The volume of water in the tank is 24 m³. Find the width of the tank.

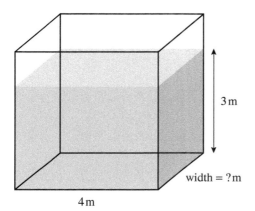

3 m

width = ? m

4 m

Solution

The depth of the water is 3 m.
Volume of water = base area × depth of water
$$24 = \text{base area} \times 3$$
$$\text{Base area} = 24 \div 3$$
$$= 8 \, \text{m}^2$$
Width = base area ÷ length
$$= 8 \div 4$$
$$= 2 \, \text{m}$$

Practice 11.1

Level 1

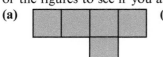

1. Which of these figures do you think will form a cube when folded? Explain your answers. Now copy and cut out these figures. Try forming a cube from each of the figures to see if you are correct.

(a) **(b)**

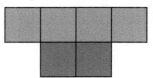

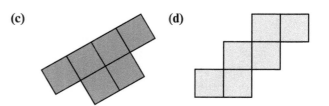

(c) **(d)**

Solution

(a) It will not form a cube because it only has 5 sides while a cube has 6 sides.

(b) It will form a cube.

(c) It will not form a cube because the bottom 2 flaps will overlap.

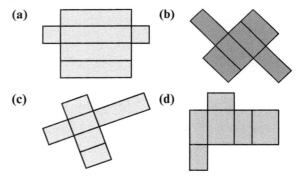

(d) It will form a cube.

2. Predict which of these figures will not form a cuboid when folded. Explain your answers. Now copy and cut out these figures. Try forming a cuboid from each of the figures to see if your prediction is correct.

(a) **(b)**

(c) **(d)**

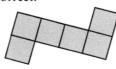

Solution

(a) It will form a cuboid.

(b) It will not form a cuboid because some of the adjacent sides do not fit each other.

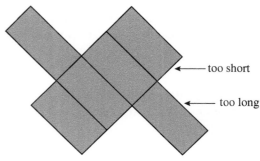

too short

too long

(c) It will not form a cuboid because some of the adjacent sides do not fit each other.

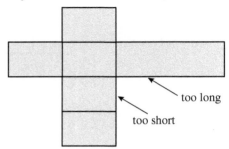

too long

too short

(d) It will form a cuboid.

Level 2

3. On plain paper draw a cube that has edges of length 3 cm.

Solution
(diagram not drawn to scale)

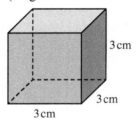

3 cm

3 cm

3 cm

4. On plain paper draw a cuboid in which two of the faces have length 4 cm and width 3 cm

Solution
(diagram not drawn to scale)

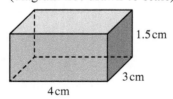

1.5 cm

3 cm

4 cm

5. On plain paper or square grid paper draw two different, accurate nets of a cube with side length 3 cm.

Solution
One possible solution shown here.
(diagram not drawn to scale)

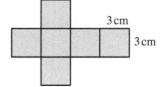

3 cm

3 cm

6. On plain paper or square grid paper draw two different, accurate nets of a cuboid with length 3 cm, width 2 cm and height 4 cm.

Solution
One possible solution shown below.
(Diagram not drawn to scale)

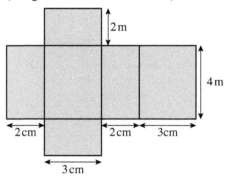

2 m

4 m

2 cm   2 cm   3 cm

3 cm

7. Copy and complete each figure so that it becomes a net of a cuboid.

(a)

(b)

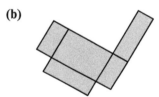

Solution
(a) One possible solution is shown below.

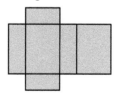

(b) One possible solution is shown below.

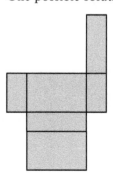

8. Copy each figure and modify one of its rectangles so that it becomes a net of a cuboid.

(a)

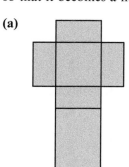

(b)

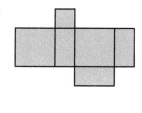

Solution

(a) One possible solution is shown below.

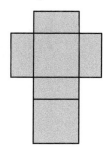

(b) One possible solution is shown below.

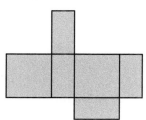

Practice 11.2

Level 1   GCSE Grade **3**

1. Find the surface area of each cube.
Hint: You can start by drawing a net of each cube.

(a)

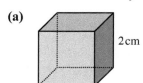

2 cm

(b)

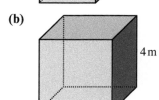

4 m

(c)

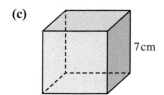

7 cm

Solution

(a) Consider the net of the cube:

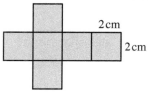

2 cm
2 cm

Each face of the cube is a square of side length 2 cm.
Total surface area of the cube
$= 6 \times (\text{area of square})$
$= 6 \times (2 \times 2)$
$= 6 \times 4$
$= 24 \, \text{cm}^2$

(b) Consider the net of the cube:

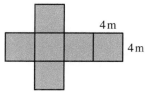

4 m
4 m

Each face of the cube is a square of side length 4 m.
Total surface area of the cube
$= 6 \times (4 \times 4)$
$= 6 \times 16$
$= 96 \, \text{m}^2$

(c) Consider the net of the cube:

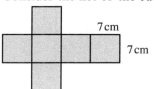

7 cm
7 cm

Each face of the cube is a square of side length 7 cm.
Total surface area of the cube
$= 6 \times (7 \times 7)$
$= 6 \times 49$
$= 294 \, \text{cm}^2$

2. Find the surface area of each cuboid.
Hint: You can start by drawing a net of each cuboid.

(a)

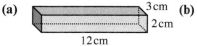

3 cm
2 cm
12 cm

(b)

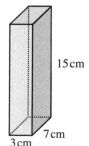

15 cm
7 cm
3 cm

(c)

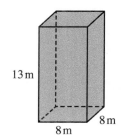

13 m
8 m
8 m

Solution

(a) Consider the net of the cuboid:

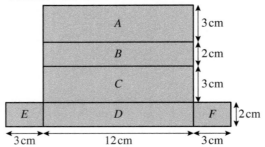

Area of rectangles A, B, C and D
$$= (3 + 2 + 3 + 2) \times 12$$
$$= 120\,\text{cm}^2$$
Area of rectangles E and $F = 2 \times (3 \times 2)$
$$= 12\,\text{cm}^2$$
Total surface area of the cuboid $= 120 + 12$
$$= 132\,\text{cm}^2$$

(b) Consider the net of the cuboid:

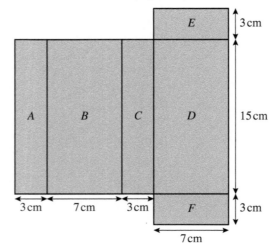

Areas of rectangles A, B, C and D
$$= (3 + 7 + 3 + 7) \times 15$$
$$= 300\,\text{cm}^2$$
Areas of rectangles E and $F = 2 \times (7 \times 3)$
$$= 42\,\text{cm}^2$$
Total surface area of the cuboid $= 300 + 42$
$$= 342\,\text{cm}^2$$

(c) Consider the net of the cuboid:

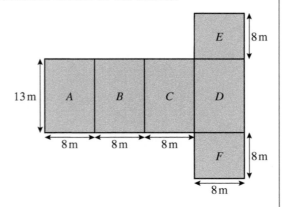

Areas of rectangles A, B, C and D
$$= (8 + 8 + 8 + 8) \times 13$$
$$= 32 \times 13$$
$$= 416\,\text{m}^2$$
Areas of rectangles E and $F = 2 \times (8 \times 8)$
$$= 2 \times 64$$
$$= 128\,\text{m}^2$$
Total surface area of the cuboid $= 416 + 128$
$$= 544\,\text{m}^2$$

Level 2　**GCSE Grade 3⁺**

3. Given the surface area of each cube, find the area of one face of the cube.

(a) Surface area $= 78\,\text{cm}^2$　**(b)** Surface area $= 108\,\text{m}^2$

Solution

(a) Consider the net of the cube:

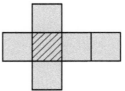

The area of one square face $= 78 \div 6$
$$= 13\,\text{cm}^2$$

(b) Consider the net of the cube:

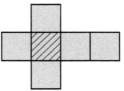

The area of one square face $= 108 \div 6$
$$= 18\,\text{cm}^2$$

4. A box without a lid is in the shape of a cube. The top of the box is open. The surface area (not including the inside of the box) is $215\,\text{cm}^2$. Find the area of one face.

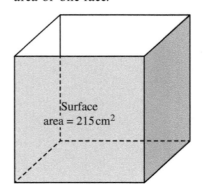

Surface area $= 215\,\text{cm}^2$

Solution
Area of one face = external surface area ÷ 5
$$= 215 \div 5$$
$$= 43 \, \text{cm}^2$$

5. A tray is made out of thin pieces of wood glued together. What is the total area of wood used to make the tray?
Hint: Start by drawing a net of the tray.

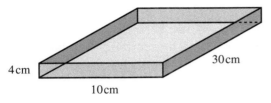

Solution
External surface area = $2 \times 10 \times 4 + 2 \times 30 \times 4$
$$+ \, 1 \times 10 \times 30$$
$$= 80 + 240 + 300$$
$$= 620 \, \text{cm}^2$$

Practice 11.3

Level 1

GCSE Grade 2⁺

1. Find the volume of each cube.

(a) 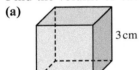 3 cm

(b) 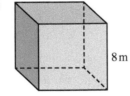 8 m

Solution
(a) The base of the cube is a square.
Base area = 3×3
$$= 9 \, \text{cm}^2$$
Volume of the cube = 9×3
$$= 27 \, \text{cm}^3$$

(b) The base of the cube is a square.
Base area = 8×8
$$= 64 \, \text{m}^2$$
Volume of the cube = 64×8
$$= 512 \, \text{m}^3$$

2. Find the volume of each cuboid.

(a) 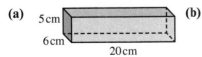 5 cm 6 cm 20 cm

(b) 5 m 3 m 2 m

Solution
(a) The base of the cuboid is a rectangle.
Volume of the cuboid = base area × height
$$= 20 \times 6 \times 5$$
$$= 600 \, \text{cm}^3$$

(b) The base of the cuboid is a rectangle.
Volume of the cuboid = base area × height
$$= 2 \times 3 \times 5$$
$$= 30 \, \text{m}^3$$

3. Which has the greater volume, a cube with side length 11 cm or a cuboid with dimensions 8 cm by 8 cm by 20 cm?

Solution
Volume of the cube = base area × height
$$= 11 \times 11 \times 11$$
$$= 1331 \, \text{cm}^3$$
Volume of the cuboid = base area × height
$$= 8 \times 8 \times 20$$
$$= 1280 \, \text{cm}^3$$
∴ the cube has the greater volume.

Level 2

GCSE Grade 3⁻

4. A rectangular tank is filled with 25 200 cm³ of water. The base of the tank is 40 cm by 30 cm. What is the depth of the water in the tank?
Hint: Draw a diagram to help you visualise the question.

Solution
Base area of the tank = 40×30
$$= 1200 \, \text{cm}^2.$$
Volume of water = base area × depth of water
$$25\,200 = 1200 \times \text{depth of water}$$
Depth of water = $25\,200 \div 1200$
$$= 21 \, \text{cm}$$

5. A container is 30 cm long, 20 cm wide and 40 cm high. 4800 cm³ of water is poured into it. Will the water overflow? Explain your answer.

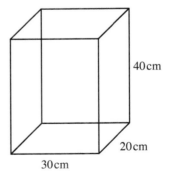

40 cm 20 cm 30 cm

Solution
The base area of the container = 30×20
$$= 600 \, \text{cm}^2$$
Volume of water = base area × depth of water
$$4800 = 600 \times \text{depth of water}$$
Depth of water = $4800 \div 600$
$$= 8 \, \text{cm}$$
∴ the water would occupy a space 30 cm long, 20 cm wide and 8 cm high. The tank will not overflow because the depth of water is less than the height of the container.

6. A rectangular tank is 4 m deep. When seven cubes filled with water, each of side length 2 m, are emptied into it, it becomes full. What is the base area of the rectangular tank?

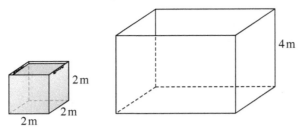

Solution

Volume of each cube of water $= 2 \times 2 \times 2$
$$= 8 \, m^3$$
Volume of 7 cubes $= 7 \times 8$
$$= 56 \, m^3$$
Volume of tank $=$ base area $\times$ height
$$56 = \text{base area} \times 4$$
$$\text{Base area} = 56 \div 4$$
$$= 14 \, m^2$$

Challenge 11

 Find the volume and total surface area of each of these solids, which are made up of 1 cm cubes.

(a) 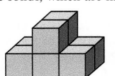   **(b)**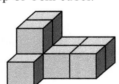

Solution

Area of a face of one cube $= 1 \times 1$
$$= 1 \, cm^2$$
Volume of one cube $= 1 \times 1 \times 1$
$$= 1 \, cm^3$$
Hence,

(a) Number of squares facing up or down $= 6 + 6$
$$= 12$$
Number of squares facing left or right $= 4 + 4$
$$= 8$$
Number of squares facing front or back $= 4 + 4$
$$= 8$$
Total number of squares $= 12 + 8 + 8$
$$= 28$$
$\therefore$ total surface area of the solid $= 1 \times 28$
$$= 28 \, cm^2$$
Total number of cubes $= 8$
$\therefore$ volume of the solid $= 1 \times 8$
$$= 8 \, cm^3$$

(b) Number of squares facing up or down $= 7 + 7$
$$= 14$$
Number of squares facing left or right $= 5 + 5$
$$= 10$$

Number of squares facing front or back $= 4 + 4$
$$= 8$$
Total number of squares $= 14 + 10 + 8$
$$= 32$$
$\therefore$ total surface area of the solid $= 1 \times 32$
$$= 32 \, cm^2$$

Total number of cubes $= 9$
$\therefore$ volume of the solid $= 1 \times 9$
$$= 9 \, cm^3$$

Revision Exercise 11

1. Predict which of these are nets of cuboids or cubes. Explain your reasoning. Now copy each figure and cut it out. See if it can be folded to form a cuboid or a cube and see if your predictions are correct.

(a)

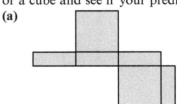

(b)

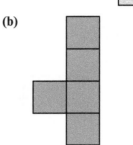

(c)

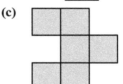

(d)

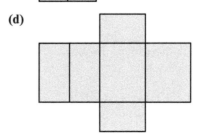

Solution

(a) is a net of a cuboid.
(b) is not a net of a cube because it only has five square faces while a cube has six.
(c) is not the net of a cube because the two square flaps on the left will overlap when it is folded up.

(d) is not the net of a cuboid. There are the correct number of faces and their dimensions are correct but they are not set out in the right order, pairs of identical faces are next to each other so will not be opposite when folded up.

2. Find the total surface area and volume of each of these cubes and cuboids.

(a)

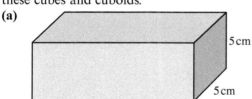

14 cm, 5 cm, 5 cm

(b)

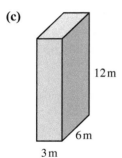

20 mm, 20 mm, 20 mm

(c)

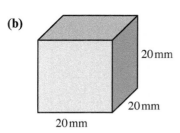

12 m, 6 m, 3 m

(d)

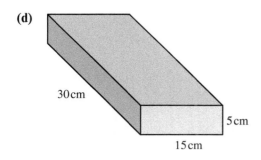

30 cm, 15 cm, 5 cm

Solution

(a) Total surface area $= 2 \times 5 \times 5 + 4 \times 14 \times 5$
$$= 50 + 280$$
$$= 330 \, \text{cm}^2$$
Volume $= 14 \times 5 \times 5$
$$= 350 \, \text{cm}^3$$

(b) Total surface area $= 6 \times 20 \times 20$
$$= 2400 \, \text{cm}^2$$
Volume $= 20 \times 20 \times 20$
$$= 8000 \, \text{cm}^3$$

(c) Total surface area $= 2 \times 3 \times 6 + 2 \times 6 \times 12$
$$+ 2 \times 12 \times 3$$
$$= 36 + 144 + 72$$
$$= 252 \, \text{m}^2$$
Volume $= 6 \times 3 \times 12$
$$= 216 \, \text{m}^3$$

(d) Total surface area $= 2 \times 5 \times 15 + 2 \times 15 \times 30$
$$+ 2 \times 5 \times 30$$
$$= 150 + 900 + 300$$
$$= 1350 \, \text{cm}^2$$
Volume $= 15 \times 30 \times 5$
$$= 2250 \, \text{cm}^3$$

3. Find the total surface area and volume of these 3D objects. Ignore the overlap of the lid in **(a)**.

(a)

5 cm, 6 cm, 15 cm

(b)

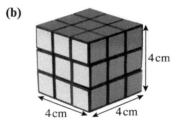

4 cm, 4 cm, 4 cm

Solution

(a) Consider a net of the box:

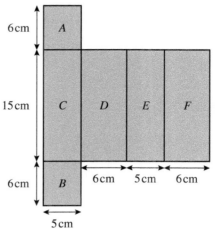

6 cm, A, 15 cm, C, D, E, F, 6 cm, B, 6 cm, 5 cm, 6 cm, 5 cm

Area of rectangles A and $B = 2 \times (6 \times 5)$
$$= 60 \, \text{cm}^2$$
Area of rectangles C, D, E and F
$$= 15 \times (5 + 6 + 5 + 6)$$
$$= 330 \, \text{cm}^2$$
$\therefore$ total surface area of the box $= 60 + 330$
$$= 390 \, \text{cm}^2$$

Volume of the box $= 15 \times 6 \times 5$
$$= 450 \, \text{cm}^3$$

(b) Consider a net of the cube:

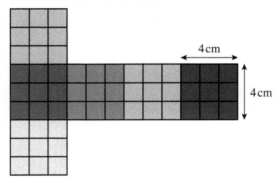

Area of each face = 4×4
$= 16 \, cm^2$

∴ total surface area of the cube = 16×6
$= 96 \, cm^2$

Volume of the cube = $4 \times 4 \times 4$
$= 64 \, cm^3$

4. If a cube has a total surface area of $1176 \, cm^2$, what is the area of one square face of the cube?

Solution
Area of one face = $1176 \div 6$
$= 196 \, cm^2$

5. Copy and complete each of these figures so that each forms a net of a cube or a cuboid.

(a)

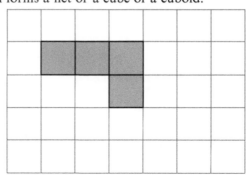

(b)

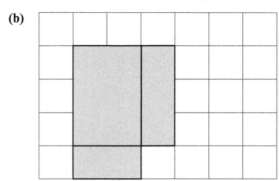

Solution
Alternatives to those shown are possible.

(a)

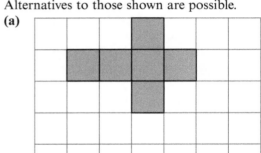

(b)

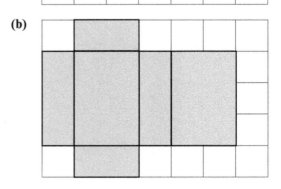

6. Draw two cuboids that each have a volume of $160 \, cm^3$. Label the length, width and height of each cuboid clearly. Explain each of your choices.

Solution
An example of a suitable answer is shown below.

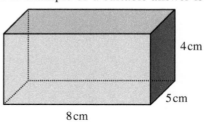

Volume = width × length × height = $8 \times 5 \times 4$
$= 160 \, cm^3$

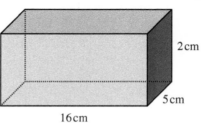

Volume = width × length × height = $16 \times 5 \times 2$
$= 160 \, cm^3$

7. Find the volume and total surface area of each of these solids, which are made up of 1 cm cubes.

Hint: Build the shapes using interlocking cubes to help you find the volume. To find the surface area, work out the area of one face, and count how many faces you can see on all sides of your shape.

(a)

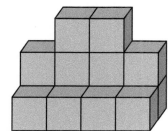

(b)

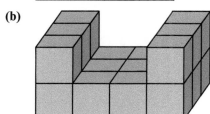

Solution

Area of a face of one cube = 1 × 1
= 1 cm²
Volume of one cube = 1 × 1 × 1
= 1 cm³
Hence,

(a) Number of squares facing up or down = 2 × 8
= 16
Number of squares facing left or right = 2 × 4
= 8
Number of squares facing front or back
= 2 × 10
= 20
Total number of squares = 16 + 8 + 20
= 44
∴ total surface area of the solid = 1 × 44
= 44 cm²
Total number of cubes = 14
∴ volume of the solid = 1 × 14
= 14 cm³

(b) Number of squares facing up or down = 2 × 12
= 24
Number of squares facing left or right = 2 × 9
= 18
Number of squares facing front or back
= 2 × 6
= 12

Total number of squares = 24 + 18 + 12
= 54
∴ total surface area of the solid = 1 × 54
= 54 cm²
Total number of cubes = 18
∴ volume of the solid = 1 × 18
= 18 cm³

8. You melt some wax of volume 80 cm³. You pour the molten wax into a mould that has the shape of a cuboid with a square base of side length 4 cm.

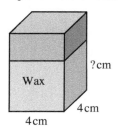

?cm

Wax

4cm

4cm

(a) What is the area of the square base of the mould?

(b) Find the height of the wax in the mould.

Solution

(a) The area of the square base of the mould
= 4 × 4 = 16 cm²

(b) Volume of the wax = base area × height of wax
80 = 16 × height of wax
Height of wax = 80 ÷ 16
= 5 cm

9. A nursery would like to build a rectangular sandpit that is 9 m long, 6 m wide and 1 m deep in the playground. Sand costs £30 per cubic metre. The budget to spend on sand is £1500. Can enough sand be purchased to fill the sandpit completely?

Solution

The volume of sand required to build the sandpit
= 9 × 1 × 6 = 54 m³

If sand is £30 per cubic metre, the budget required to fill the sandpit = 30 × 54 = £1620.

Therefore, it is not possible to completely fill the sandpit with a budget of £1500.

12 Collecting, Organising and Displaying Data

Class Activity 1

Objective: To understand how data is collected through surveys.

Task: Work in pairs to design a simple survey form.

You will need to use word processing software.

1. Design a simple survey. Your survey form should include at least three questions. Some possible topics are:
   - favourite movie,
   - favourite sport,
   - birthday months,

   - favourite singer or band,
   - number of siblings,
   - favourite food and drink.

   An example is shown.

Profile Information

1. In which month were you born?
   - ☐ January
   - ☐ May
   - ☐ September

   - ☐ February
   - ☐ June
   - ☐ October

   - ☐ March
   - ☐ July
   - ☐ November

   - ☐ April
   - ☐ August
   - ☐ December

2. What is your zodiac sign?
   - ☐ Aries
   - ☐ Leo
   - ☐ Sagittarius

   - ☐ Taurus
   - ☐ Virgo
   - ☐ Capricorn

   - ☐ Gemini
   - ☐ Libra
   - ☐ Aquarius

   - ☐ Cancer
   - ☐ Scorpio
   - ☐ Pisces

3. How many pupils in your form were at the same primary school as you?
   - ☐ 0–5
   - ☐ More than 20

   - ☐ 6–10

   - ☐ 11–15

   - ☐ 16–20

   Student's own designs.

2. Compare your survey with another pair. Which questions do you think are most effective? Why?

   Student's own answer.

Class Activity 2

Objective: To practise classifying and tabulating data.

Task: Work in a pair or small group and record your results using the method described.

You will need a six-sided dice.

1. Predict which number on the dice will show up the highest number of times in 12 rolls. Write down your guess.

2. Copy the table. Roll the dice 12 times. For each roll, mark a stroke '/' (called a **tally**) under the 'Tally' column in the same row as the outcome. To make counting easier, mark every fifth tally with a cross stroke through the previous four. Complete the table as you carry out the activity.

Number rolled	Tally	Frequency
1		
2		
3		
4		
5		
6		

The number of times each outcome occurs is called the **frequency** of the outcome. Write down the frequency of each outcome by counting its corresponding tally marks after you have recorded all 12 rolls. The table formed is called a **frequency table**.

Answer the following questions.

(a) Which number appeared most frequently?
(b) Which number appeared least frequently?
(c) Did you make the correct prediction?

Student's own interpretation of their results.

Class Activity 3

Objective: To create a pictogram from a set of data.
Task: Work in a pair or small group to create a pictogram from the data below.

Class 7S are holding a bake sale and Cassie and her friends all bring in cupcakes. Cassie brings in 12 cakes, Oliver bakes 6 cakes, Saskia brings in 15 cakes and Ahmed bakes 9 cakes.

1. Look at the data about the cake sale and decide on a suitable image to use to represent the data. You should also decide what quantity of cakes one whole image represents. Add this information into your key.

A suitable image for the cupcake would be

Each represents 4 cupcakes.

2. Using your chosen image, create a pictogram for this data.

An example of a correct pictogram.

	Number of cupcakes
Cassie	🧁 🧁 🧁
Oliver	🧁 🧁
Saskia	🧁 🧁 🧁 🧁
Ahmed	🧁 🧁 ◢
Each 🧁 represents 4 cupcakes	

3. Compare your pictogram with those of your classmates. Discuss the images you used and the choice you made about what one of your images would represent.

Student's own answer.

Class Activity 4

Objective: To create a bar chart using a spreadsheet program.

1. The following table shows the favourite ice cream flavours in a survey of a group of students.

Favourite ice cream flavour	Chocolate	Vanilla	Strawberry	Mango	Mint
Number of students (Frequency)	13	8	9	5	5

(a) Copy the data into a spreadsheet program.

	A	B	C	D	E	F
1	Favourite ice cream flavour	Chocolate	Vanilla	Strawberry	Mango	Mint
2	Number of students	13	8	9	5	5

(b) Use the data to create a bar chart.
Highlight the entire table and then click the Insert menu option →
Column or Bar Chart → 2D Clustered Column.

(c) Write down three things that you notice about the presentation of the bar chart created.

The gaps between adjacent bars are equal.
The width of each bar is the same.
The data is given on the vertical axis.

(d) Write down three statements about the data that you can make from the bar chart.

Chocolate is the most popular flavour of ice cream.
Mango and mint are the least popular flavours of ice cream.
The same number of people favour mango and mint ice cream.

(e) Change the data in your spreadsheet and see how the bar chart changes.

Student's own answer.

2. Using the same data, see if you can produce a horizontal bar chart.
   (a) How is the horizontal bar chart different from the original bar chart?

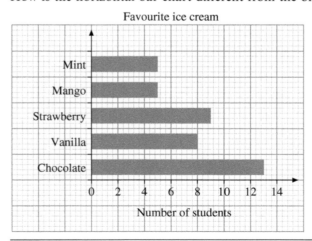

Favourite ice cream

(b) Do you think one of these charts presents the data better? If so, why?

The display of both sets of data is the same but in a different orientation. It might be easier to see that chocolate is the favourite flavour in the

horizontal bar chart, as there is more space to display the bars in the horizontal orientation.

Class Activity 5

Objective: To gather data, draw and compare pictograms, bar charts and vertical line charts.

1. Search in newspapers, online news websites or other media to find an article that includes a set of interesting data.
2. Present the data in a pictogram.
3. Present the data in a vertical line chart.
4. Present the data in a bar chart.
5. Which of the above charts do you think works best for your data and why? Why don't the other charts work as well?
6. Write your own article about your chart to present to your class. Explain what your chart shows.

Student's own answers.

Try It!

Section 12.1

1. Data was collected from a group of 40 students on their scores for a spelling test. The maximum score for the test is 10.

5	4	3	2	8	8	7	7	9	8
8	8	8	8	2	4	7	3	8	7
6	1	3	8	7	7	7	8	7	2
8	8	7	8	7	4	3	7	7	8

(a) Copy and complete the frequency table for this data.

Score	0	1	2	3	4	5	6	7	8	9	10
Tally											
Frequency											

(b) What was the highest score obtained for the test?

(c) What score was obtained by the greatest number of students?

(d) How many students scored fewer than 5 out of 10?

(e) How many students passed the spelling test if a student needed to score more than 5 out of 10 to pass?

Solution

(a)

Score	0	1	2	3	4	5	6	7	8	9	10
Tally		/	///	////	///	/	/	⦀⦀ ⦀⦀ //	⦀⦀ ⦀⦀ ////	/	
Frequency	0	1	3	4	3	1	1	12	14	1	0

(b) The highest score obtained was 9.

(c) The highest frequency is 14, so the score obtained by the largest number of students was 8.

(d) Number of students who scored less than 5 out of 10
= 0 + 1 + 3 + 4 + 3
= 11

(e) Number of students who scored more than 5 out of 10
= 1 + 12 + 14 + 1 + 0
= 28

2. This table shows the modes of transport taken by a group of students to travel to school.

Mode of transport	Number of students (Frequency)
Bus	15
Car	6
Train	12
Bicycle	4
Walk	8

(a) How many students were there in the group?

(b) Which mode of transport was used by the highest number of students?

(c) How many more students took a bus than walked to school?

(d) What fraction of students in the group cycled to school?

Solution

(a) Total number of students in the group
$$= 15 + 6 + 12 + 4 + 8$$
$$= 45$$

(b) Bus

(c) $15 - 8 = 7$
7 more students took a bus than the number who walked to school.

(d) Fraction of students in the class who cycled to school

$$= \frac{\text{number of students who cycled}}{\text{total number of students in the class}}$$

$$= \frac{4}{45}$$

Section 12.2

3. This pictogram shows the number of cakes sold by a shop over five days.

Day	Number of cakes sold
Monday	🟤 🟤 🟤
Tuesday	🟤
Wednesday	🟤 🟤 🟤 ◗
Thursday	🟤 🟤
Friday	🟤 🟤 🟤 ◗

Each 🟤 represents 4 cakes.

(a) How many cakes were sold on Wednesday?

(b) What was the total number of cakes sold over the five days?

(c) On which day was the smallest number of cakes sold?

(d) How many more cakes were sold on Friday than on Tuesday?

(e) What fraction of the cakes sold in the five days were sold on Monday?

Solution

(a) Since  represents 4 cakes,

🟤 🟤 🟤 ◗ represents

$$4 \times 3\frac{3}{4} = 15 \text{ cakes.}$$

∴ 15 cakes were sold on Wednesday.

(b) There are a total of $13\frac{1}{2}$ 🟤.

∴ Total number of cakes over the five days
$$= 13\frac{1}{2} \times 4$$
$$= 54$$

(c) The smallest number of cakes was sold on Tuesday.

(d) Number of cakes sold on Friday = 15
Number of cakes sold on Tuesday = 4
Difference in number of cakes = 15 − 4
$$= 11$$

∴ 11 more cakes were sold on Friday than on Tuesday.

(e) $\dfrac{\text{number of cakes sold on Monday}}{\text{total number of cakes sold in the 5 days}} = \dfrac{3 \times 4}{54}$

$$= \frac{2}{9}$$

4. This vertical line chart shows the favourite pets in a survey of a group of students.

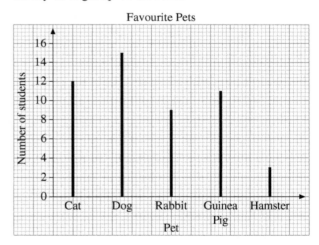

Favourite Pets

(a) Which pet is the most popular?

(b) How many people like cats or dogs best?

(c) How many people didn't choose a guinea pig?

Solution

(a) Dog has the highest frequency of 15, so dogs are the most popular pet.

(b) Number of people who like cats or dogs best
= frequency of cat + frequency of dog
= 12 + 15
= 27
27 people like cats or dogs best.

(c) Number of people who didn't choose a guinea pig as their favourite pet
= sum of all other options
= frequency of cat + frequency of dog + frequency of rabbit + frequency of hamster
= 12 + 15 + 9 + 3
= 39

5. The table shows the number of hours that a surveyed group of students spent on their homework in one week.

Number of hours	1	2	3	4	5
Number of students	12	8	9	7	3

Draw a vertical line chart to represent the data.

Solution

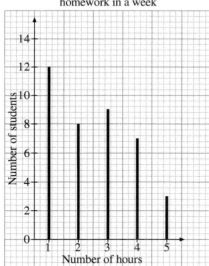

6. This table shows the types of sport played in a survey of students.

Type of sport	Football	Badminton	Rugby	Tennis	Basketball
Number of students (Frequency)	16	6	2	4	12

(a) Copy and complete the bar chart to represent the given data.

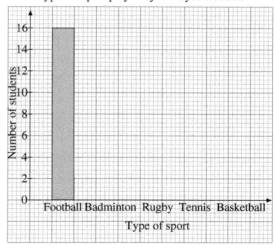

(b) Which sport was the most popular?

(c) What percentage of the students in the survey played football?

(d) What percentage of the students in the survey did not play basketball?

Solution

(a)

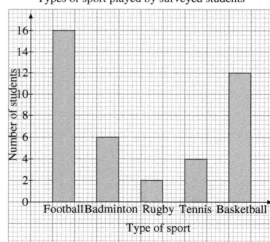

(b) The most popular sport was football.

(c) Total number of students in the class
= 16 + 6 + 2 + 4 + 12
= 40

Percentage of students who played football
$$= \frac{\text{number of students who played football}}{\text{total number of students in the class}} \times 100\%$$
$$= \frac{16}{40} \times 100\%$$
$$= 40\%$$

(d) Number of students who did not play basketball
= 40 − 12
= 28

Percentage of students who did not play basketball

$$= \frac{28}{40} \times 100\%$$
$$= 70\%$$

7. The table shows the number of pets owned by students in a survey.

Number of pets	1	2	3
Number of students	11	18	5

The data is represented in the bar chart below.

Point out three faults in the chart and redraw the chart.

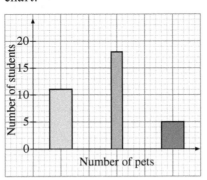

Solution

The three faults in the chart are:
1. The width of the bar for two pets is half the size of the other bars. When comparing the areas of the bars, it provides a wrong impression that the number of students with two pets is smaller than the number of students with one pet.

2. There is no scale on the horizontal axis. This makes it impossible to read the number of pets each bar represents.

3. The chart has no title. This makes it hard to know exactly what the chart is showing.

An improved bar chart is shown below.

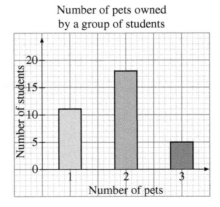

8. The horizontal compound bar chart shows the favourite drinks, from a vending machine, of students in a survey.

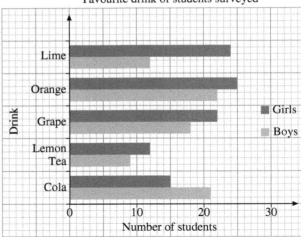

(a) How many students were surveyed?
(b) Which drink was liked by more boys than girls?
(c) Which drink was the most popular?
(d) What was the ratio of the number of boys to the number of girls whose favourite drink was grape? Give your answer in its simplest form.

Solution

(a) Total number of students surveyed
= 24 + 12 + 25 + 22 + 22 + 18 + 12 + 9 + 15 + 21
= 180

(b) Cola was liked by more boys than girls.

(c) Orange was the most popular.

(d) Number boys who like grape = 18
Number of girls who like grape = 22
Ratio of boys to girls who like grape
= 18 : 22
= 9 : 11

Section 12.3

9. The frequency table shows the number of emails received by a group of colleagues on a particular day.

Number of emails received	21–40	41–60	61–80	81–100	101–120
Frequency	13	24	19	12	5

(a) How many people received fewer than 61 emails?
(b) Draw a line chart to represent the data.
(c) Find the ratio of the number of people received from 81 to 100 emails to the number of people who received from 41 to 60 emails. Express your answer in the simplest form.

Solution

(a) Number of people who received fewer than
61 emails = frequency of 21–40 class +
frequency of 41–60 class
= 13 + 24
= 37

(b)

Number of emails received

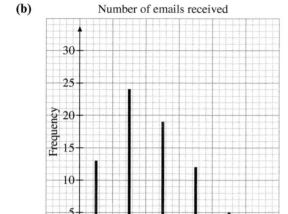

(c) The ratio of the number of people who
received 81–100 emails to the number of
people who received 41–60 emails
= frequency of 81–100 class : frequency of
41–60 class
= 12 : 24
= 1 : 2

10. A vet recorded the masses of 25 dogs. The results
in kg are:

19.0 9.7 11.5 12.0 8.3 13.4 16.8 17.4 24.7

21.4 13.0 6.8 7.5 14.6 17.0 11.7 20.9 26.4

23.2 18.7 28.9 19.1 22.8 18.9 18.5

(a) Copy and complete the frequency table.

Mass (x kg)	Tally	Frequency
$5 \leq x < 10$		
$10 \leq x < 15$		
$15 \leq x < 20$		
$20 \leq x < 25$		
$25 \leq x < 30$		

(b) Find the percentage of dogs with masses less
than 15 kg.

Solution

(a)

Mass (x kg)	Tally	Frequency
$5 \leq x < 10$	////	4
$10 \leq x < 15$	₩₩ /	6
$15 \leq x < 20$	₩₩ ///	8
$20 \leq x < 25$	₩₩	5
$25 \leq x < 30$	//	2
	Total	25

(b) Percentage of dogs with masses less than 15 kg

$= \dfrac{\text{number of dogs with masses less than 15 kg}}{\text{total number of dogs}} \times 100\%$

$= \dfrac{\text{frequency of class} 5 \leq x < 10 + \text{frequency of class} 10 \leq x < 15}{25} \times 100\%$

$= \dfrac{4+6}{25} \times 100\%$

$= \dfrac{10}{25} \times 100\%$

$= 40\%$

Practice 12.1

Level 1 **GCSE Grade 1**

1. Conduct a survey in your class to find out how
many siblings each student has. Copy and complete
the table and answer the questions.

Number of siblings	0	1	2	3	4	>4
Tally						
Number of students (Frequency)						

(a) How many students were there in your survey?
(b) How many students had three siblings?
(c) How many students had fewer than two siblings?

Solution

Student's own answer

2. Data was collected about the ages of students in a
cheerleading team.

10	14	13	12	15	14	13	13
12	13	11	10	14	15	15	12
12	10	11	14	14	13	12	12

(a) Copy and complete the frequency table to represent
the given data.

Age	Tally	Frequency
10		
11		
12		
13		
14		
15		

(b) How many students are there in the cheerleading team?

(c) How many 11-year-old students are there?

(d) Are there more students who are under 11 years old than students who are over 14 years old?

Solution

(a)

Age	Tally	Frequency
10	///	3
11	//	2
12	### /	6
13	###	5
14	###	5
15	///	3

(b) Total students in the cheerleading team
$$= 3 + 2 + 6 + 5 + 5 + 3$$
$$= 24$$

(c) The number of 11-year-old students is 2.

(d) Students under 11 years old = 3
Students over 14 years old = 3
No, there are not more students under 11 than over 14 years, there are 3 students in each category.

Level 2 — GCSE Grade 1^+ / 2^-

3. The table shows the numbers of movies that a surveyed group of people watched in a month.

Number of movies	0	1	2	3	4	5
Number of people (Frequency)	37	42	24	18	8	9

(a) How many people participated in the survey?

(b) How many people watched fewer than three movies in a month?

(c) What fraction of the people watched at least three movies in a month?

Hint: Remember that 'at least three' means three movies or more.

Solution

(a) Number of people who participated in the survey
$$= 37 + 42 + 24 + 18 + 8 + 9$$
$$= 138$$

(b) Number of people who watched fewer than 3 movies in a month
$$= 37 + 42 + 24$$
$$= 103$$

(c) Number of people who watched at least 3 movies in a month
$$= 18 + 8 + 9$$
$$= 35$$

Fraction of people who watched at least 3 movies in a month

$$= \frac{\text{number of people who watched at least 3 movies per month}}{\text{total number of people surveyed}}$$

$$= \frac{35}{138}$$

4. The table shows the favourite colours of a group of students.

Favourite colour	Pink	Green	Yellow	Red	Blue
Number of students (Frequency)	14	10	9	17	13

(a) Which colour is the most popular?

(b) How many more students preferred pink to yellow?

(c) What is the fraction of students whose favourite colour is not red?

Solution

(a) Red is the most popular as it has a frequency of 17.

(b) Pink frequency – yellow frequency
$$= 14 - 9$$
$$= 5$$

(c) Fraction whose favourite is not red

$$= \frac{\text{the total of all other colours}}{\text{the total of all colours}}$$

$$= \frac{14 + 10 + 9 + 13}{14 + 10 + 9 + 17 + 13}$$

$$= \frac{46}{63}$$

Practice 12.2

Level 1 — GCSE Grade 1 / 2^-

1. This pictogram shows the earnings of three stalls at a food fair.

Stall	Earnings
A	
B	
C	

(Each represents £100.)

(a) Work out the earnings of Stall A, Stall B and Stall C.

(b) How much more did stall A earn than Stall B?

(c) Find the ratio of the earnings of Stall B to the earnings of Stall C in its simplest form.

Solution

(a) One 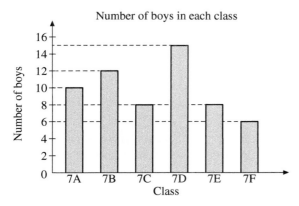 represents £100.

Amount earned by Stall A $= £100 \times 5 + \frac{1}{2}$ of £100

$$= £500 + £50$$
$$= £550$$

Amount earned by Stall B $= £100 \times 3$
$$= £300$$

Amount earned by Stall C $= £100 \times 4 + \frac{3}{4}$ of £100

$$= £400 + £75$$
$$= £475$$

(b) Difference in earning between Stalls A and B
$$= £550 - £300$$
$$= £250$$
Stall A earned £250 more than Stall B.

(c) Amount earned by Stall B : Amount earned by Stall C
$$= 300 : 475$$
$$= 12 : 19$$

2. This bar chart shows the number of boys in each class.

Number of boys in each class

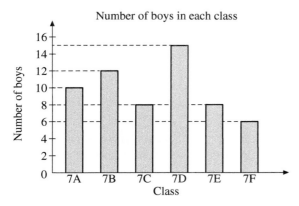

(a) What is the total number of boys in the six classes?

(b) Which class has the highest number of boys?

(c) Which class has the lowest number of boys?

(d) Which two classes have the same number of boys?

(e) Which class has half as many boys as class 7B?

Solution

(a) Total number of boys in the six classes
$$= 10 + 12 + 8 + 15 + 8 + 6$$
$$= 59$$

(b) Class 7D has the highest number of boys.

(c) Class 7F has the lowest number of boys.

(d) Classes 7C and 7E have the same number of boys.

(e) Class 7B has 12 boys.

$$\frac{1}{2} \times 12 = 6$$

∴ Class 7F has half as many boys as class 7B.

3. The vertical line chart shows the favourite flavours of jelly of a group of 50 people responding to a survey.

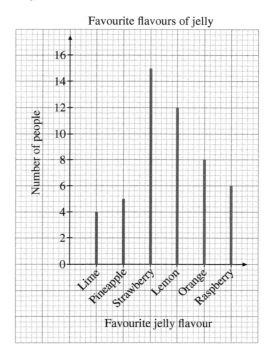

(a) Which is the least popular flavour of jelly from the survey, and what is its frequency?

(b) What percentage of the people surveyed like orange jelly best?

(c) If you add the numbers for the two most popular flavours together, what is that sum as a percentage of the total?

Solution

(a) The least popular has the lowest frequency. Lime is the least popular flavour with a frequency of 4.

(b) The percentage of people who like orange the best $= \dfrac{\text{frequency of orange}}{\text{total of people surveyed}} \times 100\%$

$$= \frac{8}{50} \times 100\%$$

$$= 16\%$$

(c) Percentage of the two most popular flavours added together

$$= \frac{\text{frequency of strawberry} + \text{frequency of lemon}}{\text{total of people surveyed}} \times 100\%$$

$$= \frac{15 + 12}{50} \times 100\%$$

$$= 54\%$$

GCSE Grade 2

4. This table shows the number of copies of different types of publication sold in a bookshop.

Type of publication	Newspapers	Novels	Magazines	Comics
Number of copies sold	120	80	145	95

(a) Draw a bar chart to represent the data.
(b) What fraction of all the publications sold are newspapers? Give your answer in its simplest form.

Solution

(a)

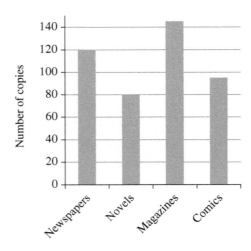

Number of copies sold for different types of publications

(b) Total number of copies of publications sold
= 120 + 80 + 145 + 95
= 440

Fraction of all publications sold that are newspapers

$= \dfrac{\text{number of copies of newspapers sold}}{\text{total number of copies of publications sold}}$

$= \dfrac{120}{440}$

$= \dfrac{3}{11}$

5. This table shows the number of students from a year group who are members of uniformed groups. No student is in more than one group.

Uniformed group	Girl Guides	CCF	Scouts	Red Cross
Number of students	12	14	8	6

(a) Draw a vertical line chart to represent the data.
(b) What fraction of the students who are members of uniformed groups are members of CCF?

(c) There is a total of 100 students in the year group. What is the ratio of the number of students who are not in any uniformed group to the total number of students? Give your answer in its simplest form.

Solution

(a)

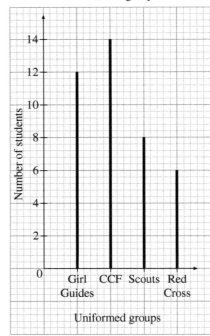

Number of students who are members of uniformed groups

(b) Total number of students in the uniformed groups
= 12 + 14 + 8 + 6
= 40

Fraction of students who are members of uniformed groups are members of CCF

$= \dfrac{14}{40}$

$= \dfrac{7}{20}$

(c) Number of students who are not members of any uniformed group
= 100 − 40
= 60

Number of students who are not members of any uniformed group : total number of students
= 60 : 100
= 3 : 5

6. Draw a bar chart to show the rainfall in a year in the city or county where you live. Put the months of the year on the horizontal axis.

Solution
Student's own answer

Practice 12.3

Level 1

1. The table shows the number of calls received by a company on 70 working days.

Number of calls	10–19	20–29	30–39	40–49	50–59
Frequency	7	12	23	18	10

(a) On one particular day 22 calls were received. Which group does this belong to?

(b) On how many days were the number of calls more than 49?

(c) Find the ratio of the number of days with 30 to 39 calls to the number of days with 40 to 49 calls.

(d) Draw a bar chart to represent the data.

Solution

(a) 22 belongs in the class 20–29.

(b) 10 days

(c) Frequency of class 30–39 : frequency of class 40–49 = 23 : 18

(d)

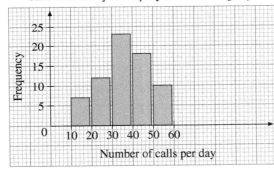

Calls received by a company on 70 working days

2. The table shows the time taken to run 400 m by 50 athletes.

Hint: $48 \leq t < 50$ means that the time taken is more than or equal to 48 seconds, but less than 50 seconds.

Time (t seconds)	Frequency
$48 \leq t < 50$	3
$50 \leq t < 52$	9
$52 \leq t < 54$	16
$54 \leq t < 56$	12
$56 \leq t < 58$	6
$58 \leq t < 60$	4

(a) Find the number of athletes whose times taken are less than 50 seconds.

(b) Find the percentage of athletes whose times taken are greater than or equal to 54 seconds.

Solution

(a) Athletes whose times are less than 50 seconds = 3

(b) Percentage of athletes whose times are greater than or equal to 54 seconds

$$= \frac{\text{frequency of } 54 \leq t < 56 + \text{frequency of } 56 \leq t < 58 + \text{frequency of } 58 \leq t < 60}{\text{Total number of athletes}}$$
$$\times 100\%$$
$$= \frac{12 + 6 + 4}{50} \times 100\%$$
$$= 44\%$$

Level 2

3. A magazine conducts a survey about the ages of its readers. The results, in years, are:

41	25	34	59	31	43	35	50	31	45
26	28	56	68	39	43	62	37	33	51
29	35	47	53	34	46	64	58	28	53

(a) Copy and complete the frequency table.

Age (years)	Tally	Frequency
20–29		
30–39		
40–49		
50–59		
60–69		

(b) Find the number of readers whose ages are 50 or above.

(c) Find the percentage of readers who are in their thirties.

Solution

(a)

Age (years)	Tally	Frequency
20–29	IIII I	5
30–39	HHI IIII	9
40–49	HHI I	6
50–59	HHI II	7
60–69	III	3

(b) Number of readers whose ages are 50 or above
= frequency of age 50–59
   + frequency of age 60–69
= 7 + 3
= 10

(c) Percentage of readers whose ages are in the class '30–39'

$$= \frac{\text{frequency of age } 30-39}{\text{total number of readers}} \times 100\%$$

$$= \frac{9}{30} \times 100\%$$

$$= 30\%$$

4. The volumes in cm^3 of hydrogen produced in 25 repetitions of an experiment are recorded below.

14.3 12.8 16.2 13.6 15.7 10.8 14.9 19.3 17.2

19.6 10.8 15.4 18.2 17.9 21.4 15.0 13.5 14.7

17.6 18.5 12.5 11.7 16.0 15.6 11.4

(a) Copy and complete the frequency table.

Volume (x cm³)	Tally	Frequency
$10 \le x < 12$		
$12 \le x < 14$		
$14 \le x < 16$		
$16 \le x < 18$		
$18 \le x < 20$		
$20 \le x < 22$		

(b) Find the ratio of the frequency of the class '$12 \le x < 14$' to the frequency of the class '$16 \le x < 18$'. Give your answer in its simplest form.

(c) Find the percentage of times that the volume is not less than $18\,cm^3$.

Solution

(a)

Volume (x cm³)	Tally	Frequency
$10 \le x < 12$	IIII	4
$12 \le x < 14$	IIII	4
$14 \le x < 16$	ℍ II	7
$16 \le x < 18$	ℍ	5
$18 \le x < 20$	IIII	4
$20 \le x < 22$	I	1

(b) The frequency of the class $12 \le x < 14$ is 4.
The frequency of the class $16 \le x < 18$ is 5.
The ratio of the frequency of the class
'$12 \le x < 14$' to the frequency of the class
'$16 \le x < 18$' = 4 : 5

(c) Percentage of times not less than 18

$$= \frac{\text{frequency of } 18 \le x < 20 + \text{frequency of } 20 \le x < 22}{\text{total}}$$

$$= \frac{4+1}{25} \times 100\%$$

$$= 20\%$$

Challenge 12

GCSE Grade 3 25 people go to a fancy dress party. Two people dress as animals. Three more people dress as celebrities than those that dress as animals. Twice as many people dress as fictional characters than those that dress as animals.
The remaining people dress as clowns. Draw a horizontal bar chart or a vertical bar chart that shows the different outfits at the fancy dress party.

Solution

There are 25 people at the party in total. The types of fancy dress are:

animals, celebrities, fictional characters, and clowns. This makes four categories for the bar chart.

A table is not asked for but can help with solving the problem.

Costume	Frequency
Animal	2
Celebrity	(2 + 3) = 5
Fictional character	(2 × 2) = 4
Clown	(25 − 2 − 5 − 4) = 14
TOTAL	25

A horizontal bar chart is shown, students may decide to take the option of a vertical bar chart.

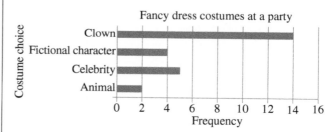

Revision Exercise 12

1. 50 people were interviewed to find out the type of houses they lived in.

Type of house	Tally	Number of people
One-bedroom	ℍ ℍ	10
Two-bedroom		6
Three-bedroom	ℍ ℍ ℍ I	
Four-bedroom		11
Five-bedroom	ℍ II	7

(a) Copy and complete the table.
(b) Which type of house was the most common?
(c) What fraction of the people interviewed lived in a two-bedroom house?

Solution

(a)

Type of flat	Tally	Number of people
One-bedroom	‖‖ ‖‖	10
Two-bedroom	‖‖ ∣	6
Three-bedroom	‖‖ ‖‖ ‖‖ ∣	16
Four-bedroom	‖‖ ‖‖ ∣	11
Five-bedroom	‖‖ ∥	7

(b) Three-bedroom houses were the most common.

(c) Fraction of people interviewed who lived in a two-bedroom house

$= \dfrac{6}{50}$

$= \dfrac{3}{25}$

2. The frequency table shows the number of sit-ups achieved in one minute by 75 students. The data is grouped into classes of equal sizes.

Number of sit-ups	25–27	28–30	31–33			40–42
Frequency	9		24	17	8	2

(a) Copy and complete the table.
(b) Display the data in a line chart.
(c) Which class has one-third the frequency of the class '31–33'?
(d) What fraction of the students achieved more than 33 sit-ups in one minute?

Solution

(a)

Number of sit-ups	25–27	28–30	31–33	34–36	37–39	40–42
Frequency	9	15	24	17	8	2

(b)

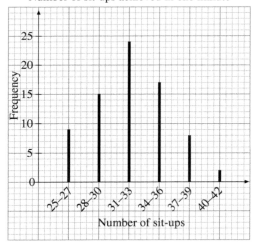

Number of sit-ups achieved in one minute

(c) Class '37–39' has a frequency one-third of class '31–33'.

(d) Students who achieved more than 33 sit-ups

$= \dfrac{\text{frequency of '34–36'} + \text{frequency of '37–39'} + \text{frequency of '40–42'}}{\text{total}}$

$= \dfrac{17+8+2}{75}$

$= \dfrac{27}{75}$

$= \dfrac{9}{25}$

3. This table shows the number of fish in each of six fish tanks.

Tank	A	B	C	D	E	F
Number of fish in tank	15	14	17	15	10	9

(a) Draw a bar chart to represent the given data.
(b) Which tank has the smallest number of fish?
(c) Which tanks have the same number of fish?
(d) What fraction of the total number of fish is in tank B?

Solution

(a)

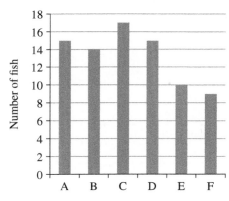

Number of fish in each fish tank

(b) Tank F has the smallest number of fish.

(c) Tanks A and D have the same number of fish.

(d) Total number of fish = 15 + 14 + 17 + 15 + 10 + 9
= 80

Fraction of fish that are in tank B

$= \dfrac{\text{number of fish in tank B}}{\text{total number of fish}}$

$= \dfrac{14}{80}$

$= \dfrac{7}{40}$

4. A toy-box contains a variety of plastic squares, triangles, pentagons and circles. This chart shows the number of different shapes in the toy-box.

Shape	Number of shapes in the toy-box
Square	♠ ♠ ♠ ♠
Triangle	♠ ♠ ♠ ♠ ♠ ♠ ♠ ♠ ♠
Pentagon	♠ ♠
Circle	♠ ♠ ♠ ♠ ♠

(Each ♠ represents 2 shapes.)

(a) What is the name for a chart that uses a symbol or picture to represent a certain number of things?

(b) Make a table to show the number of each type of shape in the box.

(c) Find the total number of shapes in the box.

(d) One week later, four plastic squares and two triangles were lost. What fraction of the remaining shapes are circles? Express the fraction in its simplest form.

Solution

(a) Pictogram

(b)

Shape	Number of shapes in the toy box
Square	8
Triangle	18
Pentagon	4
Circle	10

(c) Total number of shapes = 8 + 18 + 4 + 10
= 40

(d) New total number = 40 − 4 − 2
= 34

The fraction of remaining shapes that are circles
$= \dfrac{10}{34} = \dfrac{5}{17}$

5. A mushroom grower is interested in the masses of his mushrooms. He weighs 40 of the mushrooms he has picked on one day and the results, in grams, are shown.

20.8 26.0 10.7 16.0 24.7 29.3 24.1 26.4 34.5 23.7

27.0 24.6 16.3 32.5 11.7 18.3 17.4 13.2 21.3 18.5

26.5 23.8 15.4 22.2 27.1 19.0 25.6 23.1 15.9 21.7

32.8 30.9 21.5 28.8 22.8 27.1 31.5 23.9 28.0 32.4

(a) Copy and complete the frequency table. The classes should be of equal size.

Masses of mushrooms (x g)	Tally	Frequency
$10 \le x < 15$		
$15 \le x < 20$		
$30 \le x < 35$		

(b) Find the ratio of the number of mushrooms, with mass x g, in the class '$15 \le x < 20$' to the number in the class '$30 \le x < 35$'.

Solution

(a)

Masses of mushrooms (x g)	Tally	Frequency
$10 \le x < 15$	|||	3
$15 \le x < 20$	₶₶ |||	8
$20 \le x < 25$	₶₶ ₶₶ |||	13
$25 \le x < 30$	₶₶ ₶₶	10
$30 \le x < 35$	₶₶ |	6

(b) Number of mushrooms in class $15 \le x < 20$:
Number of mushrooms in class $30 \le x < 35$
= 8 : 6
= 4 : 3

Integrated Examples and Review Exercise 3

Try It!

1. *ABN* is a straight line and $\angle ANC = 90°$.
    $AB = 3$ cm, $BN = 2$ cm and $CN = 2$ cm.

    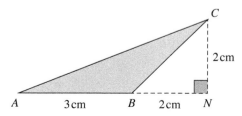

    (a) Measure $\angle ABC$.
    (b) Calculate the area of $\triangle ABC$.
    (c) Four of $\triangle ABC$ are placed together to form the figure below.

    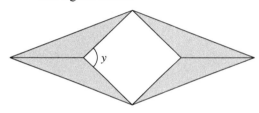

    (i) Find the size of $\angle y$. Give the reason for your answer. Draw a bar model to explain your reasoning.
    (ii) Describe the symmetry of the figure.

Solution

(a) Measuring with a protractor,
     $\angle ABC = 135°$.

(b) Area of $\triangle ABC$
     $= \frac{1}{2} \times AB \times CN$
     $= \frac{1}{2} \times 3 \times 2$
     $= 3 \text{ cm}^2$

(c) (i) $\angle y + \angle ABC + \angle ABC = 360°$
          (Angles at a point add up to 360°.)
          $\angle y + 135° + 135° = 360°$
          $\angle y + 270° = 360°$
          $\angle y = 360° - 270°$
          $\angle y = 90°$

     (ii) The figure has two lines of symmetry. Thus, it has reflection symmetry. It has rotation symmetry of order 2.

2. Janice measured 16 angles in a book. The results are listed.

    | 123° | 12° | 89° | 347° | 98° | 143° | 46° | 257° |
    | 168° | 270° | 57° | 256° | 30° | 128° | 143° | 155° |

    (a) Copy and complete the table for the list of angles.

Acute angle	
Obtuse angle	123°,
Reflex angle	

    (b) Identify pairs of angles from the list that will form angles on a straight line.

    (c) Draw a vertical line chart to display the number of each different type of angle that Janice measured.

Solution

(a)

Acute angle	12°, 89°, 46°, 57°, 30°
Obtuse angle	123°, 98°, 143°, 168°, 128°, 143°, 155°
Reflex angle	347°, 257°, 270°, 256°

(b) Angles on a straight line add up to 180°.
     Here, $12° + 168° = 180°$,
     and $57° + 123° = 180°$.
     These two pairs of angles, (12°, 168°) and (57°, 123°), form angles on a straight line.

(c) The vertical line chart below displays the number of different types of each angle.

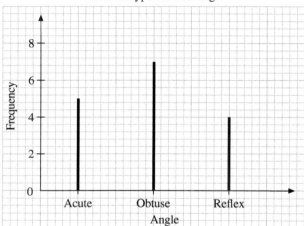

Different types of each angle

3. A rectangular box is 5 cm long and has square ends with sides that are 2 cm.

   (a) Find the perimeter and area of one
     (i) square face,
     (ii) rectangular face.

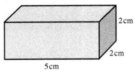

   (b) Draw a net of the box.
   (c) Find the surface area of the box.
   (d) Find the volume of the box.
   (e) The pictogram shows the sizes of some boxes in a shop. Which size of box is represented by the smallest number of symbols? How many boxes of that size are there?

Sizes of boxes

Small	▦ ▦ ▦ ▢
Medium	▦ ▦ ▦ ▦
Large	▦ ▦ ▢
Extra large	▦ ▦ ▦ ▦ ▫

▦ represents 5 boxes

Solution

(a) **(i)** Perimeter of a square face
      = 4 × length of side
      = 4 × 2
      = 8 cm
      Area of a square face
      = side × side
      = 2 × 2
      = 4 cm^2

    (ii) Perimeter of a rectangular face
      = 2 × (length + width)
      = 2 × (5 + 2)
      = 2 × 7
      = 14 cm
      Area of a rectangular face
      = length × width
      = 5 × 2
      = 10 cm^2

(b) Two possible nets of the box are shown below.

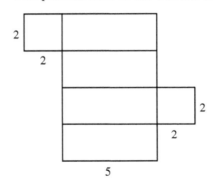

(c) Surface area of the box
    = 4 × area of the rectangular face + 2 × area of the square face
    = 4 × 10 + 2 × 4
    = 48 cm^2

(d) Volume of the box
    = length × width × height
    = (5 × 2) × 2
    = 20 cm^3

(d) In the pictogram, the 'Large' size has the smallest number of symbols. Hence, the 'Large' size has the smallest number of boxes. The number of 'Large' size boxes
    = 2 × 5 + 4
    = 14

Review Exercise 3

1. Measure angles *a*, *b* and *c* and state their types.

GCSE Grade 2

Hint: You can extend the sides of an angle to make the angle easier to measure.

Solution
∠*a* = 82° is an acute angle
∠*b* = 324° is a reflex angle.
∠*c* = 123° is an obtuse angle.

2. *DEF* is a straight line. Find the sizes of angles x, y and z.

Hint: Use bar models to explain your reasoning.

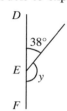 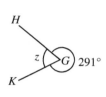

A *B*
56°
x
C

D
38°
E y
F

H
z *G* 291°
K

Solution

$\angle x + 56° = 90°$ (Angles at a right angle
$\quad \angle x = 90° - 56°$ add up to 90°.)
$\qquad = 34°$

$\angle y + 38° = 180°$ (Angles on a straight
$\quad \angle y = 180° - 38°$ line add up to 180°.)
$\qquad = 142°$

$\angle z + 291° = 360°$ (Angles at a point add
$\quad \angle z = 360° - 291°$ up to 360°.)
$\qquad = 69°$

3. Copy the diagrams and draw any lines of symmetry.

(a)    **(b)**

Solution

(a)

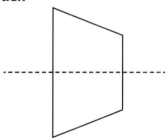

(b)

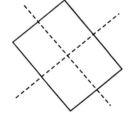

4. State the order of rotation symmetry about the given centre of rotation of each diagram.

(a)   **(b)**

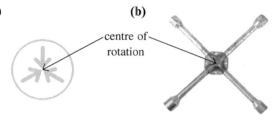

centre of rotation

Solution

(a) The order of rotation symmetry is 3.

(b) The order of rotation symmetry is 4.

5. (a) Each side of a square is 7 cm. Draw a diagram and find
    (i) the perimeter of the square,
    (ii) the area of the square.

Hint: Draw a diagram to help you.
(b) A rectangular lawn is 8 m by 5 m. Draw a diagram and find
    (i) the perimeter of the lawn,
    (ii) the area of the lawn.

Solution

(a) (i) Perimeter of the square $= 4 \times 7$
                          $= 28$ cm

    (ii) Area of the square $= 7 \times 7$
                            $= 49$ cm^2

(b) (i)

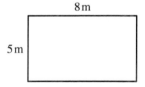

8 m
5 m

      Perimeter of the lawn
      $= 2 \times (8 + 5)$
      $= 2 \times 3$
      $= 26$ m

    (ii) Area of the lawn
             $= 8 \times 5$
             $= 40$ m^2

6. (a) Find the area of $\triangle ABC$.

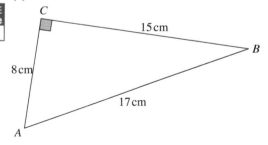

C
15 cm
B
8 cm
17 cm
A

(b) Find the area of $\triangle PQR$.

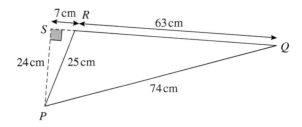

Solution

(a) Area of $\triangle ABC$

$= \frac{1}{2} \times \text{base} \times \text{perpendicular height}$

$= \frac{1}{2} \times AC \times BC$

$= \frac{1}{2} \times 8 \times 15$

$= 60\,\text{cm}^2$

(b) Area of $\triangle PQR$

$= \frac{1}{2} \times QR \times PS$

$= \frac{1}{2} \times 63 \times 24$

$= 756\,\text{cm}^2$

7. Each edge of a wooden cube is 5 cm long.

(a) Draw a net of the cube.

(b) Calculate the surface area of the cube.

(c) Calculate the volume of the cube.

Solution

(a) Possible student's diagram:

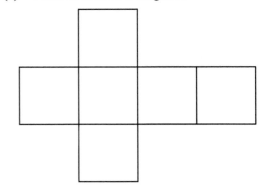

(b) Surface area of the cube
$= 6 \times \text{area of one square face}$
$= 6 \times (5 \times 5)$
$= 6 \times 25$
$= 150\,\text{cm}^2$

(c) Volume of the cube
$= 5 \times 5 \times 5$
$= 125\,\text{cm}^3$

8. An aquarium tank is 60 cm long, 28 cm wide and 50 cm high. You can use a calculator for this question.

(a) Draw the net of the tank. Remember that the top of the tank is open.

(b) Calculate the surface area of the four walls and the base of the tank.

(c) Calculate the volume of the tank.

(d) Draw another tank that would hold the same volume of water. Explain your answer.

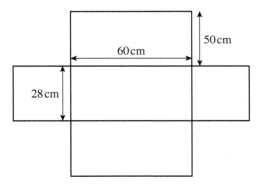

Solution

(a) There are several possible nets. One example is shown below.

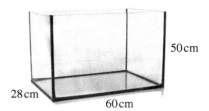

(b) The required surface area
$= 2 \times (60 \times 50) + 2 \times (50 \times 28) + 60 \times 28$
$= 6000 + 2800 + 1680$
$= 10\,480\,\text{cm}^2$

(c) Volume of the tank
$= 60 \times 28 \times 50$
$= 84\,000\,\text{cm}^3$

(d) There are several possible alternative tanks. One example is shown below.

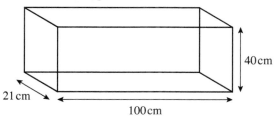

Volume of the tank = $100 \times 40 \times 21$
                                $= 84\,000\,cm^3$

Therefore this tank can hold the same volume of water as the original tank.

9. The vertical bar chart shows the prices of three items bought by Zoe.

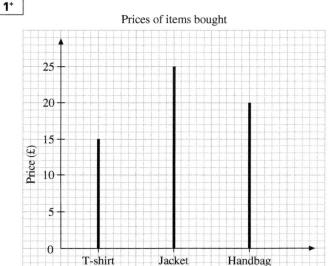

(a) What is the difference in price between the T-shirt and the handbag?
(b) What is the total price of the three items?

Solution
(a) The Handbag has a price of £20, and the t-shirt has a price of £15.
Therefore, difference in price = 20 − 15 = £5

(b) Total price of the three items
= £(15 + 25 + 20)
= £60

10. The pictogram shows the number of daffodils in four flowerbeds.

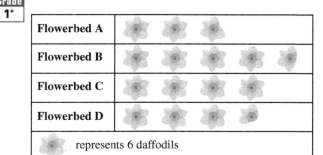

(a) Which flowerbed has the greatest number of daffodils?
(b) What is the difference between the number of daffodils in flowerbeds A and D?

Solution
(a) Flowerbed B has the greatest number of daffodils.

(b) The difference = 21 − 17
              = 4

11. *ABCD* is a rectangular playground measuring 7 m by 4 m, and *BE* = 3 m.

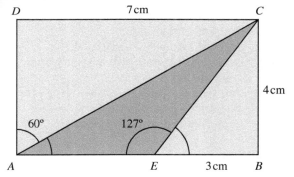

Calculate
(a) $\angle BAC$, giving the reason for your answer,
(b) $\angle BEC$, giving the reason for your answer,
(c) the perimeter of the playground,
(d) the area of $\triangle AEC$.

Solution
(a) $\angle BAC + \angle DAC = 90°$ (Angles on at right
        $\angle BAC + 60° = 90°$ angle add up to 90°.)
        $\angle BAC = 30°$

(b) $\angle BEC + \angle AEC = 180°$ (Angles on a straight
$\angle BEC + 127° = 180°$ line add up to 180°.)
$\angle BEC = 53°$

(c) Perimeter of the playground
$= 2 \times (7 + 4)$
$= 2 \times 11$
$= 22\,m$

(d) $AB = DC$ (sides of a rectangle)
$= 7\,m$
$AE = AB - EB$
$= 7 - 3$
$= 4\,m$
Area of $\triangle AEC$
$= \frac{1}{2} \times AE \times CB$
$= \frac{1}{2} \times 4 \times 4$
$= 8\,m^2$

12. The diagram shows two arrows
joined to form a double-headed arrow.
(a) Copy the diagram and draw any
lines of symmetry.
(b) State its order of rotation
symmetry, and show where the
centre of rotation should be.
(c) Add two more arrows to your
diagram so that its
order of symmetry becomes 4.
(d) Does your diagram still have reflection
symmetry?
(e) Can you add just one arrow to the original
diagram so that it has both reflection
symmetry and rotation symmetry?

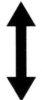

GCSE
Grade
2⁺

Solution
(a)

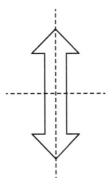

(b) Order of rotation symmetry = 2

(c) A figure with rotation symmetry of order 4 is
shown below.

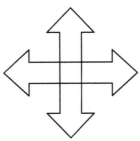

(d) Yes, the example shown in part **(c)** still has
reflection symmetry.

(e) No, if you add one more arrow to the
diagram, it is possible for the diagram to still
have reflection symmetry but it would have no
rotation symmetry.

13. The diagram is a net of a cube of edge 7 cm.

GCSE
Grade
3

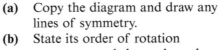

7 cm

(a) Find the surface area of the cube.
(b) Find the volume of the cube.
(c) Which face is opposite to face A when the net
is made into a cube?
Hint: To verify your prediction, you could draw the
net, cut it out and fold it up.

Solution
(a) Surface area of the cube
$= 6 \times$ area of one square face
$= 6 \times (7 \times 7)$
$= 6 \times 49$
$= 294\,cm^2$

(b) Volume of the cube
$= 7 \times 7 \times 7$
$= 343\,cm^3$

(c) Face F is opposite to face A in the cube.

14. The frequency table shows the number of push-ups that some students can do in one minute.

GCSE Grade 3⁻

Number of push-ups	Frequency
10–14	12
15–19	19
20–24	32
25–29	11
30–34	6

(a) What does 10–14 mean in the table?

(b) Find the total number of students recorded in the table.

(c) How many students can do more than 29 push-ups in one minute?

(d) What is the ratio of the number of students who can do 10–14 push-ups to those who can do 20–24 push-ups in one minute? Express your answer in the simplest form.

Solution

(a) 10–14 represents 10, 11, 12, 13 and 14 push-ups.

(b) Total number of students recorded
= total frequency
= 12 + 19 + 32 + 11 + 6
= 80

(c) Number of students who can do > 29 push-ups in one minute
= number of students who can do 30–34 push-ups
= 6

(d) From the frequency table, 12 students can do 10–14 push-ups and 32 students can do 20–24 push-ups.
Hence, the required ratio
= 12 : 32
= 3 : 8

A. Rushton Triangular Lodge

Rushton Triangular Lodge is an extraordinary building in Northamptonshire. It was built by Sir Thomas Tresham in 1593. Many things in the Lodge involve the number three. The Lodge has three external walls that are all 33 feet long. Each side has three triangular windows and three triangular points, called 'gables', one above each window. There are three floors and a triangular chimney.

1.

The diagram shows the upper floor plan of the Lodge. Explain why the triangle formed by the three external walls is an equilateral triangle.
Hint: Read the introduction again to help you answer this question.

Solution

Since each external wall is 33 feet long, all three walls are equal in length.
Hence, the walls form an equilateral triangle.

2.

The image shows a trefoil window of the Lodge.
(a) Does the window have reflection symmetry? If so, sketch the window and draw on its lines of symmetry.
(b) Does the window have rotation symmetry? If so, what is its order of rotation symmetry and where is its centre of rotation?

Solution
(a) The window has reflection symmetry. It has three lines of symmetry as shown below.

(b) The window has rotation symmetry of order 3.

---

3. (a)

A French tourist would like to know the length of the external wall, in metres. Note that 1 foot = 12 inches and 1 inch = 2.54 cm. Express the length of the external wall
(i) in inches,
(ii) in centimetres, to the nearest 10 cm,
(iii) in metres, using the result in **(ii)**.

(b) It is shown that the perpendicular height of an equilateral triangle is approximately 0.866 times the length of any of its sides. The triangle shown represents the upper floor of the lodge.

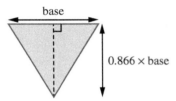

(i) Using your result in **(a) (ii)**, find the perpendicular height, in centimetres. Give your answer to the nearest 10 cm.
(ii) Convert your result from **(i)** to metres and use it to find a value for the enclosed area of the upper floor. Give your answer in square metres (m²).
(iii) Use your result from **(ii)** to find the total area of the three floors. Round your answer to the nearest 10 square metres.

Solution
(a) (i) Length of the wall = 33 feet
$$= 33 \times 12 \text{ inches}$$
$$= 396 \text{ inches}$$

(ii) Length of the wall
$$= 396 \times 2.54 \text{ cm}$$
$$= 1005.84 \text{ cm}$$
$$= 1010 \text{ cm} \quad \text{(to the nearest 10 cm)}$$

(iii) Length of the wall = 1010 ÷ 100 m
$$= 10.10 \text{ m}$$

(b) (i) Perpendicular height = 0.866 × base
$$= 0.866 \times 1010$$
$$= 874.66 \text{ cm}$$
$$= 870 \text{ cm}$$

(ii) $870 = 8.70\,\text{m}$

Ground area of the upper floor

$= \dfrac{1}{2} \times \text{base} \times \text{height}$

$= \dfrac{1}{2} \times 10.10 \times 8.70$

$= \dfrac{87.87}{2}$

$= 43.935\,\text{m}^2$

(iii) Total area of 3 floors

$= 43.935 \times 3$

$= 131.805$

$= 130\,\text{m}^2$ (to the nearest $10\,\text{m}^2$)

Notes to teachers

Some mathematical facts:

1. The main room on each floor is hexagonal, leaving three triangular corner spaces.

2. There are many mysterious numbers on the walls, such as 1626 and 1641. These numbers are divisible by 3. In addition, when the design date 1593 is subtracted from 1626 and 1641 respectively, the results are 33 and 48. According to the Bible, these are the ages at which Jesus and St Mary died.

3. There is a row of Latin texts of 33 letters on the façade of each wall. They relate to statements in the Bible.

4. Some window designs possess reflection symmetry or rotation symmetry or both.

B. Living Room Extension

The diagram shows the floor plan of a house.
$AB = 9\,\text{m}$, $BC = 6\,\text{m}$,
$CD = 5\,\text{m}$ and $DE = 1\,\text{m}$.

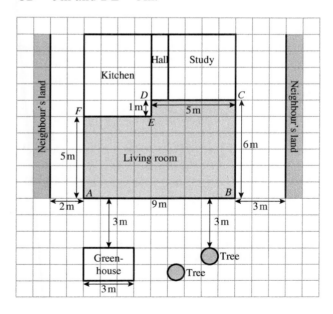

---

1. Find the perimeter of the living room.

GCSE Grade 1+

Solution

$EF = AB - CD$
$\quad = 9 - 5$
$\quad = 4\,\text{m}$

$FA = CB - DE$
$\quad = 6 - 1$
$\quad = 5\,\text{m}$

Perimeter of the living room $= AB + BC + CD + DE$
$\qquad\qquad\qquad\qquad\qquad + EF + FA$
$\qquad\qquad = 9 + 6 + 5 + 1 + 4 + 5$
$\qquad\qquad = 30\,\text{m}$

2. Find the area of the living room.

GCSE Grade 2+

Solution

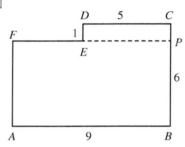

Extend FE to meet the side BC at P.

Area of the living room

$=$ area of the rectangle $ABPF +$ area of the rectangle $PCDE$

$= 9 \times 5 + 5 \times 1$

$= 50\,\text{m}^2$

(Alternative working that divides the room differently is also acceptable.)

3. Alice wishes to extend the living room by moving a wall outwards. She can move any of the outer walls, but must leave a metre between the wall and her neighbour's land, the greenhouse and any trees. She looks at extending it by extending walls AB and DC by 1.5 m to form $AGHDEF$.

GCSE Grade 3-

The dotted lines show the extensions.

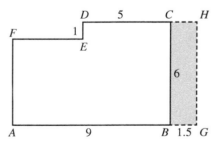

(a) What would be the area of the new living room?

(b) (i) What other options could she consider? Describe three more options: which wall will move, and by how much?

(ii) Calculate the area of the new living room for each option.

(iii) Which option would create a new living room with the largest area?

Solution

(a) Area of the rectangle $BGHC = 1.5 \times 6$
$$= 9\,m^2$$
Area of the original living room $= 9 \times 6 - (1 \times 4)$
$$= 50\,m^2$$
Hence, the new area of the living room is $59\,m^2$.

(b) (i) Alice could extend the right wall of the living room (BC) by 2 m, or the left wall of the living room (AF) by 1 m. She could also extend the bottom wall of the living room (AB) by 2 m towards the greenhouse.

(ii) If Alice extends the right wall of the living room by 2 m, new area
$$= (2 \times 6) + 50$$
$$= 62\,m^2$$

If Alice extends the left wall of the living room by 1 m, new area
$$= (1 \times 5) + 50$$
$$= 55\,m^2$$

If Alice extends the bottom wall of the living room by 2 m, new area
$$= (9 \times 2) + 50$$
$$= 68\,m^2$$

(iii) Extending the bottom wall of the living room by 2 m would create the living room with the largest area.

C. Extendable Table

The table top of an extendable table is 147 cm by 95 cm when it is not extended. It becomes 204 cm by 95 cm when it is extended.

1. Find the increase in the perimeter of the table top when its length is increased from 147 cm to 204 cm.

Solution

For the size of 147 cm by 95 cm,
the perimeter of the table top $= 2 \times 147 + 2 \times 95$
$$= 484\,cm$$
For the size of 204 cm by 95 cm,
the perimeter of the table top $= 2 \times 204 + 2 \times 95$
$$= 598\,cm$$
Increase in the perimeter of the table top $= 598 - 484$
$$= 114\,cm$$

2. Find the increase in the area of the table top surface when its length is increased from 147 cm to 204 cm.

Solution

For the size of 147 cm by 95 cm,
the area of the table top $= 147 \times 95$
$$= 13\,965\,cm^2$$
For the size of 204 cm by 95 cm,
the area of the table top $= 204 \times 95$
$$= 19\,380\,cm^2$$
Increase in the area of the table top
$$= 19\,380 - 13\,965$$
$$= 5415\,cm^2$$

3. The table top is made of solid pine. Its thickness is 4 cm. Estimate the mass of the extended table top in kilograms (kg). State any assumptions you made for your calculation.

Hint: You should find out what the mass of $1\,cm^3$ of pine is. The mass of $1\,cm^3$ of pine is called the 'density' of pine.

Solution

Assume the density of pine is 0.5 gram per cm^3. (The density of pine, depending on its species, varies from 0.42 grams per cm^3 to 0.67 grams per cm^3. Students are expected to search for this on the Internet. Students' calculations may differ from this according to the density value they chose.)
Volume of the extended table top $= 204 \times 95 \times 4\,cm^3$
Mass of the extended table top $= 204 \times 95 \times 4 \times 0.5$
$$= 38\,760\,grams$$
$$= 38\,760 \div 1000\,kg$$
$$= 38.76\,kg$$

D. Carat Gold

Carat is a unit for measuring how pure gold is. Pure gold is 24 carats, denoted by 24k. Therefore, 24k gold means 100% gold. Canadian Maple Leaf gold coins are made from pure gold.

1. South African Krugerrand gold coins are 22 carat gold. This means each one contains 22 parts gold and 2 parts other metals by mass. Find the ratio of the mass of gold to the mass of other metals in a Krugerrand coin. Give your answer in the simplest form.

Solution

Ratio of the mass of gold to the mass of other metals in a Krugerrand coin
$$= 22 : 2$$
$$= 11 : 1$$

2. 18 carat gold contains 18 parts of gold and 6 parts other metals by mass. It is mainly used for gold jewellery. The FIFA World Cup Trophy 2018 is also made of 18 carat gold and has a malachite base. Find the percentage of gold in 18 carat gold.

GCSE Grade 2⁺

Solution

18 parts + 6 parts = 24 parts

Percentage of gold in 18 carat gold $= \frac{18}{24} \times 100\%$
$$= 75\%$$

3. 9 carat gold contains 9 parts of gold and 15 parts of other metals. 22 carat gold contains 22 parts gold and 2 parts of other metals. A jeweller has 200 grams of gold. He makes bracelets in either 9k gold or 22k gold and each bracelet weighs 48 grams. How many 9k and 22k bracelets should he make in order to use as much of the 200 g gold as possible?

GCSE Grade 3

Solution

There are 24 parts in each bracelet, and each bracelet weighs 48 g. Therefore, each part weighs $\frac{48}{24} = 2$ g.

The jeweller has 200 grams of gold, therefore he can use $\frac{200}{2} = 100$ parts of gold.

A 22k bracelet has 22 parts gold, and a 9k bracelet has 9 parts gold.

Therefore, (22 × no. of 22k bracelets) + (9 × no. of 9k bracelets) should be less than or equal to 100.

Using trial and error, we get (22 × 2) + (9 × 6) = 98

Therefore, he should make two 22k bracelets and six 9k bracelets to use as much gold as possible.

E. Height of a Tree

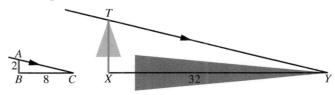

AB is a vertical pole of height 2 m. It casts a shadow BC of length 8 m on the horizontal ground. At the same time, a tree TX casts a shadow XY of length 32 m on the horizontal ground.

1. Measure $\angle ACB$ in the book, which is the angle that the sun ray makes with the horizontal ground.

GCSE Grade 2

Solution

Using a protractor to measure,
$\angle ACB = 15°$

(Values from 13° to 17° are acceptable.)

2. **(a)** Find the fraction $\frac{\text{length of } AB}{\text{length of } BC}$, expressing your answer in its simplest form.
  (b) Find the ratio of the length of AB to the length of BC.
  (c) Express the length of AB as a percentage of the length of BC.

GCSE Grade 3⁻

Solution

(a) $\frac{\text{length of } AB}{\text{length of } BC} = \frac{2}{8}$
$$= \frac{1}{4}$$

(b) Length of AB : Length of $BC = 2 : 8$
$$= 1 : 4$$

(c) The required percentage $= \frac{1}{4} \times 100\%$
$$= 25\%$$

3. It is a useful fact that the angle the sun ray makes with the ground in both of these triangles is the same, meaning that $\angle TYX = \angle ACB$. It is hence known that the fractions $\frac{\text{length of } AB}{\text{length of } BC}$ and $\frac{\text{length of } TX}{\text{length of } XY}$ are equivalent. Use your knowledge of equivalent fractions to find the height of the tree TX.

GCSE Grade 3

Solution

Since the fractions $\frac{\text{length of } AB}{\text{length of } BC}$ and $\frac{\text{length of } TX}{\text{length of } XY}$ are equivalent,

$\frac{\text{length of } TX}{\text{length of } XY} = \frac{\text{length of } AB}{\text{length of } BC}$

$\frac{\text{length of } TX}{32} = \frac{2}{8}$

Finding the number that relates the two fractions
$32 \div 8 = 4$

$\frac{2 \times 4}{8 \times 4} = \frac{8}{32}$

$\therefore$ Height of the tree $TX =$ length of TX
$$= 8 \text{ m}$$